Dr Andrew Lees, MD, FRCP, is Consultant Neurologist to the National Hospital for Neurology and Neurosurgery and the Middlesex Hospital, and Medical Adviser to the Parkinson's Disease Society. He was born on Merseyside and has been a lifelong supporter of Liverpool Football Club. His previous books have been on Parkinson's disease and tics.

RAY OF HOPE

**DR ANDREW LEES AND
RAY KENNEDY**

PENGUIN BOOKS

PENGUIN BOOKS

Published by the Penguin Group
Penguin Books Ltd, 27 Wrights Lane, London W8 5TZ, England
Penguin Books USA Inc., 375 Hudson Street, New York, New York 10014, USA
Penguin Books Australia Ltd, Ringwood, Victoria, Australia
Penguin Books Canada Ltd, 10 Alcorn Avenue, Toronto, Ontario, Canada M4V 3B2
Penguin Books (NZ) Ltd, 182–190 Wairau Road, Auckland 10, New Zealand

Penguin Books Ltd, Registered Offices: Harmondsworth, Middlesex, England

First published by Pelham 1993
Published with minor revisions and additional material in Penguin Books 1994
1 3 5 7 9 10 8 6 4 2

Printed in England by Clays Ltd, St Ives plc

A proportion of the royalties from the sale of this book will be going to the
Ray Kennedy Appeal for Parkinson's Disease
under the aegis of the Parkinson's Disease Society.

To my mother whose sacrifices and encouragement made possible my medical career and to my father who despite his allegiance to 'the Mancs' catalysed and kindled my football obsession.

Contents

Dr Andrew Lees' Acknowledgements

THIS book could not have been written without Ray Kennedy's co-operation and commitment. Nevertheless it has been a tortured voyage for a man who had previously resisted exposure of his private life. Many of our chats were curtailed by Ray's 'switch-offs' during which he lost the initiative to explain and the capacity to assemble his thoughts. Through his determination, however, bit by bit I was able to tease out his fading or repressed recollections.

For the most part his responses to my questions were an admixture of self-denigration and old-fashioned directness. It was hard to get him to acknowledge and talk about his achievements on the football field, but he was keen to communicate what it was like to live with Parkinson's disease. I remember him telling me one day, 'All footballers feel like old people when they hang up their boots, but I move like one too.' Without Ray's blessing I could not have divulged his medical intimacies. These are presented in the hope that they will enhance understanding and compassion for a malady which most of the public still do not recognize. In this regard I must also thank all the 'Parkinsonian autobiographers' from whose books I have quoted liberally, and the many patients from whom I have learned what it is like to have Parkinson's disease.

One of the pleasures of writing a biography of a compliant contemporary is that you are introduced to his circle. It has been fascinating and interesting for me, as a football fan, to meet a generation of players I cursed, railed against and occasionally cheered from the terraces. Ray's memory of his playing days, even with the help of his scrapbooks, has shrunk to little more than isolated flashbacks and vague heartaches, and watching games has become a deep hurt. Ray was generally popular with his peers and I am grateful to his many team-mates, the coaching staff at Highbury, Anfield and the Vetch Field, and the band of sports journalists who followed his career for more than a decade. As members of my profession tend to be acknowledged masters of the delicate expression of uncertainty, talking to football people was a refreshing and, at times, enriching experience. With their help I have been able to embellish Ray's 'lost games'.

My thanks also go to Ken Friar at Arsenal and Peter Robinson at Liverpool who allowed me a glimpse of the inner workings of the citadels they administer. At both clubs I felt comfortable, as their ritualistic and homely atmosphere bore a remarkable likeness to a London teaching hospital. Almost all the Arsenal Double side contributed anecdotes or assessments of Ray's abilities, but I am particularly indebted to Frank McLintock, Bob Wilson and Geordie Armstrong. Steve Burtenshaw and Don Howe provided invaluable testimonies, and Ray's mates from the Arnos Arms, Malcolm Sale and Terry Felton, put his Arsenal days into perspective. Gooners Richard Artus and Clem Cattini also merit acknowledgement. At Liverpool the boot room of Graeme Souness, Ronnie Moran, Roy Evans and Tom Saunders provided friendly encouragement, and Ken Addison and Joe Fagan emphasized Ray's popularity. Tommy Smith and Jimmy Case deserve my particular gratitude for providing a detailed tapestry of life at Anfield, and Phil Thompson my thanks for his hospitality. Eddie Marks and innumerable other Scousers contributed substantially to the fabric of the Liverpool chapters.

My special thanks, however, must go to Ray's parents, his brother Trevor, sister Janet and children Cara and Dale for making me feel at home and supplying vital early details. Mr Allen, a folk historian and the Kennedys' neighbour, guided me through Seaton Delaval's history, and Rob Bryden, Ray's teacher, John Maley, his manager at New Hartley, and Mr J. Welch, his employer at the toffee factory at Whitley Bay, were other essential witnesses.

There are also many journalists to thank, but I would particularly single out Mike Ellis, Bob Harris and John Keith from the national press, Phil McNulty from the *Liverpool Echo* and John Burgum from the *Swansea Evening Post*. Ian Cole at the *Daily Express* and Colorsport supplied a few of the photographs. Richard Shepherd at BBC Wales, Jimmy Case and Jonathan Plummer at Granada provided video clips of Ray's career, and Neil Duncanson of Chrysalis permitted me free access to all the footage collected during the production of *Ray of Hope*. John Toshack, manager of

Real Sociedad, and Sir Stanley Matthews were not afraid to tell their side of the story. Dr Koulis Kyriallis, Nicosia neurologist and Red supporter, supplied information and photographs from Ray's Larnaca days and my colleague, Dr David Bates from the Royal Victoria Infirmary in Newcastle-upon-Tyne, provided details of the onset of Ray's Parkinson's disease.

Jo Butler and Jill Ockelford prepared the manuscript and provided oodles of psychotherapy, my father proof-read and Arianne Burnette at Pelham Books edited judiciously. My wife Juana not only convinced me that I should take on this labour of love, but also helped with much of the background research in the North-East. George, my son, helped with data collection and has been instrumental in rekindling my passion for football. Finally, to my daughter Nathalie, my thanks and kisses for her timely interventions with encouragement and cups of coffee.

Ray Kennedy's Acknowledgements

WITHOUT Dr Andrew Lees this book would never have been written. Over the past three years he has become a valued and trusted friend. He has kept me going emotionally as well as medically, offering encouragement and support whenever I needed it most. It is hard for me to begin to express my gratitude for all that he has done and continues to do for me.

The doctor has generously given endless hours of his free time to research and write this book, and I haven't heard him complain once in all our sessions together. Somehow he has managed to convey what I wished to say but didn't always know how to express. In the process, he has created an accurate picture of my life, and me as a person, with an objectivity that has helped me to understand events more clearly.

There is really no adequate way for me to thank Dr Lees for undertaking this project. If I had my choice, the present I would most like to give him is the honour of finding the cure for Parkinson's disease – he deserves it.

The authors and the publisher are grateful to the following for kind permission to reprint copyright material:

Aitken, Stone & Wylie Ltd for 'Upton and Other Parks' by Sebastian Faulks and Sheil Land Associates Ltd for 'Selling Spurs Short' by Hunter Davies in *Saturday's Boys: The Football Experience* edited by H. Lansdown and A. Spillius (HarperCollins); Faber & Faber Ltd for 'Digging' in *Death of a Naturalist* by Seamus Heaney and 'The Men of Terry Street' in *Terry Street* by Douglas Dunn; The Gallery Press and the author for 'One of the Boys' in *Poems 1956–86* by James Simmons; Frank Graham Ltd for 'Sweet Springs in Geordieland' in *A Tree with Rosy Apples* by Sid Chaplin; Victor Gollancz Ltd for *Fever Pitch* by Nick Hornby; A M Heath & Co Ltd for *News of the World* by George Barker; Steven Kelly for extract from *Through the Wind and Rain*; Jeff Kent, Reg Berks and Mick Cullerton for extracts from *Port Vale Tales*; Lennard Publishing for *Mark Lawrenson: The Autobiography*; Littlewood Arc for 'Urban Programme' by Steve Edwards in *Northern Poetry* No. 1 edited by C. Byron and J. Lyons; The Estate of Roald Dahl and Murray Pollinger for *Charlie and the Chocolate Factory* by Roald Dahl (Penguin Books Ltd); Peterloo Poets for 'Elegy for My Mother' in *Late Harvest* by John Ward; Peters Fraser & Dunlop Group Ltd for 'Bulletins' and 'Head Injury' in *After the Merrymaking* by Roger McGough; Robbins Music Ltd and Ewan MacColl for 'Dirty Old Town' by Ewan MacColl; Robson Books for *Terry-Thomas Tells Tales: An Autobiography* with Terry Daun; Routledge for 'Ghosts' by Peter Redgrove; Seven Locks Press for *Inside Parkinson's: A Patient's View* by Sidney Dorros; Sheil Land Associates Ltd and Mainstream Publishing for *The Glory Game* by Hunter Davies; Stanley Paul for *Brian Clough* by Tony Francis; Dr Cecil Todes and *The Lancet* for 'Inside Parkinsonism – A Psychiatrist's Personal Experience' by Dr Cecil Todes; Warner Chappell Music Ltd and The Smiths for 'Half a Person' by Morrissey and Johnny Marr; A. P. Watt Ltd for *Only a Game?: Diary of a Professional Footballer* by Eamon Dunphy; Weidenfeld & Nicolson for *Back in Touch* by Stanley and Mila Matthews with Don Taylor, *A Lifetime in Football* by Bob Paisley and *I Did It the Hard Way* by Tommy Smith. Appendix 5 is reproduced by kind permission of Raven Press, New York.

Introduction

THE first really effective treatment for Parkinson's disease became available on prescription in 1971, the year Arsenal won the Double. It was also about the time that George Best was banned for disreputable behaviour, Bobby Moore was framed in Colombia before the Mexico World Cup, and sixty-six people died tragically at Ibrox during a Rangers *v* Celtic derby. Edward Heath had come to power and the postmen were out on strike. I was house physician at St Stephen's Hospital, Chelsea, and will never forget the effect of L-dopa on a helpless, chairbound, trembling wreck of a lady who had been admitted from a local nursing home. Two weeks after starting the new therapy, she was able to leave the hospital, walking unaided, and for the first time in eight years could dress, feed and bathe herself. Several years earlier, as an impressionable and aspiring scientist, I had been equally amazed by the first *Your Life in Their Hands* programme, introduced by Sir Charles Fletcher, in which a brain surgeon delicately introduced a probe deep into the brain, burnt away a few thousand nerve cells, and stopped a devastating hand tremor on the opposite side of the body dead in its tracks.

I first met Ray Kennedy in a newspaper photograph: a matador oozing control, force and steel, an image linked in my subconscious with strains of 'Maggie May' and 'Let It Be', and King's Road dolly birds. The names of Kennedy and Radford were scribbled on schoolgirls' exercise books, revered in the Islington tap rooms and feared by visiting defences. On quiet autumn evenings I can sometimes pull back Arsenal cameos: Charlie George's decisive strike in the Cup Final against Liverpool still induces pangs of colic, and there are lasting memories, too, of Peter Storey ruthlessly cutting high-flying strikers down to size. Ray Kennedy's crucial header against Spurs to win the League title, however, is nowhere to be found among these mental images.

When Bill Shankly resigned from Liverpool in 1974 I was studying for postgraduate examinations and I remember thinking that Liverpool would be back in the Second Division before too long. Ray Kennedy's simultaneous transfer has disappeared into a vacuum, and I have no recollection of his first troubled games for Liverpool, up front with Phil Boersma, then Kevin Keegan. I suspect, in common with many other Liverpool supporters at the time, Ray grew on me slowly and, even after seven distinguished years at the club, remained something of an enigma, ever present yet difficult to categorize. I was more impressed by the mercurial cunning of Kenny Dalglish, the spectacular threatening outside hiking runs of Steve Heighway and the uncompromising defiance of Tommy Smith. However, I can still picture Ray Kennedy's life-saving goals in Europe – Liverpool often with their backs against the wall – his uncanny vision and his searching first touch balls down the left side. Souness, McDermott, Case and Kennedy, the best midfield ever to grace British football: together they were an impregnable wall; individually, unique talents all capable of scoring spectacular goals. Kennedy was the ghost in the Liverpool machine, his style of play was singularly unusual for the English game, and his modesty resulted in an underestimation of his worth by the footballing public. His fellow professionals, on the other hand, were in no doubt about his natural abilities, and the Kop, though never sanctifying him, grew to respect him. In Europe he was considered one of England's finest players.

During his playing career, despite being rated by Jimmy Greaves as the player of the seventies, Kennedy had always rejected overtures by journalists to write his life story, largely I suspect because he rightly considered that football was for playing. To Ray, playing football was Heaven, talking about it was Hell, and writing about it was a waste of time.

At the age of thirty-five, Ray Kennedy was diagnosed as having Parkinson's disease. Four years later, in 1990, the face of a football hero filed away among fond Anfield memorabilia became that of my patient, in need of advice, support and care for a constellation of capricious and enigmatic disturbances of body movement. Not long after we had met for the first time, Ray drew a parallel between himself and the Elephant Man. It was an indication of how desperate he felt. As a medical student at the Royal London Hospital, Whitechapel, I had learned my human anatomy beneath the Elephant Man's skeleton. I had been milk-nursed on the melodramatic tale of the deformed fairground freak, Joseph Merrick, who had been rescued by a young surgeon, Frederick Treves. Treves was responsible for arranging permanent accommodation for Merrick in a room in the garret of the London Hospital. At the end of each day he would visit Merrick and, with time, learned to decipher his strained and faltering speech. Treves, who had initially considered the Elephant Man to be a dullard and simpleton, concluded that he possessed a considerable innate intelligence which was barred from expression by his facial mask and problems with communication. Many patients with Parkinson's disease are also quite wrongly accused of being cold and unfeeling because of their facial impassivity, or are treated as drunks or imbeciles because of their slurred speech. A whole segment of Treves's life and career became intertwined with Merrick's destiny.

Like Merrick, Ray Kennedy has become a famous patient, known to all travellers on the London Underground, where his face can be seen on posters promoting the good works of the Parkinson's Disease Society. Like Treves, I have become engrossed in my patient's predicament, and he has undoubtedly become a special case. There the similarities between the stories end. Ray is not physically deformed and, at times, he is accused by members of the public of malingering because he looks so well. However, without warning he can become even more incapacitated than Merrick, out of control, unable to move and incapable of making binding decisions.

My case report published in the medical press and appended to this book is my tribute to Ray Kennedy as a patient. It is a clinical account in which his fascinating medical history has been used to marshal evidence for a scientific hypothesis.

This story is my tribute to Ray Kennedy as a man and a friend trying to face life as an invalid. It is a biography of human movement in health and illness, if such a thing is possible. Descriptions of goals can never compete with being there, or even with video footage. At best they are essays of regret. Nor can descriptions of Parkinson's disease ever convey the desolation and restrictions the illness brings. Authorized biographies by definition are censored documents, but Ray would have hated a ghost-written hagiography. His full co-operation has also enabled me to convey intimate details of his illness which would otherwise constitute a breach of professional confidence.

In Ray's mind the emergence of Parkinson's disease provided

the justification for this book and explains his choice of biographer. While many of his contemporaries navigate the stormy seas of football management, Ray daily confronts an even fiercer adversary. He has been reborn as a hero of the people, but his fans are no longer chanting on the North Bank or on the Kop, instead they are the thousands of people battling against Parkinson's disease to whom his courage and unshakeable optimism have given renewed hope and inspiration.

1 The Shaking Palsy

I'm grateful and will always be grateful for a Geordie upbringing, a Geordie twang and the Geordie sense of humour which has given me about sixteen million laughs against all the odds in this sad and sticky world.

And if I am ever up against it — and I mean really fighting — I hope there's one voice around to shout 'Gan on kidder, get stuck in.'

Then win or lose, I shall be ready to square my account.

(SID CHAPLIN)

IN 1986, on one of those bleak, early autumn evenings with the wind whipping in off the Northumbrian coast and the night falling like a lead weight from the sky, Dr Daniel McDonald Kerr, after a particularly hectic evening surgery, popped into the Three Horse Shoes in Horton. There he was greeted by one of his patients, Ray Kennedy, who was having a drink with his mates after their weekly five-a-side football game. Ray was drenched in sweat and looked drained, and Dr Kerr became concerned when he learned that the men's match had finished more than two hours earlier. (In fact, since his return to the North-East, Ray had visited Dr Kerr's surgery on a number of occasions with vague complaints of tenseness, chest discomfort and shaking, and had been referred to the local hospital for a barium meal X-ray which had reassuringly been reported as normal.) Before leaving the pub, he told Ray to come to the surgery the following day so that he could take a look at him. Dr Kerr's blunt request brought to a head Ray's mounting concern that there was something drastically wrong with him. He found this hard to put into words, but it culminated in a feeling that his head would explode.

That night in bed, like Alexander the Great, Ray knew that his life would be glorious, but short. Nightmares of the cajoling and well-meaning bullying he had received from the Liverpool boot room to get him properly fit flooded back, and painful flashbacks of his unhappy days at Swansea Football Club loomed like threatening pit heads in the gloom. Ignominious hallucinations of his pathetic lumbering and staggering at Hartlepool Rovers reared out of the black emptiness. He recalled those first ephemeral quivers of his right index finger after gruelling training spells and relived the horrors of his failing abilities to stretch for balls on the right side. He suffered the nauseous, suffocating burning in his throat first kindled in those solitary training laps at the Vetch Field – a punishment meted out by his desperate manager. The watershed age of thirty had been used to explain his lacklustre, wooden and sluggish performances and the recurrent muscular injuries to his right leg, but did it really explain his alarming loss of vision and positional sense?

Even in the company of those not fit to lace his boots, he had floundered. Why had he been reluctant to run when coaching in Cyprus? Why had a single drink caused his speech to slur and his right hand to start trembling again? Why had his car started to career involuntarily towards the middle of the road, and why did he always veer to the right when he swam? For two years he had noticed that his handwriting, which had previously been neat, had deteriorated to a childish scribble. He re-lived the acute embarrassment of hardly being capable of signing his name, haunted by the scornful jeers of parents as their children showed his pathetic scribble to them.

Obtuse feelings of his brain wanting to switch sides had been commonplace. Then he remembered that no one had said anything. Surely, if he was so sick, they would have commented. As the perspiration dried, momentarily he was reassured that everything was all right, but then he broke out in sweat again, remembering the difficulty he had had fastening his bootlaces over the last year, the compulsion to move his right hand towards his mouth and the struggle to get his legs working. Why did he now use his left hand to rub shampoo into his hair and why did he have such difficulty wet shaving?

Over the next week or two Ray visited Dr Kerr's surgery several times and was found to have mildly elevated blood pressure; again he complained of shaking and choking. Reluctantly, Ray agreed to go to Newcastle to see a heart specialist at the Royal Victoria Infirmary. Ray remembers that during the consultation on 10 November 1986 he had difficulty keeping still and in finding a comfortable position on the examination couch. The specialist noted his frightened look and persistent trembling, and arranged for him to be seen by Dr David Bates, a consultant neurologist at the hospital.

The following week, Ray's hands were shaking as he turned the pages of a newspaper in the waiting room. On being ushered into the consulting room, he was asked to take his coat off and, before Dr Bates had even asked him what the problem was, to Ray's surprise, the doctor turned to him and said, 'I know what's wrong with you'. Ray remembers that the neurologist put his right wrist through a full range of movements and detected a rachet-like jerkiness. Dr Bates's letter to the heart specialist read as follows:

Dear Doctor,
Thank you for referring this gentleman whom I saw on 17 November 1986. Mr Kennedy is a thirty-five-year-old right-handed publican and former professional footballer who has complained of intermittent shaking of the right hand for the past three years and who, together with his wife, has noticed a progressive slowing of his movements. I regret to say that on examination there can be no reasonable doubt but that he has Parkinson's disease, which is more marked on the right than the left, and although he has little tremor his habit of heading footballs may be of more than coincidence. I am arranging for him to have a brain scan and I have asked Dr Kerr to give him treatment with Sinemet Plus, half a tablet three times daily. I will review him in five weeks' time.

On hearing Dr Bates's diagnosis Ray was stunned, but subconsciously completely rejected it. He recalled a stooped, cachectic old man called Joe who drooled, shuffled and shook from Parkinson's disease, who regularly frequented Ray's pub, the Melton Constable, and whose disabilities bore no resemblance to his own. Dr Bates went on to inform Ray that, although he could not cure him, tablets would control his symptoms, and recommended some reading material about the malady. Ray's vehement

denial of the diagnosis led to an immediate row with Jenny, his
wife, who in a tearful, distressed state warned Ray that he might
end up in a mental hospital if he did not confront the situation
realistically. Why me? How did I get it? were the questions that
Ray kept asking as the anger and fear welled up. However,
within a few days Ray felt strong enough to tell his parents
about the diagnosis, and his mother recalls him informing them,
almost with a sense of relief, that finally the doctors had got to
the bottom of his problem. Veronica Kennedy had known for
some time that Ray was not himself. She remembered commenting to her daughter, Janet, that the drenching sweats and
trembling her son had experienced after he and Jenny had taken
over the Melton Constable were not normal. His complaints of
tiredness and of his head feeling too heavy for his body and his
increasing irritability had finally been diagnosed as 'the old man's
disease'. Over the next weeks and months she prayed that the
diagnosis was wrong and that her beloved son would be cured
by a miracle.

Ray was obliged to wait in suspense until after Christmas
when the brain scan could be carried out. He had become
increasingly anxious that a tumour or cyst would be found, and
on the day of the test was in a dreadful, terrified state. On
learning that the scan was clear, he was so overjoyed that for a
few hours he forgot altogether that there was supposed to be
something wrong with him and felt back to his old self. As the
tablets prescribed by Dr Bates began to take effect over the next
few weeks, Ray started to feel better than he had done for
several years, and finally began to accept that the diagnosis was
correct.

After the diagnosis of Parkinson's disease had been made,
family, friends and acquaintances began to talk. Ray's tiredness
had been a standing joke at home for many years. His mother
remembers him having to return home from many family outings
prematurely because of fatigue, even in the heyday of his playing
career. On New Year's Day, 1983, Ray's brother Trevor remembers Ray complaining of aching down the whole of the right
side, stiffness of the right shoulder and an inability to move
freely.

By 1985, people who knew him commented that he looked
like an old man and that he was becoming more and more nervy.

His friends noticed that he was stooped and that he had great difficulty using his right hand, although he could run reasonably well during a game of football. When Ray mentioned some of his symptoms to people in the pub, they would rationalize them by saying, 'Oh, this is a big comedown for you', and attributed his complaints to the difficulty of coping with the curtailment of a glamorous career in football. Try as he might, he was unable to convince people that anything was wrong. The mild slurring of his speech, the shakiness when holding pints or handling change in the till, his irritability and withdrawal raised suspicions of alcohol abuse among the Melton Constable's clientele. Dr Kerr, too, had attributed his early symptoms to an agitated depression brought on by the painful adjustments all famous footballers have to make on retirement. He also knew that Ray's marriage was going through an extremely difficult time. So gradual are the inroads of Parkinson's disease and so unusual is the disorder in a young man that such a diagnosis had never been contemplated.

Yet within six years of reaching the peak of a glittering, lucrative and highly successful football career, during which he had won every honour in the game, Ray Kennedy, former England international, had been left to fight his battle against an incurable movement disorder alone, abandoned by a fickle public, in debt and soon to be divorced. His struggles were now those of getting dressed, feeding himself, walking to the end of the road and making himself understood clearly. Aspirations of a successful career in football management had become no more than a pipe dream, and even kicking a ball in the street with his son was a Herculean task. A man whose sheer physical presence had sent shivers down opponents' spines was now an isolated, insecure, increasingly suspicious, shuffling shadow at the mercy of hangers-on, oddballs and cheapskates.

2 Seaton Delaval

My grandfather cut more turf in a day
Than any other man on Toner's bog.
Once I carried him milk in a bottle
Corked sloppily with paper. He straightened up
To drink it, then fell to right away
Nicking and slicing neatly, heaving sods
Over his shoulder, going down and down
For the good turf. Digging.

The cold smell of potato mould, the squelch and slap
Of soggy peat, the curt cuts of an edge
Through living roots awaken in my head.
But I've no spade to follow men like them.

(SEAMUS HEANEY)

SEATON DELAVAL is the improbable name of a former pit village, its rambling council estates now suspended in limbo somewhere between heritage Northumbria and the more genteel northern suburbs of Newcastle-upon-Tyne. It conjures up vistas of a fading south coast spa with grand esplanades, a rusting pier-head and decaying rows of dingy hotels. Indeed, Seaton Delaval seems as misplaced as the swarthy Kennedys who have lived in this settlement near the sea since its stirrings with the rush for black gold one hundred and fifty years ago. Boys still kick footballs in Seaton Delaval, the pub remains, but its heart was ripped out thirty years ago, with the closure of the pit leaving people with an impenetrable emptiness and aching nostalgia.

Heading north from the Tyne Tunnel you suddenly turn into the Avenue, a regal, windswept thoroughfare bordered by tall sycamores whose branches caress and intertwine above the road, walling off the lowering mackerel sky. As you walk its length you can imagine momentarily the ruling noblemen of France cantering sedately back from the hunt, but then the railway webs, Stephenson's Rocket and the never-ending caravans of pig iron, slack and human sweat flood in to interrupt and confuse the tapestry. Nearby two stone pillars mark the spot where Admiral George Delaval was dragged, dying, after he fell from his mount. Then, a little way further on, just off the path, cold grey walls announce Seaton Delaval Hall. Gales howl through balustrades built in the wake of storms; the Hall's huge courtyard stretches its arms to the sea and Scotland. Generations of miners' children have watched from outside the walls of this enchanted palace, hoping for a glimpse in the gloam of the White Lady peering from her room on the first floor on the north side of the building, and in these forbidden territories the Kennedy boys spent halcyon days bird-nesting. To the villagers of Seaton Delaval the Hall was a mysterious foreign world, but one which had controlled and moulded them far more than they would ever discern from the occasional public garden party.

The Delaval family came to Seaton Moor from France at the time of the Norman Conquest, and then resisted the Magna Carta before engaging in a series of border forays into Scotland. In the seventeenth century Sir Ralph Delaval built Seaton Sluice to carry out salt and coal, and a century later John Delaval made the long cut between the rocks, providing a new entrance and a deep-water dock, which led to the rise of the port to an importance even greater than that of its rival, Blyth. At the same time, John's brother Thomas opened a glass factory, a brickyard and a brewery, bringing skilled workers into the town from Germany. Not long after Vanbrugh had built the present Hall, the Delaval ram's head crest spoke and decreed that none of the male members of the family would die in their beds of natural causes. This prophecy was eerily fulfilled in the next three Delaval generations, and the family then seemed to go into an inexorable moral decline in the era of the Gay Delavals, renowned as practical jokers, spendthrifts and great lovers of the arts. On Edward Delaval's death in 1814, the ancestral home for more than seven hundred years passed into the hands of Sir Jacob Astley from Melton Constable, a Member of Parliament for Norfolk. Shortly after this transfer of power from one established English family to another, a fire gutted the central block, which then remained derelict until the present Earl Hastings, who lives in the west wing of the Hall, began restoration. The Earl has been President of the British Epilepsy Association for many years; his eldest son, born in Delaval Hall, is now a member of the cast of *The Archers*, under his stage name, Delaval Astley.

Although a small, thriving community remained at Seaton Sluice into the nineteenth century, only a few scattered farmhouses existed on Seaton Moor, and the hamlet of Wheatridge, which was to become Seaton Delaval, had a static population of only two hundred and forty people in 1820. Coal had been mined in this area of Northumberland since the thirteenth century, when it was dug by the monks, and bell pits, in which labourers gnawed into the seams and then packed them up again, had been in operation since the sixteenth century. A few mine shafts, going down fifty to seventy metres and worked by forty to fifty miners, were also in operation in the eighteenth century; the coal was used for domestic fires and the local brewing, soap and brickmaking industries. Large quantities of this 'sea coal' were also shipped to London, so that by the late eighteenth century more than a thousand ships of various kinds were carrying coal out of the North-East. The coal was pulled in trucks, by pit horses, along wooden wagon ways to the staithes at Seaton Sluice and Blyth and then transferred to the colliers for shipment south.

The mining explosion in the North-East really took off in the wake of the Industrial Revolution with the development of the steam engine and new methods of mass production in the iron industry. People flooded down from Scotland, and Welsh sheep farmers and Cornish tin miners headed north in the hope of steady labour. Although the bulk of the Irish fleeing the potato famine settled in the north-west, many also came through Scotland to the north-east, hoping to reap rich rewards from the black diamond rush. By the middle of the nineteenth century, the whole of south-east Northumberland had been turned into a frontier zone. Ashington, a few miles up the road from Seaton Delaval, and the home of the Milburns and the Charltons, was transformed within a few years from a hamlet of homesteads to the biggest pit village in the world. Squalid rookeries of miners' rows were crammed between increasing numbers of pit heads linked by ever deepening shafts to form an impressive web of industry. Felham Down, Bothal, Duke, Carl, Shilbottle, Pegswood, Woodham and Whittle were names which rang out with the newfound Geordie pride. The back-breaking labour and the need for teamwork led to intense feelings of loyalty, clear identification with the local pit and tightly knit communities. Around these industrial shrines new and lasting roots were being forged in the hope of future prosperity and a better life.

In 1826, the Cramlington pit was sunk by the Seaton Delaval Coal Company, and such was its success that Sir Jacob Astley, then owner of Seaton Delaval Hall, granted a lease for Joseph Lamb, William Wharton Burdon, Thomas Barnes and John Straker of Cramlington to sink another pit in 1838. Three shafts were sunk by a German company and named AB Shaft, CD Shaft and EF Shaft. This pit became known as the Seaton Delaval pit and, together with the neighbouring shafts at Cramlington and Hartley, was soon connected to the sea by a standard gauge railway through Seghill; the wagons were pulled by the very first steam locomotives. With the help of newly invented steam engines and exhaust fans, drainage and ventilation could be considerably improved, allowing the miners to go ever deeper with their picks, shovels and Davy lamps. Pit ponies pulled trucks through the main underground passages, but in the narrower confines women and children still had to go down on all fours with trucks harnessed to their waists and carry loaded baskets up ladders to the surface.

It is probable that the Kennedy family arrived in Northumberland about this time, together with hordes of other Celtic labourers, hard as steel, used to living rough and raised on a diet of gruelling uninterrupted manual labour. Strong Irish communities continue to this day in the Newcastle suburbs of Jarrow and Hebburn or, as the locals call it, 'a little bit of Hebburn'.

Within three years of the sinking of the pit, the population of Seaton Delaval had grown to 1,568, and by 1850 it had doubled. At its peak the pit was producing 207,000 tons of coal a year and employing eight hundred men. The Hastings Arms was built to provide Saturday solace for the miners, and a clutch of Anglican chapels to restore their faith and provide hope; a Co-op store supplied them with groceries. The outside world became more accessible once a small railway station was built in 1847. Boxes with slate lids built from locally quarried stone were the people's homes. First Row, close to the shaft, was built for the gaffers and their families, then came long parallel rows of back-to-back miners' cottages separated by cart tracks and pungent quagmires. For a hundred years, shift in shift out, generation after generation, teams of men dug coal shoulder to shoulder, hour after hour,

locked in darkness like caged animals. The people of the new
Seaton Delaval village lived out of one another's hands, married
among themselves, shared burdens and troubles, and rejoiced at
minor triumphs such as bonuses or the birth of a healthy child.
Even the supervisors and pit owners, the gentry of First Row,
mixed freely with the men and played an active part in the
community. Help never had to be sought in Seaton Delaval, it
was offered automatically and this created a feeling of belonging and emotional security. However, strangers or newcomers,
although greeted courteously, were not easily accepted or welcomed. Most of the villagers were decent folk with stereotyped,
conformist existences, some never going beyond the confines of
this narrow world from cradle to grave. Individuality was not
encouraged. Men were distinguished by virtuous prowess on the
field of play or by reputations as drinkers, fighters, gamblers or
womanizers. These were the only available ways of breaking free
from an obligatory social and cultural corset. Faced with these
adversities, the women became fanatically houseproud, tidy and
possessive of their men. Loss of a husband from TB or silicosis
frequently meant the loss of what amounted to a tithe home.

It was into this world that Martin Kennedy, his three brothers,
Larry, Howard and Jim, and his elder sister, Jenny, were born. It
was a world centred on a thriving pit, supplying Britain's needs
with coal to spare to export profitably to other parts of Europe;
but the miners' standard of living improved hardly at all. By
1926 winds of change were blowing; the mining industry was
running into trouble from keen European competition and a
failure to modernize uneconomical pits. It was a time of wage
cuts and dismissals. Money was always in short supply, and the
threat of ill-health was a constant dread for families. Damp,
insanitary housing, minimal education and appalling child mortal-
ity figures led to an overwhelming despair that culminated in the
Jarrow Hunger March, in which miners demanded better pay,
living conditions and working hours, and in the ill-fated General
Strike, with class conflict continuing to motivate industrial unrest.
At this time more than two-thirds of the National Wealth was
owned by one per cent of the population. During the General
Strike the army blocked food supplies to mining villages, and the
middle and upper classes volunteered to take over the miners'
work for the good of the country. All this was becoming harder

and harder to bear as newsreels, movies and magazines brought images to the mining villages of a better life and world outside.

The Kennedy home, on a miners' row, consisted of a large room downstairs and an upper room reached by a ladder. Water came from a tap outside and the communal toilet, the 'netty,' was across the road. When Martin Kennedy was a small boy, his grandfather used to deliver coal by horse and cart to the family home and sell ducks' eggs to the neighbours. Martin had the standard rudimentary education, considered a blessing only in the sense that it mercifully postponed subterranean life for a few more years. He was one of the brightest of his class, but this made little difference to his future, as all the lads were predestined for the pits, like their fathers before them. The possibility of other options was not even discussed. Football was not the major love of Martin's life, and he was only called on to make up the numbers. At the age of fourteen he was sent to the Seaton Delaval pit and started on the night shift from midnight to 8 a.m. He can still remember his terrifying journey down the back row and across a field full of terrifying phantoms and imaginary intruders to reach the security of the pits where he met the other novices who would become his 'marras', or work-mates. Martin's father also was working the night shift, but was allowed to arrive at the pit a little later than his son; their contact at work was minimal. For the next twenty years Martin Kennedy would work these shifts, grateful for continuing employment.

Florence Veronica Armstrong, Ray's mother, was born of good Northumbrian stock, an intermingling of Roman, Viking and Pict, tough-minded, long-suffering and full of common sense. Her father, too, went down the Seaton Delaval pit, but died of meningitis when she was only nine years old. This led to eviction from their colliery house. Her brother was sent to live with Nan Armstrong and her mother went out to work to boost her widow's pension of ten shillings a week. A woman's life in a pit village was, if anything, even more narrow than a man's and was geared round learning to keep her menfolk content by massaging their egos. Girls played with dolls while boys kicked balls.

Veronica recalls many happy summer days walking to Dickie Birds corner on the Avenue leading to Seaton Delaval Hall. After she left school, she worked in a small bakery preparing the staple

Geordie diet of discus-shaped stotty cakes; her brother joined the Air Force as an engineer and some of her friends cycled to Whitley Bay to clean the big seafront houses. Whereas a few lucky men might escape the pits through professional football, occasionally girls escaped the drudgery of a pit man's wife by taking a secretary's job in a solicitor's office in Newcastle.

When Veronica went to visit her grandmother, who lived in the nearby homestead of Seghill, she sometimes met Martin Kennedy, whose aunt lived next door. Their friendship blossomed over the next three years into a full-blown courtship fed by weekly visits to one of the three Seaton Delaval dance halls. On 31 July 1948, when Veronica was nineteen and Martin twenty-five, they were married in the little church in Seaton Delaval and went to live in an upstairs tenement at 24, Milbourne Terrace, above Veronica's mother.

Each evening Martin would cross the fields with his marras and return eight hours later crusted with grime, scarred blue and ready for his hot bath in front of the huge colliery fire. The family tin bath was kept on a hook on the wall; the water was heated by Veronica over the fire and stirred with blades. Martin frequently left his back unwashed, as superstition decreed that scrubbing a miner's shoulder blades sapped his strength. He remembers one of his friends at the weekly dance starting to perspire profusely, whereupon his filthy back left a huge embarrassing black stain on his shirt, which did his chances with the young lady he had invited to dance no good at all. On getting out of the tub, Martin would dress and light his pipe, and sit relaxing on his cracket, a three-legged stool kept downstairs.

Each Wednesday Veronica 'dadded' his clothes against the back wall to shake off the asphyxiating dust and congealed mud. They were then dumped in the poss-tub with grated blue soap flakes. The heavy wooden poss-stick, with prongs at its base and a shovel-like handle at the top, was then thumped up and down for hours by the women who, not surprisingly, developed muscles to match their husbands'. During these back-breaking sessions the women in the lane would congregate in the wash-house while the clothes boiled, and talk through their news and troubles. Ironing was an equally onerous chore done with huge gas irons.

In his spare time Martin grew leeks and entered them for competitions at the Astley Arms, or played billiards or bowls at the Seaton Delaval Miners' Institute. On a Saturday night Martin would have his statutory dose of 'broon-dog' dressed in the regimental flat cap and muffler. The men of Seaton Delaval were hard and dour, called a spade a spade and took pride in their work at the coal-face. The brutality of their lives made them feel apart from other men and in a sense more deserving of their transient escapes into the pubs and dance halls. Occasionally, a guest speaker would come to talk to them about politics or local history, and there was a small selection of books at the Institute which the miners could take home on loan. Martin sometimes attended the Northumberland miners' galas at Bedlington or Blyth, where all the pit men would congregate to listen to the trade union leaders, the Labour politicians of the day, and the local brass bands. Groups of pit men stuck tightly together on these occasions, each with its own special line of patter: some debated pit conditions, while others talked about football. Leeks, whippets and pigeons were other staple topics of conversation. To most miners these were red-letter days, looked forward to with great excitement for months in advance.

Three years after their marriage, on 28 July 1951, Raymond Kennedy was born with his umbilical cord knotted round his neck. It was a sultry evening and the whole of the long road was out sitting and talking in the back row. The next day everyone flocked in to see the new bairn. Many were struck by the distinctive olive skin and black hair inherited from his father, which were relatively uncommon in the North-East but ubiquitous on the west coast of Ireland, where commercial links with Spain and Portugal over centuries led to frequent intermarriage. Ray was weaned on his mother's milk and baptized at the little village church.

His mother took him, when he was still a baby, to Wheatridge Park to soak in the atmosphere of the football matches. Almost as soon as he could walk he was out kicking a ball: thud, thud, thud against the coal-house door for hours on end, except when his father was home from the night shift and needing sleep. Only darkness, snowstorms, meals or bedtime interrupted this heaven-on-earth existence. A trip to the shops was turned into a wonderful opportunity to try to tame the capricious playmate who ran away from him and refused to be controlled by naked aggression, but could be held fleetingly to ransom by skill and imagination. Ray's first field was the back row where he lived, the goal was the end of the street, his opponents lampposts. This was his idyllic childhood world, though in some senses it was impoverished and restricted. Hour after hour, week after week, he would juggle the ball with his feet until he laid down motor programmes which would be automatically and intuitively recalled in adult life. The ball became an appendage. Ray remembers 'banging the ball against the garage doors at the back for hours, taking the ball on the first bounce and hammering it back, seeing how many times I could do this without stopping. When the ball ran away from me I would put myself under pressure by saying that if I could control it before it reached a certain mark on the ground I'd play for England. If I did it I'd feel reassured; if I didn't I'd just carry on until I'd mastered it.'

This is the stereotyped, intense, ritualistic dedication that is described over and over again in the biographies of our football heroes. For example, Sir Stanley Matthews from the age of seven was kicking a rag ball all day on the Meakins, or dribbling a tennis ball between kitchen chairs or ten or twelve people he had lined up in a row. Hughie Gallagher, born in the coal and steel town of Belshill ten miles from Glasgow, kicked anything that moved — stones, cans, bundles of rags — before he graduated to become a 'tanna ba' player biffing a tuppenny rubber ball on the playground. Jackie Milburn would kick a stone all the way down the gutters of unmade streets and hurry home to start up a football game with twenty or thirty of his friends. George Best was so football daft that he would take his ball to bed with him for comfort.

As a small boy, Ray Kennedy clung to Veronica's apron strings, pulling on her arm if she dared to stop and chat with neighbours, pursuing her to the netty and spending long happy hours with her in the kitchen. Ray describes himself as 'a mummy's boy', who helped with all the domestic chores, particularly with the baking which he loved, always licking the cake mixture bowl clean with his tongue at the end. Like many first-born children, he developed an especially close relationship with his mother, who showered him with love and affection. Ray would cry and scream if she ever tried to escape from the house for an occasional night out. If she went to have an afternoon nap at her mother's, Ray would become so distressed by her absence that he would go to shake and rouse her. Once she was so desperate to get out of the house that she decided to make a lifelike dummy and place it on the chair in the living room in the hope that Ray, playing outside with his friends, would not guess that she had slipped out for an hour or two. If his mother disappeared even for a few minutes, Ray remembers getting into a blind panic and screaming the place down.

When Raymond was three, the family moved to a slightly larger colliery home at 55, Foremans Row, a long row of terraced cottages with a pub at one end and a shop at the other. There was a large stuffy room downstairs dominated by the statutory hearth and colliery fire. Across the busy road at the front was the garden where Ray kept his pet rabbit and Martin grew leeks. The back path was made of clinkers; the middens were on the other side. Blacklocks (Geordie cockroaches) abounded in the walls of the houses. Not long after the move Raymond's brother Trevor was born; the two boys were extremely close throughout childhood and remain good friends.

Toilet facilities continued to be primitive in the pit villages, with the netty in the back row consisting of an earth closet and a seat with a large hole below it. Men in midden cars would come down the back lane every day, lift up the flap and shovel the excrement rapidly into the car. An amusing incident occurred when Raymond was four or five years old: 'I remember going to the netty on my own, sitting there, when suddenly a train nearby blew its whistle and I was so shocked I fell down the hole and had to be rescued and then cleaned up'.

Ray started school in Seaton Delaval at the age of five; he cried his eyes out for a day at the thought of leaving home, but his parents were adamant that he must go. However, within an hour or two of arriving at the school, he soiled his pants and had to be taken home by his grandma, and spent the rest of the day with her. His education was to prove one long game of football with a bit of learning thrown in.

If you go past Ray's old school playground today, you will still see tangles of boys engrossed in chasing a ball, their faces set fiercely against defeat. In Ray's day lads from Seaton Delaval were still being bred for the pit although, if they wished to venture further afield, opportunities were available in the shipyards or in the building trade, and light industry was arriving on the Cramlington Industrial Estate. Art galleries, the poetry of Keats and quantum physics were irrelevancies reserved for the gaffers' children or the patronizing middle classes of Gosforth. Art for the masses, Melvin Bragg and *The South Bank Show*, and Eric Burdon and the Animals had not yet arrived in Seaton Delaval. Imaginative expression, when and where it existed, was channelled into the poetry of football.

These were still the days when top professional footballers were perceived as representing all that was heroic in the English working class. They were romantics who played for honour and enjoyment, not for money. These were the times when the players lived in terraced tenements near the pit shaft and somewhere near you. The players were respected locally but ignored elsewhere. Alf Ramsey, who had thirty-one international caps, went on Eamonn Andrews' popular television programme *What's My Line* and was not recognized by a single member of the panel even when they took their blindfolds off. Here, in the dotted clusters of ball-kicking youths seen on every corner and in every park, survival was at play. Within a few of these moving dots, poverty bred an anger and a hunger and, with it, an unquenchable desire for fame and success.

Ray was one of these dots driven on by his mother's love and his own fear of failure. He wanted to be one of those brutalized and alienated, hard and damaged Geordie boys who dodged the rat traps and glimpsed the golden skyline. As a result of these early confrontations, Ray soon became aware that he had some natural ability, but quite how much was something which bedevilled him throughout his subsequent professional football career. He went immediately into the school junior team, playing against older boys, and had his first match when he was six or seven years old:

We used to play these games at Wheatridge Park where Seaton Delaval played their senior matches. I remember the pitch looked enormous and the goal so wide it seemed impossible to miss. Our team scored an early goal and the opposition keeper kicked the ball towards the centre for a kick-off. The ball landed at my feet. I didn't know that you had to restart play from the centre after the kick-off, so I just blasted the ball straight back past the goalie for what I thought was a great goal.

Over the next few years, Ray continued to measure himself against other boys in what proved to be an explosive learning curve facilitated by his innate athletic and ball-controlling skills.

In 1960 the Seaton Delaval pit closed and Ray's father was transferred to Longhirst Drift Pit near Morpeth, where he was to work for a further twelve years. Seaton miners were promised another eighty years' work at Longhirst, but in reality the Northumbrian coal industry was already on its last legs. Many men failed to get work at all, some were transferred to Bates Pit and others sought work on the new industrial estate. Even those Seaton Delaval men who were fortunate enough to find work in other pits felt displaced and disorientated; despair set in, and was often alleviated temporarily in the Astley Arms or some other local hostelry. After he left Longhirst Drift Pit, Martin Kennedy was offered a place at Dudley Pit, a short distance from Seaton Delaval, but at the age of forty-seven he had finally had enough. After a brief spell on the dole, he became the caretaker at the Holywell Junior School, where he worked until his retirement. Veronica found work at the local factory which made Old Spice.

Martin continued his gardening and would meet his former pit mates regularly in the pub at weekends. Although never a football man himself, he supported his son's interest and advised him shrewdly later in his career. Ray's football genes probably came from his mother's side, where some distant football pedigree can be found. Veronica Kennedy's mother's cousins were the talented Stevenson brothers, one of whom – George – played for Aston Villa and England. The other, Clem, started his playing career with Blyth and New Delaval and then joined Herbert Chapman at Huddersfield Town before becoming manager of the Yorkshire side. Another relative of Veronica Kennedy's was Billy Moore, born in 1892, who played for Sunderland and then joined West Ham, where he played in the first Wembley Cup Final in 1923 and gained England amateur international honours. Billy Moore stayed with West Ham as a trainer, and died in the East End of London about the time Ray began his professional career.

Ray's early childhood was happy; he was a robust, hearty child who had hardly a day's ill-health. Despite the industrial morass accumulated in the wake of the mines, Seaton Delaval remains, in many sense, a country village. One of Trevor and Ray's favourite pastimes was to go to Holywell Dene and spend the morning jumping over the beck on a rope, trying to tip the water with their feet. Invariably they would return home soaked in foul-smelling water, which meant even more washing for their hard-pressed mother. Another favourite pastime was bird-nesting in the local nature reserve; Trevor got hold of books to identify the species and their eggs. In those days, however, the nature reserve was patrolled by a tyrannical gamekeeper whose job it was to guard the pheasants on Lord Hastings' estate. If he caught the boys with birds' eggs, he would make them put them between their teeth and then would press their lower jaw until the shells cracked. Ray remembers: 'One day me and a friend were spotted by the gamekeeper, who chased after us across the fields. I escaped easily, but my friend's jeans were so tight he couldn't run and he was caught.'

Ray's childhood was filled with such hilarious escapes from authority. Once he was sitting eating turnips and carrots in a cornfield in New Hartley when the farmer arrived with his men and savage dogs to round up all the children. Ray was one of the few to escape by crawling silently on his knees through the cornfield and out the far side. Even when his come-uppance seemed inevitable, his mother was always there to rescue him. One day, when a policeman knocked on the door to complain that the Kennedy boys had been messing about in the cornfields again, Veronica came to the door and said, 'Get them lasses rounded up before you start picking on the lads, they are three times as bad'. Although the boys were always up to mischief, it was nothing more than the usual childish misdemeanours, for the Kennedy children were brought up with strict moral values and a basic sense of decency and pride.

Michael, Ray's younger brother, was born six years after Ray and three years after Trevor. Like most younger brothers, he had a difficult time and spent most of his early childhood trying to keep up with the two older boys, who would do everything in their power to escape on their own. Michael was the imp of the family and small for his age. Ray can remember Trevor's resentment towards their mother when Michael was born.

When Ray was eight, all the inhabitants of Foremans Row

were moved lock, stock and barrel to Tillmouth Avenue, a long road on a newly built council estate in Holywell. The Kennedys' new home gave the family more room and was kept meticulously tidy by Veronica. Ray had his own little bedroom, and his brothers shared another. The family have remained there ever since, along with most of their neighbours from Foremans Row.

All Veronica Kennedy's energies went into doing the best for her children, making sure they had all the love that she could give them, regular meals and the best clothes they could afford. She did everything in the home, with Martin leaving all the difficult tasks and emotional demands of the family to her. When she was out in the street once with her bairns, a neighbour said to her, 'Eeh, Mrs Kennedy, Ahve yet to see you by yourself, you've always got the bairns with you. You've got the patience of Job with them'. One day, when Ray was about nine years old, he hit a spoilt, adopted girl, who lived up the road, after she had thrown stones at him. The girl's mother had given Ray a clout round the ear which had made him cry. On coming home from bingo and hearing about this, Veronica could not let things rest and stayed up all night tossing and turning. The next day she went round to the girl's house, spoke sharply to the mother and slapped the girl in the face, leaving with the words, 'Well, now you know how I felt the other night. Never touch my son again. Anyone who hurts my family hurts me'.

One of Seaton Delaval's continuing claims to local fame is Arrighi's, its Neapolitan ice-cream parlour, reputed to be the best in the North-East, whose ice-cream is bought by the bucket-load by the locals. The Arrighis have been in the village for more than fifty years now, but when the ice-cream parlour first opened Mr Arrighi would say to Mr Kennedy, 'I'll swap you one of your bambinos for one of my daughters', so impressed was he by the Kennedys' Mediterranean appearance.

Sometimes, when Veronica was out and the boys were alone, Ray was left in charge and given half a crown to buy ice-creams. As soon as their mother went out, the three boys would start fighting and rolling about on the floor. When the ice-cream van's refrain was heard outside, the pandemonium would stop and Ray would rush out to buy the ice-creams. Peace would ensue for fifteen minutes or so while they all licked their cones, after which the playful skirmishing resumed.

Walking was a favourite Kennedy pastime, and they often covered long distances in biting winds heading for the coast at Whitley Bay, Cullercoats or Tynemouth. Ray now jokes that the locals would whisper to one another, 'Watch out, the Kennedys are coming', as the four sturdily built males of the family strode by in similar cardigans. On other occasions Ray would walk several miles to South Shields with his brothers, have chips, lick the top of the sauce bottle and then return home, an exercise which undoubtedly hardened his physical constitution, and introduced him to the North Sea.

Despite their poverty, the family took regular summer holidays for two weeks in caravans, rented flats or boarding houses, usually at the east coast resorts of Scarborough, Whitby or Skegness, but on one occasion they headed west to Morecambe and on another they went even further afield to Kent. Martin Kennedy's view was: 'The only cost of a holiday is the bus fare. You still have to feed the bairns even if you stay at home'. During these holidays Ray was struck, at times, by his father's fearless, unabashed attitude. He recalls him brazenly addressing passers-by with: 'Hey, Jack, where's the Smith lodging?' One day his mother and father were walking down the front at Scarborough arm in arm, and the children were so surprised and unnerved by this that they rushed to their parents to ask whether their mother was all right. The grind and toil of pit life left little room for romance.

As Ray grew older, he became less sociable; he enjoyed his own company, and to a large extent resisted peer pressure. He was happy to spend time with his mother, but his father urged him to get out and deal with his own problems, which he usually did by fighting. Ray's brother Trevor was being terrorized and bullied by a boy who attacked him in the back row every time he went to visit his grandmother. One day Ray waited for the assailant, knocked him off his bike and pursued him. The boy never touched Trevor again. On another occasion, heeding the advice of his father, who had told him that if you can't fight your opponent with your fist pick something up, Ray grabbed a huge brick and chased a lad back to his house, and then hurled the brick through his front-door window. Despite his solitary disposition, Ray was able to take good care of himself: with his physical presence and foot-balling prowess protecting him from the local bullies.

Behind the family house and close to the Seaton Delaval pit stood a towering slag heap. The summit was coated with a shiny black sheen of coal which, if breached by the feet, would lead to the individual sinking dangerously into the powdery coal below. One day Ray and two friends were cycling up the face of this heap when the police came and intervened. Ray and his friends tried to beat a retreat over the summit, but Ray kept slipping back towards the police. Finally he capitulated and, when asked his name, he said 'Raymond Kennedy, sir', and then openly volunteered the names of the other two boys. As a result he escaped with no more than a minor reprimand. In order to survive, he had developed a canny sense of self-preservation.

Ray loved listening to stories and, as he entered his teens, he became a great reader, picking up information on all sorts of subjects. The ability to absorb and act on information given by those he respected would serve him well in the years to come.

Veronica continued to play the role of mother hen, lavishing attention on her children and protecting them against the world's knocks as best she could. Michael used to say to her every day, 'Aren't you pleased you've got me, Mam?' The family nicknamed him 'the jam and bread kid' because he finished every meal with a jam sandwich. Ray, with his highly developed Geordie sense of humour, was constantly teasing his mother and his two brothers and the house was a happy one, full of laughter. Ray recalls scrapping with Trevor and Trevor accidentally banging Ray's head against the toilet. Ray was furious and started chasing his brother all over the house; Veronica, seeing what was going on, then started chasing after Ray. Ray finally ended up on the wash-house roof, teasing his mother that she couldn't catch up with him. Another time, Martin had gone out the back door smoking his pipe and had inadvertently caught it on the washing line. He had been gripping the pipe so tightly that it was pulled out of his mouth and catapulted over into the next garden. Ray's memories of childhood are full of these everyday mischiefs and domestic escapades.

When Ray was thirteen and his mother thirty-eight, Veronica Kennedy was embarrassed to learn that she was pregnant. At first she was too shy to tell the boys, who had never even seen her walk around the house in a slip. When she sat in a chair, she would cover up the expanding abdominal bulge with a newspaper so that no one would suspect. Finally, when she plucked up courage and told them, the boys were thrilled. Because of Veronica's age, she was taken to hospital to have the baby, but Janet, the fourth Kennedy child and the first girl on Martin Kennedy's side for forty-eight years, beat them to it and was born in the ambulance. The following day Veronica had more visitors in hospital than if 'our Janet had been Jesus'. Janet looked very much like Ray, with dark skin and black hair. When Ray came to visit his mother in hospital, he cried and said, 'I want you home, Mam'. Veronica, always attentive to her sons' needs, discharged herself prematurely and came home with baby Janet. The boys adored their new sister and were extremely protective towards her. Bringing up the Kennedy children was left entirely to Veronica Kennedy which, despite the everyday drudgery and strain, brought her a deep, inner contentment. 'I loved my family so much and the children gave me such happiness that I tried to teach them proper values and the right way to live. We were a very close family, probably too close for our own good, and this has brought heartbreak and suffering.'

As Ray entered his teens, he became more suspicious, volatile and perfectionistic. He was tidy about the house, a natty dresser, and developed firm views about what he liked. Contact with his peers centred around never-ending games of football or, in the summer months, cricket, at which he also excelled. By the age of fifteen, he was already a man with an imposing physical presence, oozing a force and venom which fifty years earlier would have been put to good use by the pit owners.

Football was a release for the miners of Seaton Delaval, an exorcism from the harsh, bestial, troglodytic existence which left them drunk on fresh air and blind in sunlight. Everyone worshipped Hughie Gallagher and Wor Jackie, and most of the villagers had one black and one white eye dominantly inherited through successive generations of Magpie supporters. However, there was a sprinkling of Raich Carter admirers, including Ray's uncle Larry, who was a regular visitor to Roker Park. Nowhere else in the country do fans give footballers so much of the hero treatment. Geordies need a folk hero, particularly one who is dashing, dynamic, courageous, and wears a number nine shirt. The rivalry between Newcastle United and Sunderland is on a par with the fervour of Rangers and Celtic without religion to give it a legitimate basis for hatred. Magpie supporters define Sunderland fans as 'those who read the newspapers from the front'. To Newcastle supporters, Sunderland is 'Gateshead without the culture' and 'lacking originality'. Sunderland supporters cheer almost as loudly if Newcastle lose as they do when their own team wins. In 1973, when Sunderland beat Leeds United, then the premier team in the land, such was the fanaticism that television cameras were able to capture Sunderland turned into a ghost town for ninety minutes. Everyone in the North-East supported their local team as well, and Seaton Delaval's ground at Wheatridge Park attracted huge crowds for local derbys in the 1950s. The network of interdigitating leagues can still be found in the region, even if fervour has paled a little with the loss of community loyalty in many of the young.

The players of Seaton Delaval were judged by the miners' own strict, hard-living code, and boys were inculcated from an early age by their parents and grandparents with the history, language and culture of football. The Welfare provided the basic sporting facilities which led to the South Northumberland football factory spawning dozens of local lads who, at weekends, were prised from the pit shafts to play with grown men in violent rival encounters. Running in their blood were the miners' grit and an unquenchable ambition which usually focused on Roker or Gallowgate. The round ball gave these boys the possibility of an easy option, the only escape from a crippling, choking, numbing and frequently short-lived existence. Most of those who were good enough to get out were ruthless and uncompromising, straightforward and reliable, but most of all grateful. The thought of their marras 'stuck down the mines risking their lives day after day' was never far from their thoughts. Football to them, in a way, was a doddle, an agreeable way of extending their childhood. On the other hand, it was a risk; to return rejected from a League club was a failure hard to come to terms with, and emotional casualties of this hit-and-miss system can be found all over Tyneside. From a region that has rarely failed to produce fewer than three players in the national side, the parlous state of Newcastle United and Sunderland Football Clubs remains a deep and inexplicable hurt which can only be blamed on internecine squabbles and misdirection from those who put their own pecuniary interests and personalities above the needs of the clubs and their supporters.

3 The Great Sir Stanley Matthews

Last night I had a curious dream I've never had before
Stan Matthews on the wing for Stoke at the age of eighty-four
And indeed my lads it's true my lads
I've never been known to lie
And if you've been down Bootham Road you'll see the same as I.
(KEELE UNIVERSITY STUDENTS RAG RECORD)

WHEN Janet Kennedy was born, Ray was already heavily involved in school football. At the age of eleven he went straight into the South Northumberland Boys Team and was a regular in the Astley Comprehensive side. When he was not at school, he was out kicking a ball with his friends — games his younger brother Trevor usually managed to inveigle himself into as well. All the signs indicated that Ray was a natural. By the time he was fourteen, his precocious development allowed him to play two or three matches a weekend and compete physically with eighteen-year-olds. About this time he remembers listening to the Cup Final on the radio: 'At half-time a few of us went out into the road to have a kick about for a few minutes and then we went in to catch the second half. After the match we were back in the road, kicking a ball again'.

Ray's parents never applied any pressure or intimated any great expectations for their son on the football field. Neither of them had much of an opportunity to watch him in school games, but passive support was always there from his mother. When Ray needed new boots, he got a pair of the latest continental style one Christmas out of her bingo winnings. Ray has since often asked his mother, 'Mam, what could you have done with that money?' In my many conversations with Ray over the last two years, he has continually reminded me of his debt to her, and his sadness at the difficult life she has led.

Both Ray and Trevor were regularly supplied with a foul-smelling liniment made up at the chemist's, which Veronica would massage into their legs before a match. Michael, who was of a smaller physical frame than the other two Kennedys and the least interested in football, not to be outdone, one day insisted on having his body massaged too, even though he had no intention of playing. Trevor and Ray carried a bottle of this liniment with them in their rucksacks before matches. After games Veronica Kennedy would frequently clean their boots and stuff the insides with paper so they would dry without losing shape. Often as not she would then help the boys dubbin them to preserve the leather.

In his final year at Astley Comprehensive School, the football team had its most impressive season: they headed their league and got to the final of the Blake Cup. Ray captained the side from his inside-left position, wearing the number ten shirt. In the first leg of the Blake Cup, a trophy the school had never won, the side went down 3–1 in Newcastle. Martin Kennedy remembers saying to his son as he left the house on the night of the return leg that they would have no chance of winning. Several hours later, as dusk approached, Martin and Veronica were waiting anxiously for their son to come home. Suddenly, Ray jumped over the garden wall with an enormous grin on his face, holding the cup and happy as a sandboy. The team had defied all the statistics and finished their season on the highest possible note. Rob Bryden, Raymond's games teacher, and now a headmaster in Wallsend, remembers Ray as a skilful competitor who also excelled at other ball games, including basketball. He recalls him as a likeable lad who never got into serious trouble and did not take his school-work too seriously.

Ray's first break came at this time, when he was playing for South Northumberland Boys. Bill Emery, a senior civil servant living in North Shields, was not officially a scout, but he enjoyed watching matches and had agreed to keep an eye out for promising boys for Stanley Matthews, who had recently taken over the manager's job at Port Vale. South Northumberland Boys were not playing particularly well and he was the only scout at one of the games. He noted Ray's strength and, watching him play a second time for a local side against Dudley Welfare, he was further impressed by Ray's goal-scoring abilities as he cracked in a thirty-five-yard goal. Emery visited the Kennedy home and was struck by the great character of Ray's parents and the spotlessness of the front room in Tillmouth Avenue. He then contacted Matthews.

It is impossible to attempt to explain to the young people of today the impact that Stanley Matthews had on football. Such was his genius that people would travel hundreds of miles to watch his magical skills. No one could touch his speed over ten yards and it was virtually impossible to tackle him. The ball was so under his spell that, when dribbling, he was frequently able to take his eyes off the ball in order to mesmerize full backs. Matthews shone above a galaxy of other post-war stars like an incandescent comet. Even in the chauvinistic Tyneside cauldron every school playground had its aspirant Matthews, crossing the ball for Jackie Milburn or Len Shackleton to nod in. Not only was Matthews an undisputed maestro, but he was also respected universally for his inherent love of the game and the natural modesty which seemed to reflect the soul of the respectable working men whom he liberated each Saturday. Matthews looked old at an early age, giving him an impression of timelessness. His pinched, artisan's face and pale lips came straight from the working man's world, and his hooded, impassive eyes concealed a tragic hurt and restless panic born of the need to gain respect by doing a job well. He was the Manolete of his day, a tragic matador, lethal and incisive. Despite being unstoppable, he never exuded flamboyance or exuberance. Off the pitch he was organized, scrupulous and thrifty, always cautious in conversation, a habitual teetotaller and non-smoker with a nervous cough and a passion for carrot juice, who gave the impression that he was constantly threatened by the terrors of debt and poverty. With time, he came to symbolize the beauty and magic of the national game, but his single-mindedness made him a difficult man to live with and, during his final spell with Stoke, his marriage fell apart.

Matthews was fifty-two years old when he visited the Kennedy home in 1966, but he was still turning out regularly in friendly

matches and pursuing his lifelong self-disciplined routine of early
morning training on the Blackpool sands. Each morning he would
rise at daybreak, take a cup of weak tea and drive to the beach,
where he would start limbering up with gentle stretching and
breathing exercises. He would then put himself through a series
of gruelling sprints. This ritual would last for thirty to ninety
minutes depending on how his body reacted to the insult.
One morning, in a torrential storm, he was leaving the house at
dawn as usual, when a friend spotted him and shouted, 'Stan,
you can't be serious?' Matthews replied sardonically, 'It's my
living'.

On finally finishing his playing career at Stoke City, Matthews
was offered the manager's job at Port Vale in Burslem. When he
took over in 1966, the club was languishing, impecunious, in the
Fourth Division. However, his romanticism and love of the club
made him grasp the nettle against his advisers' wishes. He was
content to return to the grassroots of League football and to
dream of restoring a famous club to its former glory, aided and
abetted by Jackie Mudie, his assistant and old playing partner at
Blackpool, and Len Graham, the former Stoke trainer. With his
customary dedication, he threw himself into the thankless task,
leaving his Blackpool home at five o'clock in the morning,
working a fifteen-hour day and depriving himself of any wage. In
the absence of funds to buy new players, he was committed to
rebuilding the club around an active youth development scheme
and, together with Reg Berks, his chief scout, he travelled the
length and breadth of the country visiting schools in search of
new talent. He particularly concentrated his attention on the
hotbeds of the North-East, and there is no doubt that his name
there counted for much in persuading some of the schoolboy
prodigies to join him rather than the more fashionable, larger
clubs.

Bill Emery, Jackie Mudie and Stanley Matthews himself paid a
visit to the Kennedy home. Ray was playing with friends in the
park and was summoned by his brothers to come back immediately as Sir Stanley Matthews wanted to take him down to the
Potteries for trials. Ray's parents were struck by Matthews'
straightforward, almost humble, approach and by his promise
that they could hold him personally responsible for making sure
Ray would be well looked after. Veronica, however, felt that he

was being totally unrealistic as he spoke to Ray about the glory of the game and how it would be a mistake to enter it purely for mercenary reasons.

In his autobiography, *Back in Touch*, Matthews expresses his views on football:

> How the game has changed! When I was fifteen I joined Stoke City office staff at a pound a week and was thrilled — just to have the chance to play football. But by 1965 there was money in the game and things were different. For example I would travel to Newcastle to watch a fourteen year old play. Not once or twice, but three or four times. Then if I thought his game had potential I would go home to meet his family. Dad would sit at the kitchen table over a cup of tea and say 'See this bungalow, it cost £10,000' — and that was the fee Dad was looking for. If I pointed out signing on fees were illegal for youngsters Dad would grin and say 'Dare say you're right, Stan' and that would be the end of the matter. But a month later Jackie Mudie or I would read that the youngster had joined this or that club and we would know Dad had got his bungalow paid for ... Port Vale hadn't even the money to pay my salary, let alone buy bungalows for avaricious fathers. But Jackie and I persevered. Many of the boys we wanted were whisked from under our noses in bungalow deals or more honourably simply because Dad felt his son would have a better future at a bigger club. A boy in football is no different from any young lad starting out in a profession — and the best newspapermen don't all start in Fleet Street any more than the best actor on Broadway. A spell in the provinces learning the craft isn't such a bad thing for a boy. The important thing is to learn, and that often depends on the teacher as well as the pupil.

Bungalow deals never took place at the Kennedy household, but Matthews gave the family a toby jug as a memento which they have kept to this day. A woman, who happened to be at the house at the time of the great man's visit, did not wash her hand for a week after being introduced.

Although she was pleased that Ray had got such an early chance to fulfil his dreams of playing professional football, Veronica was fearful for his well-being. However, as a large group of boys from the North-East were going together, the family felt reassured. The boys' parents were taken down to the Potteries to look at the facilities and stayed in a hotel. The Kennedys came home content that Ray was being well cared for. He was sharing digs with two other boys, and plans had been made to enrol him for a City and Guilds course in the evenings. Some of the boys from the North-East came back almost immediately, but others, including Ray, signed schoolboy forms at Port Vale. At the beginning of the 1966 season Ray went back with eighteen or so other boys to join the ground staff.

When Ray first arrived at the club on 8 August, Matthews was in hospital following a road traffic accident in which he had lost all his abdominal muscles. However, on Matthews' return to the club in September, Ray was immediately impressed by his dedication and fitness, marvelling that Matthews, even in his fifties, could sprint short distances backwards and forwards faster than the apprentices. Although he settled down reasonably well, Ray does not have happy memories of his time at Port Vale:

> I can remember pulling that huge back-breaking roller over and over again across that enormous pitch at Vale Park, cleaning the first team players' boots, laying out kit and sweeping up. I can't remember playing too much football. At night I would do City and Guilds painting and decorating. I remember Sir Stanley as still an extremely skilful, nimble man, careful to keep his body in good shape, a bit of a dandy.

Ray would spend his spare time going to the cinema with some of the other boys; their conversation revolved around football most of the time, and there were no serious girlfriends. Port Vale's youth team in 1966 was a good one, which ultimately reached the quarter-final of the Youth Cup. Ray, unfortunately, was not considered good enough to make the team. However, Jackie Mudie, the player manager, and Stan Matthews, gave him a few outings as a substitute in the reserve team. Veronica Kennedy remembers going to watch Ray play at Bishop Auckland and shaking with nerves when he missed a goal. A woman behind her started barracking the youngster and Veronica gave her a sharp piece of her mind. On that particular day Ray had been marked by a former Newcastle United player and had had little chance.

Although Ray was clearly struggling to make an impact, his

attitude remained excellent. Sir Stanley Matthews now remembers him as a softly spoken, gentle, polite boy who was never any problem on or off the pitch. However, the letter which every parent with football aspirations for their son dreads arrived at Tillmouth Avenue on 23 March 1967 and read as follows:

Dear Mr & Mrs Kennedy,
I hardly know how to begin this letter as I know you will be so disappointed, but the fact is my staff and I now feel that Raymond will have difficulty in making the grade in football to take it up as a career.

He is sluggish in his movements by his natural build and it is only fair to let you know I consider he will be wasting his time here when he could be finding alternative employment.

I have not yet mentioned the fact to Raymond and so, however distasteful this may seem to you, you will appreciate I am duty bound to give you the full facts so you may decide your son's future.

Yours sincerely,
Stan Matthews

Ray was summoned to Matthews' office, where he was sadly informed of the bad news. Matthews said to him, 'Ray, I have written to your parents that I do not think you will ever make a professional football player and I suggest you go home'. Shortly after this Jackie Mudie resigned, partly in frustration and partly lured by an attractive business offer.

Ray was mortified; he was filled with shame and despair and, once alone, he burst into tears. The thought of returning home a failure was difficult to bear, and his pain cut deeper when the other three apprentices with whom he was sharing digs were kept on. All three are now married and living in the Black Country; they never made names for themselves in football.

Initial disappointments and failures are not uncommon in professional football, and many of the top players can recall early rebuffs by so-called experts. Alan Ball was rejected by Bolton and Wolves before Blackpool took him on, and Paul Gascoigne went down to Ipswich for trials with Bobby Robson. Robson at that time described Gazza as a little boy lost who seemed overawed by the whole occasion. Carruthers, the Ipswich coach who had spotted Gazza, claimed afterwards that Robson had made the right decision on the basis of what he had seen in the trial. Gascoigne, who had been playing against more experienced boys, appeared to lack pace and could not get the ball enough to show his skill. Robson later stated: 'I took Paul a year too early. If I had waited for him to be mature it may have been different'. In contrast to Ray, Paul was given positive criticism by the Ipswich staff, who advised him to lose weight and try to gain a yard or two of pace. Instead of being gloomy and dispirited, Gascoigne replied, 'Aye, I will, Sir'.

However, rejection by Sir Stanley Matthews, the most famous footballer in the country, has to be considered in a different light. Matthews was a phenomenon, a genius who transcended tribal loyalties, a player of such divine quality that even in middle age he could help Stoke City to promotion from the Second Division. Moreover, he was an honest, modest, almost prudish man who never swore and was relatively free of the bigotry and prejudices which beleaguer the professional game. Sir Stanley's unequivocal critical verdict would have been enough to kill off most sensitive, insecure fifteen-year-olds, but Raymond Kennedy was a dreamer and a determined one at that.

In fact, trouble was brewing at the Port Vale club. Sir Stanley's scouting of youthful talent had been particularly successful, and he wanted sixteen boys to sign professional forms virtually simultaneously. Unfortunately, the FA introduced a new rule which demanded that each receive a signing-on fee of £500. To the new chairman of Port Vale an outlay of £8,000 was laughable, and the club was faced with the prospect of getting rid of all the carefully nurtured youth talent or contravening the new regulation. Furthermore, illegal bonuses were negotiated for the League Cup tie against Chester which were never paid, as the team lost the game. Other bonus irregularities, including payment to amateurs, came to light when an under-age boy from the North-East, who was sent home because of bed-wetting and undisciplined behaviour, complained to his headmaster, in a fit of pique, that he had been paid illegal monies. The Football Association made enquiries over the registration fees, and Stan had a number of brushes with Alan Hardaker, who had always resented his knighthood. In March 1968, just under a year after Ray had been sent home, Port Vale were fined £2,000 by the FA and the club was briefly expelled from the Fourth Division, only to be re-elected in the summer thanks to the loyalty of their fellow members. However, there were further fines from the League and Sir Stanley Matthews resigned in disillusionment.

After Ray had embarked on a successful career, people incredulous at the hit-and-miss selection process operating in professional football asked questions, and in one article a certain Mr G. W. Tomlinson of Finchley wrote: 'Does Sir Stanley admit he blundered when he allowed Ray Kennedy to leave Port Vale and go out of football?'. Bob Harris, the *Mirror* sports journalist chased the story and tracked down Sir Stanley Matthews to obtain his opinion. Matthews replied:

> It hurts me that people back home are saying I pushed Ray Kennedy out of the game as if I did not realise his potential. Nobody is happier than me to see him doing so well for Arsenal, the club that discovered him after he had left Port Vale who had to let him go for financial reasons. We had a promising youth squad at Vale, but the club was in such debt that we could not afford to keep them. I had to release ten youngsters in all and Ray was one of them. It was obvious he had talent even though it was some three years ago and he was still developing. He was a little sluggish on the ground, but devastating in the air. I have watched his progress with Arsenal and I am delighted that things are turning out well for him. I feel sure his experience with Port Vale where he played several reserve matches did him a lot of good.

In his autobiography, he later wrote:

> One of our lads was a boy called Ray Kennedy. Ray was one of the nicest boys in the squad and we all liked him. We knew he would make the grade one day, but not next season. Jackie said he needs another year yet, maybe more. At the time Ray was a bit cumbersome and awkward, the way some boys are in their early years. He would develop for sure if we were to give him time. But under the new policy there was no time available. We had to let Ray go.

Bill Emery, the scout who first discovered Ray, summarized the episode as follows:

> Stan's a wonderful bloke, but I honestly believe he was seeing

Kennedy wrongly. He said he was a bit slow and he was. But Matthews was looking for ball play and speed in a fellow who had entirely different but equally valid attributes. The fact is that Ray has been ditched by Vale and, when a small club has not voted you good enough, it's damned hard to find your way back.

Certainly this was not Ray Kennedy's perception at the time, when he felt that his chance had gone and that he was finished. No one had taken him on one side and given him guidance or told him what was expected and what he could do to improve his game. Ray was to remain resentful and angry about his rejection for several years. Now he is relieved Port Vale let him go as he has little doubt that if he had stayed he would never have advanced his career. When I recently spoke to Sir Stanley Matthews, now back in the Potteries as president of Stoke City Football Club, he was brutally frank. He told me that both Jackie Mudie and he were astonished when Ray later made it, as nobody at the Port Vale club had thought he had any chance at all. Sir Stanley considered Ray to have been too slow, very heavy and, despite specific training, incapable of jumping well for a ball. He commented, however, that everyone at Port Vale was impressed with Ray's attitude and character. He rejected the view that financial problems were a major factor in discarding Ray at the end of the 1967 season.

Sir Stanley's present-day version of the events is independently corroborated by two of the contributors to Jeff Kent's book, *Port Vale Tales*. Reg Berks, a coach and scout at Port Vale at the time and now with Oxford United, recalls:

Stan Matthews had a lot of blame for Ray Kennedy being released, but it was not his fault. There was an apprenticeship then, so you had to be selected because you had to pay £500 for every kid that got to the age of seventeen. That was a fortune to Port Vale and all the lads came through at the same time, so some of them had to be shown the door, and Kennedy was one of them. I've always used that as a glaring example to every kid who doesn't make it at the age of seventeen. Ray showed very little promise at that time, but you have to be patient with big players. Ray had difficulty in trapping a bag of cement, but you can't convince directors that kids mature at different rates. The system was to blame and nobody's got the patience to wait for youth schemes to come to completion.

Mick Cullerton, a Port Vale player, wrote: 'I've heard a number of people say Vale should have kept Ray Kennedy, but when he came at fifteen he was a big lad and too heavy. No player in the club gave him an earthly'.

Ray returned to the North-East crestfallen and seemingly in disgrace, having failed the first major hurdle he had had to face without his mother. Prior to this episode, he had always believed that the experts were right and that there was an inherent sense of justice in the system; now he was not so sure. Ray's self-esteem, which had never been high, was lost altogether and, for a short time, he considered himself to be a total failure.

4 The Sweet Factory

'You see, Charlie,' he said, 'not so very long ago there used to be thousands of people working in Mr Willy Wonka's factory. Then one day all of a sudden, Mr Wonka had to ask every one of them to leave, to go home, never to come back.'

'But why?' asked Charlie.

'Because of spies.'

'Spies?'

'Yes. All the other chocolate makers you see had begun to grow jealous of the wonderful sweets that Mr Wonka was making, and they started sending in spies to steal his secret recipes.'

(ROALD DAHL)

AFTER his return home, Ray almost immediately began to have a recurrent dream in which he was taken south again for trials at Burnley, where he signed professional forms. At that time the First Division Lancashire club were actively recruiting in the North-East; Ralph Coates was one of their more distinguished acquisitions. Ray told his parents that it was now clear in his mind what was needed to make a go of it in football and that he was determined to prove Sir Stanley Matthews wrong. Apart from natural ability and a sound football brain, Ray had identified determination, stamina and character as crucial ingredients for success in the professional game. His irresistible desire to conquer and commitment to win had been dampened by his traumatic experience at Port Vale, but not extinguished. Opportunities to better himself in Seaton Delaval were still negligible, and the potential rewards for successful footballers were increasing all the time. Modern players were now able to escape from their working-class backgrounds and buy suburban semi-detached houses next door to successful businessmen, lawyers and chartered accountants.

The stark reality was that Ray was sixteen, seemingly rejected by professional football, and unemployed. It was essential that he find work to improve his self-esteem, and the quicker the better. The happy childhood hours he had spent in his mother's company baking and cooking attracted him to the catering trade, and he considered applying for a job as a trainee chef. However, opportunities were few, the hours were erratic and travel away from home would probably be necessary, thereby hampering Ray's attempts to rebuild a successful football career. Instead, with his mother's help, he applied for the post of a trainee sugar boiler in a long-established family business, J. W. Welch of Laburnum Grove, Whitley Bay.

Veronica accompanied Ray to what was to be a successful interview. The factory had a small band of loyal and kindly workers, and Ray settled down well to his task of humping bags of sugar and lifting huge vats of molten caramel from one part of the shop floor to the other. The glutinous toffee would stick to Ray's shoes, rooting him to the spot, a feeling which, tragically, would return spontaneously twenty years later. Welch's was mainly involved in making toffees, nougat and a number of boiled sweets, with 'black bullets' being one of the most popular. Sometimes, on his way home, Ray would be followed by two or three dogs licking the caramel off his shoes. One day he hid a metal tray of toffees in his rucksack to give to his mother but, while waiting by the bus stop outside the factory, he turned round suddenly and the tray smashed against the window, drawing everyone's attention to his misdemeanour. David Welch, the present owner of the factory, remembers Ray as an ordinary lad whose only idiosyncrasy was that he asked for a lot of time off to play in football matches. Ray never in his heart of hearts regarded the sweet factory as anything more than a stopgap as he fought for a second chance in big-time football. However, he was now a normal working-class northern lad exposed to a world of work, drinking, fighting and an occasional screw if his luck was in.

Welch's had been partly burned down in 1970, and when Ray and I visited it recently he was struck by the greater degree of automation, but it also appeared more rundown and dirty. Margot, an elderly Czechoslovakian emigrée who had mothered Ray during his time at the factory, immediately filled bags of sweets for us both, and described how she remembered Ray's obsession with football. Every lunchtime he would play football with the Whitley Bay police round the back of the factory and, as soon as the working day had finished, he would be away to the football field. Although it was clear that the factory had seen better times and was now obliged to suffer the indignities of making sugar-free sweets, it had not lost its homeliness and its communal sense of purpose. There was a feeling of resigned contentment which twenty-five years ago must have affectionately nurtured a young man's dreams and provided the emotional security and breathing space for him to attempt to achieve them.

On his return home, Ray would sometimes go to Newcastle with friends on a Saturday to swim and then on to St James's Park, where he can remember watching Bobby Moore and Jimmy Greaves. His loyalties, however, lay firmly, like those of his father and Uncle Larry, with Sunderland. At this time Sunderland were in the Second Division but were involved in a number of exciting cup ties with replays, and Ray can still reel off the names of the Roker heroes, Johnny Crossan, Charlie Hurley, George Herd, Cecil Irwin and Martin Harvey. He had determined to model himself on Bobby Charlton, whose consummate skills, unassuming modesty and similar background made him an understandable choice.

At home, Janet was pampered like all little sisters in a male-dominated family. Trevor was already following in his older brother's footsteps and showing great promise in the Astley school team. Like Ray before him, Trevor felt himself to be little more than a number in the class, even though his academic abilities had enabled him to go twelve months ahead at junior school. He can remember on one occasion going to talk to the careers officer, but otherwise receiving absolutely no guidance as to his future. At home, education was rarely mentioned.

Having found a job to pay his way at home, Ray's next priority was to join a football club. The strong and well-respected North Shields club was top of his list until John Maley, manager of New Hartley Juniors, intervened. In 1954, after beating West Sleekburn Welfare Juniors 5–3 on Easter Monday before a crowd of 2,200 at Croft Park, New Hartley Juniors was disbanded. Four years later the club was re-formed with John Maley's father as manager and John Maley junior as secretary. After its resurrection, the New Hartley Juniors club rose to become one of the top youth sides in South Northumberland, with fifty-two Cup Final appearances, six league championships and eight runners-up awards to its credit. The club has spawned an impressive list of more than twenty Football League players. Among the most distinguished of these are Billy Wilson, the son of a Seghill miner, who made more than three hundred appearances for First Division Blackburn Rovers and then went on to play for Portsmouth in the 1960s, and Bobby Cummings, a former Bates Collier face worker who led Newcastle United to promotion to the First Division in 1964, and then went on to play for Port Elizabeth in South Africa. More recently, Ron Guthrie, a former Borradon miner, played for Newcastle United and then won an FA Cup winners' medal in the famous 1973 Cup Final when Second Division Sunderland surprised the formidable Leeds United. Les O'Neill, who worked in the time office at Hartford colliery and scored the first goal for Carlisle United on their arrival in the First Division in the 1970s, was another New Hartley old boy, as was Rob Hindmarsh, who played for Sunderland and captained Derby County. At the start of the 1991 season, two former players from the club, Paul Stoneman and Stephen Cuggy, were making their League debuts for Blackpool and Maidstone United respectively.

John Maley is the archetypal football man, a taciturn, shrewd individual who has overlorded his club through thick and thin for thirty-three years. His terraced home at 33, Gloucester Street overlooks the club ground. Inside it resembles a clubhouse more than a home, with one room adorned with cups, trophies and team photographs. Maley, who worked down the pits for thirty-one years, has kept careful scrapbooks recording the history of New Hartley Juniors through its local press coverage. In the early days, he had to beg, borrow and steal to keep his pride and joy afloat, but more recently local businessmen have been generous and have put the club on a more secure footing. Maley's life revolves around New Hartley Juniors; he rarely has the opportunity to watch League fixtures as his own team are in action each Saturday. At games, even when things are going badly, he remains poker-faced, the only sign of stress being an increase in the number of cigarettes he smokes.

The small mining village of New Hartley is a few miles from Seaton Delaval and has a similar tradition. The pit at Seaton

Delaval, the New Hartley pit which opened in 1877, the New
Delaval pit and the High Pit at Cramlington amalgamated in
1929 as the Hartley Coal Company and close links developed
among the four. Forty years ago, Seaton Delaval had a strong
football team and Wheatridge Park would attract crowds of
several thousands for the big local matches. Distinguished old
boys included Ronnie Cooke, Harry Wake, both of whom went
on to play for Newcastle United, and Frankie Brennan, a Newcastle
United and Scotland player who worked down the Seaton Delaval pit. By the 1960s, aspirant footballers from Seaton Delaval
needed to go further afield to win their spurs to either Cramlington, Alan Shearer's club, or New Hartley. The New Hartley
Juniors pitch looks onto the walled-up remains of the Hester pit,
where one of the most tragic pit disasters in Northumberland
occurred on 16 January 1862. On that fated day, the beam on a
pump shaft broke, wedging the pumping engine in the shaft and
blocking the egress of the miners below. All two hundred and
four men were asphyxiated, and it took the village six days to
get the bodies out. After this catastrophe, it became law that
mining companies must sink a minimum of two shafts at one site.
The pit has gone, marked only by a memorial stone, but the
swathe of green nestling between the terraced houses lingers
as a gathering point for the men of the village. This undistin-
guished patch, the home of one of the hundreds of junior sides in
the North-East, was soon to become Ray Kennedy's territory.

On learning that Ray had returned from the Potteries, John
Maley tracked him down while he was playing cricket for Bates
Welfare in the summer of 1967. Ray initially declined Maley's
invitation, saying that he had received other offers, including
one from North Shields. However, he was eventually swayed by
John's calm persuasiveness and obvious keenness to have him in
the New Hartley squad. The fact that a number of his former
school-mates from Astley Comprehensive were also playing at
New Hartley proved a further decisive factor. Ray began training
immediately and it was soon clear to Maley that he was a
definite choice for the side. Ray started the season wearing the
number nine shirt but adopted a rather versatile role in which he
tended to play deep and to the left. He struck up a partnership
with Ian Watts, a former England schoolboy international and
Newcastle United trialist, which was to prove an interesting

forerunner of the more distinguished pairing with John Radford. John Maley recalls that all the boys in Ray's day were keen to play and were prepared to put themselves out much more than the present generation, often making their own way to games by public transport without complaint.

In his first fourteen games for the club, Ray scored in every match and, with his intimidating, combative physical presence, forged a potent goal-scoring machine with Watts. By the end of the season Ray had scored fifty-six goals and Ian Watts eighty-six. The team notched well over two hundred goals in a single season and turned out to be the most successful New Hartley side ever. By the end of the year they had won the Northumberland FA Junior Cup, the East Northumberland Junior League Cup, the North-East Youth Challenge Cup, the East Northumberland Junior League Charlton Trophy, the Tyne-mouth Junior League Challenge Cup and the Magpie Trophy. They were also League Champions in the East Northumberland Junior League, and they won the *Evening Chronicle* Team of the Month award. Their only defeat came in the final of the Northumberland FA Junior Cup. Ray's fifty-six goals were accumulated in thirty-five games, and the League was won without dropping a point. Ray was also playing Sunday football, and some weekends he would squeeze in up to four matches, some involving confrontations with hardened miners twice his age. Newspaper reports of this fantastic season frequently mention Ray's contribution:

NFA Junior Cup Semi-final: Long Benton YC 0 – New Hartley Juniors 9

Hartley pressure was now constant and Kennedy scored in the thirty-fifth minute by running on to a loose ball outside the home penalty area and slamming the ball first time at goal. Goalkeeper Richards got his hands to the ball but was beaten by sheer power.

A great triumph then for the village side in which every player played a useful part. Kennedy, however, was probably the outstanding player of the game. He wore the number nine shirt, but in his roving commission was defending one minute and launching an attack in the next.

Acknowledging the work of five-goal Watts, the industry of Baxter, the cleverness of Winders, Brown and MacMillan, the man of the match award must still go to centre forward Kennedy.

The break Ray had been praying for came towards the end of the season. Unlike many players, he had not contacted League clubs or scouts to promote himself. New Hartley Juniors were playing in a cup final at Portland Park in Ashington and the Arsenal scouts, brothers Don and George Emerson from County Durham, had come to check on Ray's striking partner, Ian Watts, who had been rejected by Newcastle United. George Emerson, however, was immediately drawn to Ray who, within ten minutes of kick-off, had impressed him by his skill and balance, particularly for such a heavily built lad. At half-time the Emersons contacted John Maley, expressing an interest, and at the end of the game spoke to Mr and Mrs Kennedy, telling them that Ray had stuck out like a sore thumb and was reading the game so well that they would be interested in contacting Arsenal with a view to trials. The Emerson brothers then paid a visit to the Kennedy home in order to secure their prize. Ray, however, was keen to delay his signing by Arsenal so that he could play in the Challenge Cup Final which took place at Hillhead:

Montague and North Fenham B C 5 – New Hartley Juniors 3
Hartley's first two goals came from a player who dominated in the air, centre forward Kennedy. His first one came when he made a token reply to the onslaught his team had suffered. His second goal after forty minutes was a superb piece of football. He jumped high in the air and succeeded in reaching a high cross from the right wing, heading the ball powerfully into the net in true Wyn Davies fashion.

Steve Wolstencroft, a local journalist who had followed Ray with New Hartley, remembered Ray scoring a beautiful goal in this game and being literally head and shoulders above the rest of the players.

John Maley was in Keswick on holiday with his wife when Ray and I went to talk to him in 1991. He had kept in contact with his star pupil and remembers him in his New Hartley days as a very strong, tall boy who was extremely adaptable and able to read a game with a maturity well beyond his years. As well as his finishing skills, Maley's lasting images of Ray were of a powerhouse of a boy always to be found in the open spaces of the pitch. Ray was a dedicated trainer, organized, reliable and smart in his dress. John Maley thought that for much of that season Ray was passed by because he had had a chance and blown it. He remembers Martin Kennedy as a regular spectator, puffing his pipe laconically on the touch-line, and saying very little.

By the late spring of 1967, Martin Kennedy and Trevor were waving goodbye to Ray as he caught the train to King's Cross from Newcastle Station. Veronica Kennedy, meanwhile, was tearing her hair out with frightening premonitions of her son getting into fights and all sorts of trouble in the fleshpots of the big city.

Ray still remembers his panic on leaving home: 'I was crying long before Gazza. I sobbed all the way to the station. I stood in the train corridor all the way down. I was frightened someone might talk to me.'

5 Novillero

Call me morbid, call me pale
I've spent six years on your trail
And if you've five seconds to spare
Then I'll tell you the story of my life
Sixteen, clumsy and shy
I went to London and
I booked myself in at the YWCA
I said I like it here can I stay?
(THE SMITHS)

IN a historic meeting which took place in the Prince of Wales
pub, Plumstead, in October 1886, Dial Square Football Club
was founded by four football enthusiasts from the north who
had moved south to work in the munitions factory at Woolwich Arsenal. Two months later, in their first match, the club
beat Eastern Wanderers 6–0 at Millwall, with two of the
founder members, Fred Beardsley, a former Notts Forest goalkeeper, and David Danskin, a Scot from Kirkcaldy, playing in
the team. By the end of December, and after another meeting,
this time at the Royal Oak in Woolwich, the name of the club
was changed to Royal Arsenal. The first games under the new
name were played on Plumstead Common and then on Plumstead Marshes. In 1889 Royal Arsenal appeared in the FA
Cup, and an early success was the winning of the London
Senior Cup in which St Bartholomew's Hospital were thrashed
6–0 at the Oval. By now the club was playing at the Invicta
Ground in Plumstead. Increasing success led to a unanimous
decision to adopt the professional code, which at the time was
regarded as a heretical step by the authorities in the south.
Woolwich Arsenal Football and Athletic Company Limited

were now playing at the Manor Ground, where they remained for the next twenty years.

After a promising start, with rapid promotion to the First Division, the club's playing fortunes declined and by 1910 the financial situation was grave. In fact, the club was kept alive only through the intervention of Henry Morris, chairman of Fulham Football Club, who proposed that the club move to Craven Cottage, where it would either ground-share or amalgamate with Fulham. The League refused to allow it and, in 1912, Arsenal were relegated. Morris recognized the urgent need to move the club from Plumstead, which was difficult to reach by public transport from the centre of town, and finally found the ideal site for the club in Highbury in 1913.

On the resumption of football after the war, the League allocated one of the two newly created First Division slots to the Arsenal, and they have never been humbled by relegation since. Morris realized that if success was to be gained, a new manager must be found, and in 1925 he successfully enticed Herbert Chapman, an enterprising Yorkshireman who had already tasted success as manager of Huddersfield Town, to take over the reins. In his nine years with the club Chapman made prodigious changes. The East Stand went up, the North Bank was built, and Chapman was instrumental in getting London Transport to change the local tube station's name to Arsenal. More importantly, in 1929, Arsenal won the FA Cup, beating Chapman's old side, Huddersfield Town, 2–0. The following year, with legendary players like Alex James and Cliff Bastin in the side, Arsenal became the first southern club to win the Football League title.

These achievements paved the way for a decade of unprecedented supremacy, which continued after Chapman's sudden death in 1934 into the reign of George Allison, with three successive League Championships between 1932 and 1934, another in 1938 and a second Cup victory in 1938 in which Ted Drake, an Allison acquisition, scored the winner against Sheffield United. In the year of Chapman's death seven Arsenal players represented England against Italy at Highbury. These were the years against which all future Arsenal performances would be measured, and the period when the club's traditions were established. However, as with all hallowed institutions, fame can weigh heavily on future generations, and it is reputed that one distinguished manager of the club cursed every time he passed Chapman's bust in the club foyer.

By the time Raymond Kennedy arrived at Arsenal in 1967 the club had drifted into mediocrity. The League title had not been won since the 1951–2 season, and for over ten years Arsenal had failed to finish in the top three. Their last FA Cup victory had been even further back, in 1949. In 1962, for the first time in their history since Chapman's appointment, Arsenal broke with tradition and appointed a manager from outside the club. Billy Wright, the former captain of Wolves and England, who had declined the position of coach a few months earlier, readily accepted the offer of a managerial post. Although in his four-year reign he brought no honours to Arsenal, he developed a promising youth team which formed the foundation of the successes to come. Wright's lack of ruthlessness and the impatience of the club and its supporters for results led to his dismissal in June 1966; his successor was named as the club's physiotherapist and trainer, Bertie Mee. Mee was a neat, genial man, a miner's son from Bulwell, Nottinghamshire who, after a playing career as winger with Derby County and Mansfield Town, had six years' service in the Royal Army Medical Corps, followed by a long period as a rehabilitation officer to disabled servicemen. He had already been at Arsenal for six years at the time of his appointment as trainer and physiotherapist, and knew the club's way of doing things. His dapper appearance, reminiscent of a bank manager rather than a footballing man, earned him the affectionate nickname 'Burlington Bertie'. However, despite his veneer of modesty, he was not to be underestimated and proved to be a shrewd administrator who insisted on professionalism at all levels. He was a stickler for discipline and good conduct, and felt that players should be encouraged to shed their working-class oafish habits and replace them with behaviour appropriate to young men about to be elevated financially in the world. He instructed the players on table manners, warned them against the dangers of carnal temptation on overseas trips, encouraged payment into pension schemes and organized educational visits; he also advised the playing staff on good dietary habits. He despised a lack of attention to hygiene, drunkenness and slovenly conduct. Mee's benign paternalism, together with his considerable motivating skills and shrewd man-management gave the club's players a feeling of security. The involvement of money-men and agents in today's game has made Mee's approach look like a quaint anachronism.

At the beginning of the 1966–7 season, Mee brought George Graham, Bob McNab and Colin Addison to Highbury to strengthen his squad with experienced players. The club finished seventh that season after two finishes in the lower half of the table in previous seasons – encouraging signs of a resurgence in Arsenal's fortunes were beginning to emerge.

Bertie Mee had set extremely high standards during the first full season after his official appointment as manager in March 1967. The playing staff had already realized that the promoted physiotherapist was not going to be a pushover, and Mee had established a reputation for being strict but fair. Mee had also had the good fortune of acquiring the services of his old friend Dave Sexton as first team coach. Sexton's inherent gift of communicating with players without raising his voice and his qualities of leadership commanded respect even among the senior players. Together Mee and Sexton were trusted to build a team that was prepared to roll up its sleeves and battle to the end even for seemingly lost causes.

Mee opened the 1968–9 season with the following side: J. Furnell, D. J. Court, P. Storey, F. McLintock, W. J. T. Neill, P. F. Simpson, G. Johnston, J. Radford, G. Graham, J. C. Sammels, G. Armstrong. In February 1968, Mee signed the Coventry goal-scorer Bobby Gould for a record £90,000 to improve the strike force. In March Bob Wilson was promoted above Jim Furnell as first team keeper. Don Howe, who after a distinguished career with West Brom and England had come to Arsenal in 1964 as a player, was promoted from reserve team coach to chief coach after Dave Sexton left in the middle of the season to become manager at Chelsea. Much of the distress felt by many of the senior players, including Frank McClintock, the club captain, at Sexton's departure was erased within a matter of weeks of Howe's appointment.

In March 1968, Arsenal came up against Don Revie's Leeds United in the League Cup Final, a match that was to be the forerunner of future titanic battles. Leeds United by that stage had acquired the reputation of always being 'the bridesmaid and never the bride', and their football was somewhat unfairly regarded as methodical, cynical and full of gamesmanship. Before a Wembley crowd of 90,000, to the bitter disappointment of the Arsenal team — particularly Frank McLintock, who had now been on the losing side at Wembley three times, twice at Leicester City — Arsenal lost to a hotly contested Terry Cooper volley. However, the club finished the season on a positive note, with five consecutive victories and a respectable ninth position in the League.

In May 1968 Ray Kennedy arrived at King's Cross Station apprehensive and alone. His instructions were to take a taxi to Highbury Stadium, where he was to ask for Ernie Collett. At Highbury Ray was immediately struck by the palatial surroundings and the marked contrast between his new home and Vale Park. He was escorted by Collett to the Pembury Hotel in Seven Sisters Road, a popular temporary haven for the new apprentices. After signing apprentice forms on 6 May 1968, Ray had intensive trials and, a few weeks later, had made his first club appearance for the Metropolitan League side against the Metropolitan Police.

After successful trials, Ray returned to the North-East with instructions to report back to the club at the beginning of the next season. However, within a week, one of the Emerson brothers was knocking on the Kennedy family's door to inform Raymond that he was wanted immediately for a youth tour in Switzerland. In this tournament, Arsenal were beaten in the final by Newcastle United.

On his return to London in August 1968, Ray was accompanied by his parents, who were put up at the Royal Alexandra Hotel in Finsbury Park. Ray was living at the Pembury Hotel, where he shared a room with two other apprentices, Geoff English and Glen Johnson. Their company and the excitement of his new life left little time for loneliness during the week, but at weekends the other boys went home. The hotel owners illegally sublet the apprentices' rooms and on one frightening occasion, an itinerant Irish painter and decorator who was moved in for the weekend asked Ray where there was to go in London on a Saturday evening. Ray was so terrified that he left the room and walked around until the early hours, but late that night, after he had fallen asleep exhausted, the man came back drunk and tried to get into bed with him. On another occasion, some of the apprentices had been given free tickets for the Finsbury Park Astoria and had gone to watch the newly released film *Ten Rillington Place* about the mass murderer J. R. H. Christie. The following night, after the Irishman had moved out, a travelling salesman with a small briefcase and wire-rimmed National Health glasses, who closely resembled Christie, moved in, and Ray stayed awake all night terrified he would be attacked. Only his desire to avoid a second failure kept him from leaving for home immediately. After this he insisted on moving rooms and was put in the basement of the hotel: 'When I looked out of the window all I could see were people's legs hurrying by outside, and I remember the water steadily running down the walls'.

During that first week back Ray was involved in a number of make or break trial matches. In one of these he was down to play against Bob Ritchie, the brother of the famous Stoke City striker John Ritchie; before the game he felt pessimistic about his chances. However, at half-time the two boys were put on the same side. Ray eventually signed professional forms on 11 November 1968.

Ray was moved to digs at 12, South Lodge Drive, Oakwood, which he shared with Paul Davis, the younger brother of Ron Davis, the Southampton striker, and Geoff English. The apprentices' needs were well looked after by their kindly landlady, Mrs Baynton, who acted as their surrogate mum; their welfare was also supervised by the former Arsenal and England right back, George Male, who had played for the club in the Chapman era and lived just down the road.

Young Kennedy was soon made aware of Highbury's obsession with its former glories and its supporters' craving to rekindle the halcyon days nostalgically recalled by their fathers. After the grinding labour at Port Vale, Ray found apprentice duties at Highbury a doddle, and there was even time to play some football. The apprentices would be picked up by coach from Cockfosters Station, and training would start at London Colney at 10 a.m. sharp. The apprentices' chores at that time included pumping up the balls, sweeping snow from the pitch, cleaning the baths after the first team players and being on duty at Highbury on Saturday afternoons to clean the changing rooms. Tony Donnelly, the kit manager, a Dubliner and a strict disciplinarian who is still at the club, would get the apprentices to scrape the mud off the first team players' boots before he would polish them. The youth team would frequently have matches on Saturday mornings and then the boys would go back to Highbury and have fish and chips for lunch before going on duty for the first team or reserve match. Going to the Wimpy Bar at Finsbury Park for the first time was a memorable occasion for Ray who had his first Coca-Cola and loved it so much he drank the newly discovered beverage continuously for half an hour. The Wimpy Bar became a favourite meeting place for Ray and other members of the team. In the evenings they would go back to the digs to watch television or go out to play snooker or to the cinema. On a wage of £5 a month they were unable to hit the West End even if they had wanted to. Geoff English, Ray's digs partner, had some interesting nocturnal habits and Ray can remember watching him sleep-walk into the kitchen where he would open drawers, urinate in the cupboards and raid the larder. English, after playing in the Arsenal youth team at left back, went on to play League football for Barnsley, and is now a market trader in the town.

Ray remembers youth training under the strict Ernie Whalley as a punishing experience. Whalley insisted on Ray doing weight training to develop the upper part of his body, which Ray felt was unnecessary. Whalley would continually force his head down when he was doing bench presses, which Ray now recalls with dread. However, Kennedy's period with the youth team was brief.

John Maley wrote to Arsenal enquiring about Ray and begging financial support for the impecunious New Hartley Juniors. Bob Wall, the executive secretary, replied on 14 November 1968, noting Ray's progress to full-time professional three days earlier, and enclosing a cheque for ten guineas.

John Maley was by now harnessing another precocious Kennedy talent: Trevor had just joined New Hartley Juniors, having captained Astley Comprehensive School and played in the South Northumberland Boys Team. His school reports had been reasonably good but, like his elder brother, he was more interested in sport. On leaving school at fifteen he started work in a butcher's shop. Maley observed in Trevor the same gifts as Ray, and it was not long before the League scouts were on the younger Kennedy's tail. Trevor is now stoical about his failure to make the grade:

I desperately wanted to be a footballer when I left school. After I'd been for trials at Burnley my world was shattered when they said 'we'll keep an eye on you'. I was less disappointed with my later trials with Blackburn Rovers and Everton. People nowadays say I was better than Ray at fifteen. It's the luck of the draw. I probably had more opportunities and there are better players than both of us who have never made it in League football. The line between making it or not is very thin.

John Maley feels that the basic difference between the two boys may have hinged on Ray's greater ambition. Veronica Kennedy's observations may be more illuminating:

Our Trevor is a better coper than Ray. Trevor was good at football too, in some ways better than Ray but lacked the gentleman touch. He was more of a rough-house player and tended to be more selfish on the ball. In the end I think the only difference between them was that his face didn't fit; his application and determination were just as strong as Ray-mond's. Trevor would kick you and kick you again when you were down – if anything he was more eager to score goals. He always wanted to win and was more aggressive than Ray on the pitch.

One day Trevor was ill and the doctor had to be called. When he arrived and asked Veronica what was wrong with her son, she replied, 'Oh, he's not too bad, doctor, he's just offside'. Keeping onside had been a problem for Trevor during his football career.

Trevor finally resigned all hopes of playing League football but continued to enjoy the game playing for local clubs and supporting his elder brother. To this day Trevor maintains a keen interest in the local Northumberland football scene; his son Andrew plays for Cramlington Juniors and has now been offered trials with Leicester City.

Ray was now a young professional able to boast Arsenal tracksuit trousers as well as the apprentice's top. Under the guidance of Steve Burtenshaw, he was making rapid progress in the reserves, and Martin Kennedy was told by Arsenal officials that they expected his son to make the first team by the time he was nineteen years old.

Within a year of arriving at Arsenal Ray had been imbued with the pride and tradition of the club, and an efficient indoctrination

programme teaching him how to behave on and off the field
had been set in motion. Bert Owen, the club physiotherapist,
used to drill into the apprentices an aphorism which Ray was to
carry with him until the end of his career: 'Remember who you
are, what you are and who you represent'.

Ray was entering the game at a time when it had become
important for clubs and players to relate freely and positively with
the media, and it was becoming increasingly accepted for players to
mix with the press and show biz personalities. People from all walks
of life were now starting to fraternize with members of the top
clubs as football became smarter and more streamlined. Ray was
beginning to sense the pettiness, greed and injustice that prevails
in professional football, and the gulf between the master directors
and the player slaves and supporters. The days when sports fans
saw their heroes as clean-living, decent, fair-minded, team-spirited
young saints were fast receding. To a youngster, newly arrived at
the club, a player who had been worshipped on the field of play
frequently turned out to be a foul-mouthed, egotistical tyrant with a
heart of stone. Mercifully, however, the family atmosphere created
by Bertie Mee and the relative lack of interference from the directors
made life tolerable at Arsenal even for a sensitive and naïve
provincial lad. This enabled Ray's budding talent to develop steadily
and kept at bay his recurring self-doubts.

In those early days, Ray was a diffident, unpretentious, self-
effacing loner. Pauline McLelland, the wife of a former Arsenal
goalkeeper who tragically died of a brain tumour, recalls that he was
a quiet, gentle boy. She was particularly struck by the attention
he paid to her young baby, who perhaps reminded Ray of his
little sister back home. Steve Burtenshaw, a man who over the
last twenty-five years has held almost every post on the coaching
staff at Arsenal, is at present chief scout. He remembers Ray as
an innocent and rather gullible young man who initially found it
hard to cope with the streetwise banter of cockney lads such as
Charlie George. Ray was particularly sensitive to perceived slurs
on his character and, although receptive to criticism from those
he trusted and admired, he hated to be belittled in front of his
peers 'I hit Charlie because he called me an effing so and so and I
took it seriously. I didn't know in London they all talked like that.'

In training, he was keen, determined and conscientious, but
was not one of those players who would run and run for lost

causes. Although his progress appeared to be quite satisfactory, Ray was having increasing doubts about his ability to climb to the top in the face of such stern competition. He began to feel that he was not as fit or as fast as he needed to be and would sulk if he was not praised; he frequently joked of returning to the sweet factory in Whitley Bay when things weren't going well. Nevertheless, Steve Burtenshaw, who became Ray's first guiding influence, could see considerable potential in him:

> I always believed Ray could do well. For a big boy he was skilful and quite quick and we worked hard on him. He was eighteen months behind the other boys but he soon caught up because he was such a willing lad. We worked on quickening up his running and thinking and we started to see clear results on the close season tour of Holland and Germany.

Burtenshaw taught Ray to distribute the ball and shoot with his weak right foot, and instructed him in the basics of professional forward play: how and when to make telling runs, how to lay off the ball when under pressure and how to shield the ball to give his fellow forwards time to launch attacks. In his first games with the Arsenal reserves in the 1968–9 season, Ray had the opportunity to play with experienced first teamers such as George Armstrong, Frank McLintock, George Graham and Ian Ure. After he scored a goal, he would say, 'That's one for me Mam'. Although he originally came into the reserves as an outside left, it was obvious to Burtenshaw that he had talent as a striker and it was decided to develop him along those lines:

> Ray was a lot quicker than people gave him credit for, especially defenders who would frequently underestimate him. He had a marvellous first touch so that you could bang all sorts of balls up to him even under pressure. He was so strong you couldn't get the ball off him. Defenders behind him could not even see the ball half the time, he was so powerful. However I was always encouraging him to express himself more. Ray was a coach's dream, the sort of player who required a considerable amount of mechanical programming to get the best out of him.

Burtenshaw put in long hours with Ray on Mondays, Tuesdays and Thursdays at London Colney, and on other afternoons the two would work together at what are now the JVC training facilities at Highbury. Although he was a willing learner, at times Burtenshaw felt that Kennedy was in a trance, as his face would adopt a deadpan, vacant expression when he was spoken to, as if he were far away and taking nothing in during squad training sessions. Ray remembers being taken to task about this and resenting the criticism, because he knew that he was, in fact, listening attentively. A somewhat expressionless face with a slowness to respond emotionally may be one of the earliest signs of Parkinson's disease.

After a particularly tough training session on a hot day, he remembers coming off the pitch and commenting to his colleague, George Armstrong, that his right hand felt stiff and clumsy and for a few moments he was unable to undo his shirt buttons. This passed and he thought nothing more of it. He was always drenched in sweat after training, and frequently he was so exhausted that he would struggle back to his digs and fall asleep for several hours.

At times, Ray rebelled against the constant repetition of the training rituals, and kept asking why he was being singled out when other players, such as Charlie George, were spared. The reasoning behind this was that Burtenshaw thought that Ray required an extremely rigid, structured, repetitive and highly organized coaching programme to develop his skills, whereas a player like Charlie George, who relied on flair and ability, needed to be given a freer leash.

Ray's personality at that time concealed an egocentric aggressiveness beneath an exterior of disarming modesty, a defence mechanism against failure. He had already developed a highly tuned, sensual pleasure in dominating the other side, asserting himself and symbolically destroying his opponents. He realized that he was in the game of football to win glory, money and status, and not merely for the fun of playing. These sentiments, increasingly prevalent in the modern game, were expressed by Lawrie McMenemy on television some years ago: 'Football is a game that breeds selfishness. You try to encourage team work and selflessness, but in the end the professional is only in it for himself and what he can make out of it. The system, the money, bonuses, all make players think of their own interests first'.

Like many strikers, Ray was basically inward-looking and

highly strung, and needed a caring and professional environment to coax the best out of him. Arsenal more than fulfilled these requirements, and years later Ray became more and more convinced that he might never have made a success of his career if he had gone to one of the other top clubs where a more informal atmosphere prevailed. Although he soon learned to mix well and take the banter and 'in' jokes which form a footballer's everyday conversation, he remained extremely sensitive and touchy. Burtenshaw recalls that one day Ray was having physiotherapy on the bench when George Wright, the recently appointed first team physiotherapist, told the youngster to get off half-way through his massage because a first teamer had arrived. Burtenshaw immediately saw the hurt look he had grown to recognize on Ray's face and spoke sharply to the physiotherapist, reminding him that many of the young Turks in the reserves would soon be in the first team. A few weeks later Ray had bandages put on an injured leg by the physiotherapist and, in front of Burtenshaw, ripped them all off. He never forgave Wright.

Meanwhile, Bertie Mee had got the first team off to a good start, playing eleven games without a defeat. However, a loss against Leeds United at Elland Road emphasized the growing rivalry between these two clubs. An increasing tightness and solidarity was entering the Arsenal set-up under Mee. Bob Wilson the ex-schoolmaster's strength of character was becoming an important indirect influence on the side. Bob McNab and John Radford both won England honours, and Peter Simpson was emerging as an increasingly accomplished central defender. Arsenal finished a creditable fourth in the League and went out in the fifth round of the FA Cup to West Bromwich Albion one-nil before a crowd of 46,000 at the Hawthorns. Throughout the season only fifteen players were used to start games, indicating a settled side. However, the 1968–9 season will quite unjustly be most remembered for the ignominy of the Gunners' loss to lowly Swindon in the League Cup Final. This was particularly galling for the fans as Spurs had been disposed of in the two-leg semifinal. The pitch was a mud bath and many of the Arsenal players were only just recovering from 'flu. Swindon took the lead following a goal-mouth mix-up between Ian Ure and Bob Wilson. Fortuitously for Arsenal, four minutes from the end, the Swindon goalkeeper, Downsbrough, came out of his area to kick clear a

ball which instead rebounded off his knee, allowing the alert
Bobby Gould to head it into the net. Don Howe could see that
at the end of full time his players were totally exhausted.
McClintock had cramp in both legs, McNab was struggling, and
the cloying mud had already proved too much for Simpson, who
had been replaced by Graham. Howe asked the referee to
abandon the match to spare the players further stress, but to no
avail. Howe's fears were confirmed when, after fifteen minutes of
extra time, Don Rogers managed to poke the ball home from a
corner to give Swindon the lead and then, in the second period,
ran half the length of the pitch for an unforgettable second solo
goal to submerge Arsenal. Nick Hornby, in his book *Fever Pitch*,
recalls watching the game as an impressionable teenager: 'I
became aware of all the Swindon fans sitting around us with
their awful west country accents, their absurd innocent glee, their
delirious belief. I hadn't ever come across opposing fans before
and I loathed them in a way I had never before loathed
strangers'.

Four-times Wembley loser McLintock was mortified. At no
point could he have contemplated that lowly Swindon would
reinforce his Wembley agony. Ironically, a good luck telegram
from Don Revie wishing that Frank could be 'first up the steps
this time' proved to be true: the Leeds United manager had
forgotten that the League Cup Final's formalities demand that the
losers collect their medals first. For a club obsessed with kudos,
headlines such as SHAME OF ARSENAL were particularly hard for
the players to bear. The result had been prophetically anticipated
by the *Evening Standard*'s headline on 15 March: BEWARE THE
IDES OF MARCH. The underlying dissatisfaction in the stands that
had been there all season grew to a crescendo of complaints that
the club were too niggardly in buying new players and that Bob
Wall had too much authority.

Mee and Howe now had the difficult task of rebuilding morale
and weeding from their squad those players who lacked the
desire to win that was demanded by the club. Mee had no time
for fads or fancies and hated the superstitious rituals which dog
so many football clubs. Ian Ure's concern for a particularly lucky
shirt in a match against Coventry City, together with the
emerging prowess of Peter Simpson, led to the end of his
colourful and turbulent stay at Highbury in August 1969 when

he was sold to Manchester United. Mee was also aware of the need to find a regular goal-scorer. With twenty-five years' hindsight, both Bob Wilson and Frank McLintock now believe their disgrace in losing the League Cup Final to Swindon was the first of two major turning points in the club's history which crucially contributed to their imminent glories. As Wilson put it: 'After that defeat everyone at the club craved success even more and we were all determined never to let the shame of that day happen again'.

During the 1968–9 season, Ray Kennedy made twenty appearances for the Arsenal reserves in the Football Combination and also played for the youth team in the Youth Cup, in which the team went out to Chelsea 2–1. In that team were Geoff English, Ray's digs partner, Charlie George and the Glaswegian Eddie Kelly. The Arsenal reserves had a superb season, winning twenty of their twenty-five games, drawing four and losing only one. Seventy-one goals were scored, with only eighteen against, and they ended up as Division One champions. Ray scored eight. Reasonably satisfied with his first full season as a professional, he excitedly returned home to his family in the North-East loaded with presents, particularly for his young sister Janet. This was a cycle he was to repeat throughout his playing career: joining in training with his old club New Hartley Juniors and fortifying himself for the following season's battles. Later he was to recall that in the one season when he did not return home in the summer his play the following year suffered greatly.

At the beginning of the 1969–70 season, John Maley wrote again to Arsenal asking for further financial support for his club in view of Ray's progress. Bob Wall wrote back: 'It would appear that Kennedy may possibly have a good future with the club, but at this stage it is by no means conclusive'. No further donations were given to augment the ten guineas already sent to New Hartley at the beginning of the 1968 season.

Despite Wall's cautious response, Ray had already tasted first team action, coming on for John Radford on 29 September 1969 in Northern Ireland in a match against Glentoran in the first round of the Fairs Cup. Charlie George, who was nine months older than Ray, had forced himself into the first team for the first League match of the season against Everton, and had demonstrated exceptional talent and flair. However, the self-destructive side of George's nature was shown in Ray's debut match, when the talented cockney was sent off for dissent.

After their early successes in the first team, both George and Kennedy were back starring in the successful reserve team side, while the first team went through a dismal autumn without a win for ten matches, and the need for an improved strike force became more and more apparent. Bobby Gould, who had left the field in tears at the end of the 1969 League Cup Final against Swindon, was unable to find a regular first team place and at the end of the season was transferred to Wolves. Uncertainties in defence led to a crucial suggestion by Gordon Clark, the chief scout at Arsenal, that Frank McLintock be moved from wing half to central defence. McLintock was very much against this at the time, taking it as a personal insult to his abilities. However, it was a move which in the end proved beneficial to both player and club. McLintock later expressed his feelings about this traumatic period in his career:

> When I look back I think now I was a better wing half for Leicester than I was for Arsenal. I came for a record fee at a time when we weren't a very good team and I got caught up in the chase for honours. I lost discipline and used to chase all over the place trying to make us successful. Going back to centre half meant that I had to be more controlled. I tended to stray forward at first, but Bob McNab was particularly helpful and used to yell at me about my positional play. Thanks to him and the other defenders I learned the job quickly and we became very well organized at the back.

The 1969 season also marked the signing — for a record £100,000 — of the nineteen-year-old striker Peter Marinello from the Edinburgh club Hibernian. Marinello was to prove the typical innocent abroad, a player with flamboyant skills and immense natural abilities whose boyish looks, jet black Beatle haircut and unusual film star name made him an instant magnet for the media's attention. By the time he arrived at Highbury, Marinello had already earned himself the tag of the 'Scottish George Best'. In his first game for Arsenal he scored a goal away at Manchester United but, tragically, this was to be the high point of his short-lived and much-publicized stay with Arsenal.

Despite Mee's customary skill in protecting his players from the avaricious media, Marinello's arrival at Arsenal was greeted like the second coming, and the transfer was announced on the nine o'clock news. Long before he had won his spurs in the English League he was drawing £500 wages and huge sums from advertising appearances, and had a column in the *Daily Express*. Ten years later he was to comment wryly: 'I didn't realize I was a commodity rather than a footballer — I wish I had understood it more at the time'. Not surprisingly, Marinello was too immature to cope with all the hype and his life lurched out of control.

Over the next fifty matches Marinello scored only three more goals and was dropped. Immediately his new 'friends' in the press and pop business deserted him. During a period of profound loneliness and depression, Marinello tried to win his place back in the Arsenal first team as an auxiliary midfield player but failed abjectly and, after unpleasant disputes with the club, was transferred to Portsmouth, then in the lower depths of the Second Division: Marinello had been dismissed as a failure at the tender age of twenty-one. It was not long before he was back in Scotland playing for Motherwell. After brief periods with Fulham, Hearts and Phoenix Infernos, he left football to buy two public houses in Edinburgh. Within a short period of time he was bankrupt, his house was repossessed, his marriage had collapsed and, after losing over £250,000, at the age of forty he was living in the south of England with his two sons on state benefit of £63 per week.

The bright lights of London were also to be the undoing of that other talented Scotsman, Charlie Nicholas, bought by Arsenal thirteen years later to inject flair into a team of stolid mediocrity. Despite adoration from the North Bank, Nicholas, like Marinello, never fulfilled his potential. Marinello, who lived in the shadow of George Best, could never match the Irishman's natural skill, but at least he avoided the self-destructive excesses of drunkenness and promiscuity. While Best's decline was conducted in the full glare of self-seeking publicity, Marinello suffered in relative obscurity, a tragic victim of a game where winning is everything, a game polluted by hatred, jealousy and a callous disregard for the rules of fair play. As George Orwell expressed it, 'serious sport is war minus the shooting'.

Meanwhile, Ray Kennedy was making steady, inauspicious

progress, coming on as substitute on 18 October at an away match against Sunderland which ended in a one-all draw. On 17 January 1970 Ray made his first full first team appearance in the 3–0 defeat at home to Chelsea. At the end of February he scored his first goal for the first team in a 3–1 home win against Sunderland.

After the fantasy of European travel, when he came on as substitute in a match against Dynamo Bacau in Romania, Ray was soon brought back firmly to ground with the everyday cut and thrust of the fight for survival in the club. Arsenal would take one or two of the reserve players who looked likely to break through into the first team to away matches, and Ray was invited to accompany the club to Goodison Park for the match against Everton. This led to an incident which at the time he felt might have ruined his career, but in retrospect may have done him more good than harm:

Shortly after I had been made a professional Arsenal took me to Everton with the first team. On our arrival at Goodison Park, Tony Donnelly, the boot man, realized he had left the team's shin pads in the hotel and he asked me to go back to get them. I arrived back in the changing room with the pads in time, and sat down on one of the changing benches next to Raddy and Geordie Armstrong, moving some of the kit and a tin of Vaseline to one side. George Wright, the club physiotherapist, then picked up the Vaseline and snapped at me, 'Pick that fucking kit up'. Don Howe then came over and said, 'That's a nice suit you're wearing'. I was so upset by Wright's behaviour that I couldn't even answer Don Howe, who then said to me, 'Sorry I spoke to you'. I then replied to him, 'You never do normally'. After that he started to make an effort to acknowledge me at London Colney.

In the semi-final of the Fairs Cup, Arsenal came up against Ajax from Amsterdam, who boasted Cruyff and Keizer, Suurbier and Krol among their talented squad. This Ajax team went on to become three-time European Cup winners. However, Arsenal had the mercurial George, who scored a brilliant long-range goal in the first leg which set Arsenal up for a 3–0 cushion. A week later, in a bitter struggle in Holland, Arsenal held the talented Dutch side to a single goal.

Seventeen years without a major trophy was a long time for a club like Arsenal and expectations were mounting as they went back to the continent on 22 April 1970 to play the first leg of the final against Anderlecht in the Parc Astrid in Brussels. Anderlecht had conquered Inter-Milan in the semi-final and were brimming with confidence. Their most talented player was Jan Mulder, a Dutch international, but there were others with ability, including Paul van Himst and four Belgian internationals, one of whom was a colossal Congolese half-back. The matchbox-sized stadium for 30,000 was filled to the brim with wildly partisan Flemish supporters. Early in the match the Arsenal forwards were subjected to massive provocation, with frenzied tackles from the Belgian defence, and it was not long before Mulder was tearing holes in what suddenly looked like a paper-thin Arsenal defence. De Vrindt unsettled the Arsenal team further with an opening goal in the first half which kept the local support in good spirits and voice. In the second half, just when Arsenal seemed to be getting to grips with the game, Mulder had an inspired period and produced two brilliant finishes, seemingly dooming the North London side to another loss in a major final. As time began to tick away Frank McLintock, in the centre of the Arsenal defence, began to see the demoralizing spectre of defeat staring him in the face once again. With five minutes to go and the tie hopelessly lost, George Wright turned to Don Howe and said, 'What the hell. Why not put Ray on as Charlie is not doing well?' Howe concurred, and the raw eighteen-year-old was thrown on for a brief taste of the big time. Almost as soon as Kennedy had taken up position at the front of the Arsenal attack, a long Armstrong cross came over. He rose majestically to head the ball past the Anderlecht keeper to provide a valuable away goal which would count double if the sides were equal on aggregate after the second leg. With no more than a minute to go, he nearly notched a second, thudding a cracking twenty-yard shot into the chest of the Anderlecht keeper. Ray remembers: 'I came on with seven minutes to go. I wasn't nervous at all because I did not really feel I was part of the whole thing, being so much on the fringes. The ball came over and I nodded it in'.

The match finished 3–1 to Anderlecht and, despite the fillip of a late goal by their rookie youngster, the atmosphere in the Arsenal dressing room was sombre. McLintock berated his side, cursing the fact that Arsenal appeared to have blown it. However, by the time he came out of the shower, McLintock's mood had changed and he was breathing fire. Ray now recalls: 'Frank's whole attitude had changed. He told us we could paralyse the bastards in the return and that their centre half wouldn't get in the Arsenal third team. In no time at all, from being as low as one could possibly feel, we all knew we could do it. Frank lifted our heads again and we went home knowing we would win'.

These dominant powers of leadership, strength of purpose and an unnerving capricious impulsivity characterized McLintock's captaincy. Through his resolute example on the pitch and his paternal regard for his team-mates off it, he held the complete loyalty of his troops and was a wonderful asset to Howe and Mee as a self-appointed coach and manager. Howe considered McLintock a better captain than either Dave Mackay of Spurs or Bobby Moore at West Ham. After the game, McLintock said of Kennedy's performance: 'Ray scored a great goal and has the potential to be one of the best strikers in the First Division. If he gets in the team he will be difficult to displace. He is good in the air, difficult to knock off the ball and has a delicate touch. All he needs now is more confidence. He doesn't realize how good he could be'.

It may be no exaggeration to say that McLintock's legendary pep talk in the Parc Astrid dressing room and Kennedy's goal finally broke the Arsenal jinx. George Armstrong, the little Geordie who is now on the coaching staff at Arsenal, was convinced that Ray's precious goal in the first leg was the single event which lifted Arsenal's morale and paved the way for future successes. Don Howe was also enthusiastic:

> Things clicked the moment Ray came on. He already seems to have the temperament for the big match and his goal turned our fortunes. He could be another Tommy Lawton. He has all the hallmarks of a classical centre forward, size, strength, bravery and skill, heading ability and a powerful left foot shot. He is a throw back to the old fashioned centre forward of yesterday, but without the crash and bash of a Ted Drake.

However, in the second leg at Highbury six days later, Ray was back on the bench. Provided Arsenal won 2–0, thanks to Kennedy's away goal, they would go up to receive the cup from

FIFA's president, Sir Stanley Rouse, and the cup would remain in England for the third successive year, Leeds and Newcastle being the previous holders.

From the kick-off Arsenal tore into their opponents and were rewarded with an early goal from Eddie Kelly. The Arsenal side was spurred on by the desperate need to cast off the heavy burden of former honours and establish themselves in the history books. In the second half, Radford exploited Anderlecht's centre half's weakness to score and Sammels then added a third to give the Gunners a clear victory without the need to rely on Ray's goal. McClintock was carried off by the delirious supporters and Charlie George had his shirt torn from him before he could collect his medal. Grown men danced on the Highbury turf and wept with relief. After the match Bertie Mee commented: 'The experience we gained tonight will be invaluable for winning our next objective, the League title'. Don Howe was also impressed and his post-match commentary was to prove prophetic: 'This can be the big break through. We can go on and on from here. The tension is off the players now. They have proved they can play football. I think this is just the beginning'.

During the close season the World Cup Finals took place in Mexico where, despite leading Germany 2–0 in the quarter-finals, England went out and the Jules Rimet Trophy was won by a Brazilian team richly endowed with speed, flair and spontaneity. However, back at home, rising stakes with fear of failing, mounting pressures to win preventing adequate team-building, packed midfields, long balls, professional fouls and victories by a single goal in congested fixture lists were the order of the day. Even the supporters were now more concerned with winning than seeing an entertaining game of football.

6 'Does this happen every year, Charlie?'

Good old Arsenal, we're proud to say the name
While we sing this song, we'll win the game
Good old Kennedy, we're proud to shout the name
While we sing this song, we'll win the game.

(SUNG TO THE TUNE OF *RULE BRITANNIA*)

DESPITE Kennedy's blooding in the 1969–70 season, he was not in the team for the first match of the new season at Goodison Park against the League champions, who had Alan Ball, Howard Kendall and Colin Harvey as a formidable midfield trio. The Arsenal side that day was Bob Wilson in goal, Pat Rice and Bob McNab as full backs, Frank McLintock, Eddie Kelly, John 'Garth' Roberts and Peter Storey as half-backs, and Charlie George, George Graham, George Armstrong and John Radford in attack. This first match on 9 August was the forerunner of much that was to come in the ensuing season, and indicated to the First Division that Arsenal were no longer a soft touch who would cave in if they went a goal down. The first half was controlled by Everton, with Joe Royle heading home from a Tommy Wright cross. Bob Wilson and Bob McNab, who saved off the line, kept Arsenal in the game. In the second half, against the run of play, Radford suddenly broke away and set up a chance for George, who equalized. Unfortunately, in scoring, George collided with the Everton keeper and fractured his ankle in two places; Marinello came on with only a few minutes to go. Everton immediately regained the lead after another Wright cross which seemed to hit Alan Ball's hand before falling to Morrissey. Arsenal were not finished, however, and George Graham floated an equalizer over the desperate Everton keeper, West, and then almost clinched the winner in the last minutes.

Two days later at West Ham, with George out, Kennedy got his chance. Jimmy Greaves was prominent in the Hammers attack, and Ray was marked by Bobby Moore. Arsenal escaped with a creditable goalless away draw. Ray, pitchforked into the limelight, responded with a competent if unspectacular perform-ance which he now remembers with embarrassment, recalling that he was continually laying the ball off long before Bobby Moore came anywhere near him. Although he never felt secure of his place, Ray did not miss another first team game all season.

Ray was now under the wing of Don Howe, the first team coach. Howe's initial impressions were favourable:

> I liked the look of Ray from the start. He was keen, big, strong and had a nice touch. It soon became clear that he could keep his cool even under severe provocation in big matches. I can recall him on occasions reading a match programme quietly just before the kick-off. He was a very phlegmatic character who seemed to take the game in his stride and who was outstanding at holding up the ball. He was medium paced, not slow, and a coach's dream who listened and acted on advice. You could make constructive criticisms and he'd take them on board. However if someone he didn't respect came up to him after a match insulting or criticizing his play, he'd lose his rag, especially after a few drinks.

Ray's confidence was lifted after the first home game against Manchester United: 'I did not really expect to get called up so early in the season but I am now out to hold my place. I just need to get a few goals; I felt very tired in the last ten minutes and need to improve my stamina'. On the following Tuesday, 25 August, Huddersfield Town were the visitors to Highbury and proved to be stubborn opponents. The match remained goalless until the last twenty minutes; Don Howe became so frustrated that he was warned for over-enthusiastic coaching from the line. Radford limped off with thigh strain after being marked tightly all afternoon by Roy Ellam. Ellam had lived down the street from Raddy and had gone to school with him in Pontefract. After

Radford's departure, Kennedy began to take a more dominant role and, following a cross from Armstrong helped on its way by George Graham, nodded the winner into the net. Ray was to have two further dangerous headers: one went inches wide and the other was handled out by a desperate defender unnoticed by the match officials. Despite a brave display, Huddersfield, like so many of Arsenal's opponents to follow, had been worn down and drummed into submission.

The sixth game of the season was against Don Revie's Leeds United who were unbeaten and top of the League. Revie, who tragically died in 1989 of motor neurone disease (Lou Gehrig's disease), was to bring the Yorkshire club its first major successes during his reign from 1961 to 1974. Revie was a single-minded workaholic who wanted to put Leeds permanently in the record books. 'The Don', as he was called, was a methodical perfectionist who planned each League campaign with military precision. However, he was hidebound by ritualistic superstition, including lucky dressing rooms and omens which led to nagging self-doubt before critical games. He realized the importance of having an old wise head in the team, so he built his first team round the skilful veteran, Bobby Collins. Billy Bremner, the fiery diminutive Celt, provided the drive and motivation for the side in much the same way as McLintock did for Arsenal, or more recently as Gordon Strachan did for Howard Wilkinson in the 1991–2 Leeds Championship side. On this bedrock, he steadily developed one of the meanest, hardest and most ruthless defences in the First Division with the four England internationals: Norman 'Bite Your Legs' Hunter, 'Beanpole' Jack Charlton, Paul Reaney, Paul Madeley and, a little later, the reliable if uninspiring full back, Trevor Cherry. Perhaps the hardest of them all was John Giles, who had been released by Manchester United and, with Bremner, shared the play-making of the Leeds side.

In fact, there were considerable similarities between Leeds and Arsenal in those days: both were equipped with mean, solid defences and strikers accomplished at capitalizing on long balls driven from the back. For several years after success had started to come to the Leeds side, they remained under-supported by an incredulous city which was immured in football mediocrity. Other teams regarded them as an unfriendly, closed lot who kept themselves to themselves. Whereas Arsenal players were accused of being boring, Leeds were accused of being dirty: their approach to the game was considered hard to the point of being criminal.

Revie doted on his players, who were regular visitors to the family home. He attended their weddings and the birthdays of their children; Billy Bremner, the club captain, would sometimes babysit for his boss. Revie had cold blue, piercing eyes which froze out all those outside his own clan. Those within the Don's extended family, however, were cosseted and he would go to extreme lengths to make life comfortable for his players. Revie was also well known for his money-mindedness, which earned him the nickname of 'Don Readies'. Although it was later claimed that Revie had left the England job for financial reasons, he stated the real reason was that the England set-up distanced him from the players and precluded the pastoral role he so cherished. Despite Leeds' indisputable successes in the Revie years, including two League Championships, one FA Cup and two Fairs Cups, they also will be remembered as a team which often fell at final hurdles, resulting in five runners-up positions in the League, three FA Cup runners-up medals and a lack of success in the European Cup. Some of this can be blamed on phenomenal success leading to exhausting involvement in too many competitions at once.

The games between Arsenal and Leeds United in the late sixties and early seventies were invariably the contests of the season, epitomizing the English game. Avoidance of defeat was always the major consideration. On 1 September 1969, Arsenal valiantly held the Leeds side to a goalless draw at Highbury and halted the Yorkshiremen. Eddie Kelly was sent off half-way through the first half for kicking Bremner, and Kennedy was continually hacked down by Hunter, who was man-marking him. A remarkable feature of the season to come would be Kennedy's ability to absorb fearsome punishment from defenders without retaliating. This was all the more notable because the game was full of professional hit men who were set by coaches to mark strikers and, if possible, disrupt their play. When asked about this remarkable aspect of his performances, Ray replied with customary honesty: 'I was always frightened to strike back in case I got sent off and lost my place in the side. In any case I always found it much more satisfying to beat my marker with skill than by fouling him'.

Although Leeds left Highbury with an away point, most of the congratulations went to the Gunners for their gritty resistance against a team already regarded as the likely champions. Arsenal continued their good run with a mid-week home victory against Tottenham Hotspur; George Armstrong scored two opportunist goals which helped him to continue to stave off the luckless Marinello's challenge for a first team place.

After a goalless draw at Ipswich in the first leg of the League Cup, Arsenal then went to Turf Moor to play Burnley, who were already rooted at the bottom of the League. In the fourth minute, Kennedy headed the Gunners in front, but Burnley refused to give in and equalized through an own goal from Roberts following a swinging Dave Thomas corner. In the closing minutes of the match, however, Roberts atoned for his error, putting Radford through to score the winner in what was regarded later as a somewhat fortunate victory because of their opponents' resilience and the late winner.

Arsenal's defence of the Fairs Cup began with the now infamous tie in Rome's Olympic Stadium against Lazio. Lazio were having a poor season and had acquired a notorious reputation for unruly discipline. Their best player was Giorgio Chinaglia, who was born in South Wales of Italian parents and who had played briefly for Swansea City. He was big, sharp and capable of creating goals out of half-chances.

Arsenal had planned their trip to Italy in their usual meticulous way and were optimistic that they could get a result. However, when the players came out into 'a colosseum of hate', they were greeted by the derisive, sadistic roar of a Roman mob demanding blood. The air was full of fireworks and smoke, and it was clear that the game would be a real battle. Kennedy and Radford were continually axed down and spit upon by the Lazio defence, but the two down-to-earth Northerners kept their heads and Radford silenced the crowd with two cool second-half goals, both provided by Kelly. Chinaglia clawed one back for the Italians in the last minute with a low drive past Wilson. Lazio were then the beneficiaries of a dubious penalty decision against McLintock, who had headed off the line, but was judged to have handled. The game finished two-all, but Arsenal were confident of success in the second leg.

After the game, the two teams were invited to a restaurant in the city where the directors and chairmen exchanged hypocritical pleasantries. When the Arsenal chairman thanked Lazio for their warm hospitality, several of the Arsenal players began sniggering, as they thought Denis Hill-Wood was referring to the reception on the field rather than the after-match entertainment. The Arsenal players had also been given leather handbags as presents which, while fashionable in Italy at the time, were considered rather effeminate in Anglo-Saxon circles. Some of the handbags began to be thrown around. On leaving the restaurant, some of the Italian players set on Ray, kicking him in the groin. In no time at all mayhem had broken out, with a full-scale brawl between the two teams spilling out into the street. McNab was thrown to the ground and Armstrong was rammed against the side of the Arsenal coach. Arsenal, innocent victims of their opponents' frustration, rallied together. The Italian police arrived and a gun was drawn on Eddie Kelly. Bertie Mee, terrified that an even greater tragedy might ensue, risked life and limb by coming between the warring players and ushering the Arsenal team quickly into their coach and away to their hotel. Lazio subsequently claimed that the Arsenal players had incited them to aggression with verbal insults. Ray believed that he had been picked on because of his cheeky face.

Lazio initially threatened to boycott the return match, but UEFA had no sympathy and fined them, warning of even greater penalties if they did not play. Arsenal were to run out easy winners, 2–0, with the German referee from the World Cup Final cautioning five Lazio players, including their other English-born Italian defender, Giuseppe Wilson.

Six days after the Lazio victory, Arsenal defeated Bobby Robson's Ipswich, 4–0, in the League Cup replay at Highbury. After Arsenal's aerial strike power had brought goals for Roberts and Radford, Kennedy scored the third. The goalkeeper had come out to gather a long ball with Kennedy and Kelly advancing. Anticipating that the goalkeeper might misjudge the ball, Kennedy intelligently held back and the ball ricocheted off the keeper's chest into Ray's path for him to slot it in. The fourth goal was another determined Kennedy effort in which, after receiving a lobbed pass from Radford that put him through the middle, he was able to hold off two defenders' challenges to score.

The following Saturday, in front of a disappointing crowd of

only 32,000, Arsenal hit another four goals past the luckless
Nottingham Forest, with Kennedy scoring a hat trick: his first
followed a miskick by a Forest defender in the first half, the
second was a touch-in and the third came from a characteristic
bustling run. Kennedy, just nineteen and the League's top scorer,
who had an onerous £200,000 price tag placed on his head by
the press, played down the media adulation: 'I usually only
dream of these things. I thought only John Radford was capable
of getting a hat trick. I am still expecting to be dropped any
minute'.

On 10 October, after a win at Luton, Arsenal made the long
trip up to Tyneside to play lowly Newcastle at Gallowgate.
Despite the fact that Newcastle had not won at home since the
opening game of the season, Ray was more nervous than usual
to be playing back home in front of his own people. In fact, for
most of the game it looked as if Newcastle would win, thanks to
a Pop Robson goal, but for the second week running Graham
rescued the London team by coolly punishing an error in the
Magpies' defence.

The following week, Henry Newton, recently signed from
Notts Forest to strengthen the Everton defence, was back at
Highbury, where two weeks previously he had been on the end
of a 4–0 hiding. Arsenal's power in the air immediately began to
trouble the re-jigged Everton defence, with Howard Kendall at
the back. Within a few minutes of the start, Graham's flick on had
allowed Kennedy to head Arsenal into an early lead. Within
twenty minutes of kick-off, Arsenal were two up after Kennedy
had towered above Kendall to score a second goal with another
header. In the second half, following a devastating long throw
from Radford, which forced the frustrated Everton defence into a
poor clearance, Kelly picked up the loose ball and shot it past the
Everton goalkeeper. Further aerial bombardment led to an Everton
hand ball which Storey converted from the penalty spot. David
Lacey of *The Guardian*, observing that three of the Arsenal goals
had come from high ball tactics and that Everton had both Henry
and Keith Newton in their defence, wrote of the Merseysiders'
performance: 'With two Newtons in the side one might have
expected Everton to deal better with round objects dropping from
the sky'. Another match report described Kennedy as 'ploughing
around the Everton defence like a lumberjack with an axe'.

In nine home games, in which they remained unbeaten, Arsenal had now scored twenty-seven goals and conceded only two. Despite this, the Highbury crowd remained critical and dissatisfied, and they were in danger of surpassing Leeds as the most carping, hardest to please, least grateful supporters in the League.

Kennedy's eleven goals were acknowledged by an England Under-23 call-up by Alf Ramsey for the match against West Germany in which Ray came in for the injured Liverpool striker, Alun Evans. The England team was:

Shilton (Leicester)	Edwards (Manchester United)
Robson (Derby County)	Todd (Sunderland)
Lloyd (Liverpool)	Kember (Crystal Palace)
Thomas (Burnley)	Bernard (Stoke City)
Royle (Everton)	Kennedy (Arsenal)
	Kidd (Manchester United)

The next round of the Fairs Cup proved to be a stern task, with the team losing 1–0 in Austria to Sturm Graz. Back at Highbury for the second leg, Kennedy cancelled out the away-goal deficit against unfancied opposition, but the Austrians held out for extra time despite the loss of their goalkeeper in the first half. An Austrian defender handled Graham's shot on the line, then Storey, with his usual coolness from the penalty spot, beat the goalkeeper to give Arsenal a 2–1 victory on aggregate.

After a goalless draw at Selhurst Park in the next round of the League Cup, and the absence of Kember and Blythe from the Palace side for the second leg, Arsenal's safe passage through to the next round seemed a foregone conclusion, made even more certain when three of the Palace players came out at the beginning of the match swathed in bandages. To everyone's surprise and Don Howe's annoyance, Arsenal went down 2–0 for their first defeat at Highbury for ten months.

In the next match back in the League at Coventry, Radford broke his wrist, but with characteristic Yorkshire grit he refused to miss any of the next few games. Despite his injury Arsenal ran out comfortable winners 3–1 with Kennedy and Radford both scoring. In the next League game at Highbury, with only three months of the season gone, Radford joined Kennedy in double figures, in a 2–0 defeat of Derby County.

Although playing better for his tender years than anyone could have expected, Ray was beginning to find the struggle to build up stamina and keep his weight down increasingly tough. Gordon Clark, the chief scout who had been instrumental in bringing Ray to Highbury and whom Ray trusted probably more than anyone else on the coaching staff, confidentially advised him not to sink down to the cynical professional level of the other players, and Steve Burtenshaw was continually encouraging him to express himself on the pitch. While Ray was dieting, Arsenal were trying to feed up the frail Marinello whose lack of form was proving to be an embarrassing nightmare. Meanwhile, Mee was confidentially predicting England honours for the Geordie youngster within two years. Ray's image off the park at that time presented a curious contrast to his fearless, composed, dashing playing style. To those who met him socially, he came over as a rather shy, highly strung, modest man, a combination which, together with his good looks, produced a charming and fascinating air of mystery to women. His approach to the media was also naïve. When asked a question he would often start by asking, 'What do you want my opinion for?'

After a 2–0 win on a heavy pitch at Maine Road, Malcolm Allison, the City manager, conceded: 'The title is already a two horse race – Leeds because they are the most powerful team in Europe and Arsenal because their number has come up and Wilson is having a great season'. Arsenal reached the half-way stage of the season with a 2–1 victory against Wolves which left them just two points behind the League leaders, Leeds. Two weeks after their victory at Maine Road, Arsenal were back in Manchester at Old Trafford. Kennedy, McLintock and Graham scored in a 3–1 victory which gave Arsenal maximum points for the season against their northern foe. Wilson required a single stitch in a scalp wound received after a coin had been thrown from the Stretford End.

This championship victory at Manchester United was followed by a disappointing goalless draw at home in sub-zero temperatures on Boxing Day. Although Arsenal had done most of the attacking and Wilson had been a virtual spectator for most of the match, they were unable to break down the Southampton defence. Next came the first round of the FA Cup, with Arsenal drawn against the giant-killing non-League side, Yeovil Town, who had destroyed Sunderland on their notorious sloping pitch in 1948. Despite the outrageous assertions of the Yeovil chairman that his side of part-timers would win decisively, Arsenal came through smoothly, with two headers from Radford and a scrappy touch-in from Kennedy.

John Radford was already established in the Arsenal team when Ray began to break into the side. Both men came from mining families: Radford was from the South Yorkshire coal belt, where his father had worked at the coal-face at Hemsworth Colliery in Pontefract. Both shared a straightforward, honest approach to football and were prepared to work selflessly for the good of the team. Radford was delighted when Ray got into the side, as he had felt for some time that there was a need for a workhorse up front to support him and George Armstrong. He saw immediately that he would be able to play with Ray. Out of this, a close and continuing friendship grew and a dynamic twin spearhead was forged. Don Howe said of them:

> Both were big powerful quiet boys, down to earth, called a spade a spade. They were so calm sticking in goals with great regularity. Of the two, Ray had the better first touch. Raddy knew exactly how to handle Ray and they became equal partners on the pitch and great friends off it. Sometimes I'd keep them both out practising shooting when everyone had gone home and they'd never complain. Both listened and worked hard on what they were told. We played 4–2–4 with the two of them as centre forwards. Ray was mobile and could run off the ball, turning big centre halves like Mike England inside out.

In the early part of the season, Radford would often talk Ray through a game, guiding and steadying him. However, as the season progressed towards Christmas, the partnership fused into a perfect marriage. The intimacy between the two players is illustrated by one of Ray's statements to the press:

> Raddy is more than just the bloke up there at the front with me sharing the knocks as well as the goals. He's my mate and I'm grateful to him for so many things. He sort of adopted me which was a great help to a youngster especially on away trips when you feel inhibited and out of place. If I am flagging he gees me up and he is always brave, with a deceptive sense

of pace. There seemed to be an immediate chemistry between us and we have developed a special understanding. Since I got in the first team he has helped me more than anyone else. I hate to think of the number of miles we run for each other; Raddy is pretty stubborn though and I would never argue with him because I know I'd always lose.

Although their roles were in many ways interchangeable, Ray acted as the target man for Bob Wilson to pick out with his long goal kicks. Ray would then hold the ball while Radford ran into a good position, by which time the midfield would be up in support. Both men sensed almost telepathically where the other would be when the ball came through. By posing such a forceful central threat, Ray freed Radford to run across the front line. John Radford, although much more reticent about expressing his feelings to the media than Ray, was equally complimentary about his younger partner:

Ray came through the youth side. We didn't know each other then but after Charlie George got injured it was the start of an incredible partnership.

At first it seemed to happen naturally, then we started to work very hard together training morning, noon and night. Ray had a great physical presence, the ability to score goals with a very short back lift and the minimum of room.

Although the two players had a working love affair so essential for striking partnerships, off the field they did not socialize all that much. Ray was now living in digs with Mr and Mrs Jock Allen at Powys Lane in Bounds Green. By Christmas, it was generally acknowledged that the Arsenal strikers, ably aided and abetted by Armstrong's crosses, were the most destructive in the League, and visiting managers would bring their players to Highbury just to watch the two hunt. The relationship that Radford and Kennedy had was not considered particularly unusual by the football fraternity at the time. As in many other walks of life, close working relationships are commonplace among professional players, helping to provide the bonding and intuitive understanding essential for success in a team game. Despite the wide mix of ages and personalities in the Arsenal side that year, close bonds were formed; the defenders, midfielders and strikers all tended to form their own cliques leading to a unified cohesion, with Kennedy and Radford representing the archetypal strike force.

The first game of the New Year was against West Ham United at Highbury. The Hammers' stars, Bobby Moore and Jimmy Greaves, were missing, having been disciplined by Ron Greenwood for an indiscretion in a Blackpool night-club the night before their FA Cup defeat. Arsenal, with headed goals from Radford and Kennedy, won through reasonably comfortably. On coming off the pitch, their delight was doubled by learning that Spurs had pulled off a surprise 2–1 win at Elland Road to reduce Leeds' gap at the top of the table to a single point. However, just when the Gunners had a golden opportunity to go to the top, Leeds' Yorkshire neighbours, Huddersfield Town, negated the favour Spurs had done Arsenal by beating the Gunners 2–1. McLintock's nose was broken early on and then, with a quarter of an hour to go, he was controversially judged to have handled the ball in the box, giving Frank Worthington the chance to win the game. The Arsenal goal had come earlier from a free kick which Graham had miscued fortuitously into the path of Kennedy, who had put a glancing header into the net.

In the next round of the FA Cup, Arsenal were drawn against Portsmouth, ignominiously languishing in mid-table in the Second Division and thirsting for a resurrection of their former glories. The match proved to be a classic English cup tie. A hand ball in the box allowed Storey to give Arsenal the lead from the penalty spot, but in the dying minutes of a fiercely fought game Trebilcock equalized. In the replay on 1 February at Highbury, Portsmouth took the lead in the first few minutes. George, reinstated in the side after his injury in the first match of the season, ran from the half-way line and rocketed a shot past the Portsmouth keeper to equalize. Simpson then volleyed in an Armstrong corner; Pompey were not finished and clawed back an equalizer. The match was settled finally by another invaluable Storey penalty following a foul on Radford, putting Arsenal through to the fifth round of the Cup, 3–2. Following an Arsenal defeat at Liverpool 2–0, Leeds' consistency made them odds-on favourites for the title with their lead now stretched to five points. Back at Highbury the following week, Arsenal endured a tough encounter against Manchester City and required all their resilience to take the points. Radford scored the winner through good positioning after the City keeper had only been able to parry out a powerful Simpson shot. Liverpool, whose form was now peaking, put in another superb game to vanquish Leeds at Elland Road and cut back their lead.

Ray, who for most of the season feared that he would immediately be dropped on George's return, had become indispensable for Arsenal success. George's return to the side, therefore, had to be in a deeper midfield role in place of Graham. The fifth round FA Cup match at Maine Road was won 2–1, with George scoring both goals and looking increasingly comfortable in his new midfield position. The deeper role allowed him extra time to linger on the ball and display his evasive skills and pinpoint passing.

By mid-February a mood of excited anticipation was beginning to settle over Highbury. Mee pointed out to the players that three trophies were in their sights and they owed it to themselves and the fans not to squander opportunities. He informed them that a gruelling two-match-a-week schedule would now be in effect until the end of the season.

George, already established as the North Bank's hero, gave Arsenal the lead in the next home game against Ipswich with a near-post header from a corner. Kennedy, with some clever play, then put Radford through for Arsenal's second goal, and McLintock made it three from another corner. However, Ipswich were not finished, and in the second half came back with two goals from Jimmy Robertson, who had already missed an open goal and had another disallowed. Arsenal clung on for a 3–2 victory. A week later Arsenal were almost written off by the press following a 2–0 defeat at the Baseball Ground against Derby County, who were led by the ferocious Dave Mackay, hero of the Spurs Double side of 1960–1. Arsenal, despite having two games in hand, were now seven points behind Leeds, in the days when a win was worth only two points. Three days later, in a rearranged fixture, Arsenal went to Wolves, who were having an excellent season and had Bobby Gould eager to prove the Gunners' decision to sell him was a mistake. Arsenal went a goal up in the first minute, which restored their confidence. Goals from Kennedy, Radford and Storey resulted in a comfortable 3–0 win. After the game, which underlined Arsenal's fighting spirit,

McLintock remarked: 'I'm sick of people writing us off. A lot can happen before the season is over. Leeds need only lose a couple to start wobbling'. For Ray, the season of wins was beginning to resemble the success he had enjoyed at New Hartley Juniors. This time John Radford rather than Ian Watts was his goal-scoring accomplice.

With twelve games left to play, Arsenal were five points behind Leeds with a game in hand, both clubs were still in European competitions, but Leeds were already out of the FA Cup, having gone out by three goals to two to Fourth Division Colchester in the shock of the season. Arsenal's fixture congestion was not eased by a goalless away draw against Leicester City in the quarter-final of the FA Cup in which Leicester had much the better chances of clinching victory. The following week Arsenal had to play three crucial games. In the first, the next round of the Fairs Cup, Arsenal threatened to annihilate FC Köln despite the presence of German internationals Overath and Lohr. McLintock scored after the German goalkeeper failed to gather a shot from Kennedy, but against the run of play the Germans equalized before half-time. Despite constant Arsenal pressure, they could only add a single goal by Storey in the second half, and they tramped off the pitch knowing that they had failed to capitalize on their chances and that Köln only needed to win 1–0 in the second leg. On the Saturday, at Crystal Palace, Arsenal achieved a gritty 2–0 victory in the League, with goals coming from the reinstated Graham and substitute Sammels. More than 57,000 turned up at Highbury on 15 March for the FA Cup replay against Leicester. After Leicester had had an early goal disallowed, shortly before half-time George rose majestically to head home an Armstrong corner. Throughout the second half, however, Arsenal's Second Division opponents ran them close, with Wilson kept just as busy as Shilton was in the Leicester goal.

In the next League game, Arsenal scraped through against what had been regarded as a cannon-fodder Blackpool side, Peter Storey scoring his first goal with his head. This success provided welcome respite for the Arsenal midfielder who, despite achieving international honours, had been lambasted in the media for his abrasive style of play and late tackles. In the second leg of the Fairs Cup in Germany, as predicted by the Köln manager,

Arsenal lost 1–0 and went out of the tournament. The Romanian
referee had proved particularly susceptible to the German's histri-
onics and awarded a contested penalty. George was so furious
that he had to be held back as he tried to pursue the referee off
the pitch; an official complaint was lodged by the Arsenal
management but to no avail.

In the semi-final of the FA Cup, to be played at Hillsborough,
Arsenal were drawn against underdogs Stoke City, while the
other tie was a glamorous Merseyside derby between Liverpool
and Everton. After an indecisive first half showing, Arsenal
deservedly left the field 2–0 down. The first goal had come as a
result of Storey failing to clear a Greenhoff corner which hit
Dennis Smith and bounced into the net. This was followed by a
disastrous back pass by George which was intercepted by Ritchie,
who coolly slotted the ball past a disconsolate Wilson. At the
other end, however, Arsenal had been denied on two occasions
by vintage Banks' saves from Kennedy. Stoke missed killing off
Arsenal altogether in the first half, with Greenhoff skying a
relatively easy shot. After the break, however, Arsenal began
to launch a series of offensives; in one, Armstrong passed to
Kennedy, who laid on a beautiful chip just in front of Storey,
who was able to drive the ball home brilliantly from twenty
yards to give Arsenal hope. Greenhoff, however, continued to
threaten the Arsenal defence; at full time Stoke had held on
to their 2–1 lead. In the few minutes added on by referee Pat
Partridge for an injury to Charlie George, McLintock was
denied from an Armstrong corner by a desperate Mahoney hand
ball. All the Arsenal fans and players began jumping up and
down as if the match had already been saved. Storey, however,
still had to get the ball past Gordon Banks. He was fully aware
that if he missed he would be branded for life and that whatever
else he did in his football career that single error would never be
forgotten. As he began to run forward he saw Banks switch his
weight to the right and he elected to blast the ball crisply to the
left. Arsenal were reprieved. Storey, the quiet man with the cold
eyes, had saved Arsenal once more.

Radford and Kennedy at this point in the season were both
going through a lean spell, neither having scored for seven
games, but in the Cup replay at Villa Park the pair combined to
give Kennedy a decisive second goal to add to George Graham's

header from George 'The Provider' Armstrong. In the other tie, Liverpool had come from behind to beat Everton, setting up a classic north *versus* south final between two of the finest teams in the land. Remarkably, the two had not met at Wembley for twenty-one years, when Arsenal had come away victors. McLintock was now totally convinced that the Gunners would win the Double. His conviction was given further support when Leeds faltered at Chelsea in the League; although still six points ahead of the Arsenal, they had now played three games more. Most of the pundits, however, still favoured Leeds, as experience had repeatedly shown that games in hand late in the season rarely convert to maximum points.

Chelsea, buoyant after their victory over Leeds, then came to Highbury, with Arsenal adopting their customary 4–2–4 system. Shortly after the interval, George dummied an Armstrong cross, letting the ball run through to Kennedy who, without any wind-up to his shot, rifled the ball into the net. Charlie George then sent his old friend from the youth squad through for a second winning goal in the second half. After this match, it was rumoured that Revie had forbidden the Leeds side to mention the name of Arsenal.

The mid-week game against Coventry was another of those games that Arsenal could easily have let slip. Somehow, the defence held out and after clever build-up work from Graham and Armstrong, Kennedy again got the winner, killing the ball brilliantly on his first touch despite the close attention of two defenders, and blasting it past the goalkeeper.

Arsenal had now conceded only six goals in the last eighteen home matches. Southampton were fighting for a European place and presented Arsenal with stiff opposition in the next League game at the Dell. Fortunately, scoring from an Armstrong cross, Radford broke his ten-game barren spell in the second half. After Terry Paine had equalized for the Saints, McLintock stretched valiantly to prod the winner home with his right foot. Leeds, meanwhile, had only been able to draw at St James's Park and in their next game another point was dropped in a goalless draw at Huddersfield Town. The recurring Leeds' self-doubt and superstitions seemed to be creeping back.

The following day Arsenal went to Notts Forest, who had won five of their last six matches. In the first minutes of the game, Wilson had to hurl himself at the oncoming feet of Martin, leading to injuries to both players. In the seventeenth minute, following an Armstrong corner, McLintock headed the ball towards the line where it seemed to have been scrambled clear, before Kennedy made it certain. The goal was later confirmed as McClintock's. Just before half-time, from a long Radford throw, Arsenal went further ahead when Graham flicked on for Kennedy to score. Uncharacteristically, Kennedy was subsequently booked for back-chatting to a linesman. Ray had probably given the official his standard retort, 'Are you demb and duff?' George made it three for Arsenal shortly before the final whistle.

Leeds now had four League games to play and were two points ahead of Arsenal, who had two games in hand. They had conquered their nerves to return from Anfield with a wonderful 1–0 victory in the first leg of the Fairs Cup. In the League, however, Leeds' jitters continued, and by 17 April Arsenal were top of the League for the first time. At Highbury, Arsenal, in one of their less convincing performances of the season, scraped through against Newcastle United, thanks to a fierce drive from George. Earlier he had been booked in what was becoming a familiar mixture of self-destructive indiscipline mixed with graceful flair and genius. At Elland Road, Leeds were struggling against West Bromwich Albion. The first West Brom goal came from what the Leeds crowd, team and management all thought was an offside situation. The crowd invaded the pitch and the club was fined, the FA further penalizing the Yorkshire club by making them play their four opening League games of the following season away from home. When Albion, who had not won away from home for sixteen months, eventually triumphed 2–1, a deep sense of grievance and disappointment fuelled Leeds' growing insecurity. Meanwhile, when the tannoy at Highbury announced the good news, the crowd erupted.

Burnley were condemned to Second Division football in a game at Highbury settled by a penalty by George, deputizing for Storey, who was playing for England against Greece. From the beginning of March until almost the end of April, Arsenal had gone unbeaten despite scoring only sixteen goals. The crucial statistic, however, was that they had conceded only a single goal. At the Hawthorns on 24 April, Arsenal came away with a 2–2 draw, with Asa Hartford scoring goals at both ends

The Seaton Delaval Pit in the 1920s. (courtesy of Mr Thomas Allen)

Milbourne Terrace, Seaton Delaval, Ray's birthplace, as it appeared in 1968. (courtesy of Mr Thomas Allen)

Astley County Secondary Football Team. Ray, aged eleven, is in the back row, far left, in this team of older boys.

County Leaving Certificate

ISSUED BY

NORTHUMBERLAND COUNTY EDUCATION COMMITTEE

NAME OF PUPIL RAYMOND KENNEDY   Date of Birth 28. 7. 51

SCHOOL ASTLEY COUNTY SECONDARY   Date of Leaving 29.7.66

SCHOOL RECORD:

SUBJECTS	ESTIMATE OF ABILITY	
English Subjects	C-	
Mathematics	C+	
Science	C-	
Geography	C+	
History	C	
Religious Knowledge	C	
Art	C+	Physical Education .A.
Woodwork	C+	Technical Drawing .C...
Metalwork		Music .C......

(NOTE.—Ability expressed as A, B, C, D, or E, where C means average for the school, B above average
A very good, while D is below average and E poor.)

PARTICIPATION IN SCHOOL ACTIVITIES AND SPECIAL INTERESTS:

School games captain. School Prefect.
Took an active part in school
games. Special interest Association
Football. A quiet and well behaved
lad who worked steadily in most
subjects.

G.A.Turnbull Head master.   C. L. Mellowes

Date 14.7.66   Director of Education.

Ray's school leaving report from Astley County Secondary, emphasizing his sporting prowess and courteous behaviour.

Arsenal Youth Team at
tournament in 1968.
Ray is sixth from the
front and Charlie George
is second from the end.

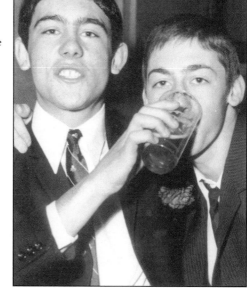

Young hopefuls –
Kennedy and George in
1969.

Ray signs professional forms at Arsenal on 11 November 1968
with Bertie Mee looking on approvingly. (Munson)

Above: Young Turk. Training alone back home in the North-East (*circa* 1969).

Centre: Ray, aged twenty, with his younger sister Janet and his mam, Veronica.

Left: Butch Kennedy and the Sundance Kid (John Radford). (Express Newspapers)

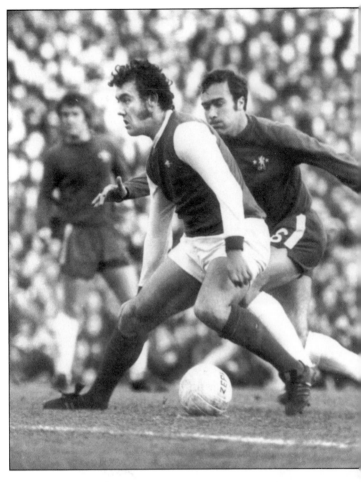

Ray, in his Arsenal days, resisting the attentions of Chelsea's
Ron 'Chopper' Harris. (Colorsport)

Kennedy in action for Arsenal against Manchester United,
22 August 1970. (Photocall Features)

Medal Man. (Harry Ormesher)

Ray presents the end of season awards at Bates Welfare as younger brother Michael (immediate right of the Master of Ceremonies) looks on, April 1973.

Kennedy, the Man in the Mask, training at Melwood, *circa* 1975, with his Liverpool team-mates, *left to right*: McDermott, Keegan, Lawler and Lindsay. (Harry Ormesher)

for West Brom. Arsenal's nine-match run of victories had come to an end. However, after the game, McLintock received the good news that he had been named Footballer of the Year. Despite a Leeds victory at Southampton, Arsenal remained top of the League with 61 points from 39 matches, with Leeds on 60 from 40 games.

On 26 April, a Monday evening, Arsenal went to Elland Road in what was regarded as a crunch game for Leeds. In front of a capacity crowd of 48,000, Leeds were desperate to win. Arsenal managed to weather the first half relatively comfortably but, spurred on by their midfield dynamos Johnny Giles and Billy Bremner, Leeds launched a relentless and ferocious second half onslaught on the Arsenal defence. In the dying minutes of the game, when it looked as if Arsenal's mass defences would survive, Madeley started another Leeds attack involving the ubiquitous and increasingly desperate Bremner, who somehow forced the ball out to Jack Charlton, who hit the post and then, amidst complaints about offside by the Arsenal defence, converted the rebound. Despite frenzied appeals by the Arsenal defence, and another booking for Charlie George, the goal stood. A last-minute Graham header whistled over the Leeds crossbar; but the single goal was enough to put Leeds back on top of the First Division.

On May Day, Leeds won again, 2–0, in their last game of the season against Notts Forest. Arsenal also kept up the challenge with a late Eddie Kelly goal in a tense game against Stoke City. Leeds United had now finished their season with a huge total of 64 points, having lost only five games and drawn ten. Arsenal, with one game to play and 63 points, had scored two fewer goals and conceded one less. The title rested, therefore, on Arsenal's final game, which was to be played at White Hart Lane on the Monday before the Cup Final.

Leeds could not have hoped for a more committed opposition than Arsenal's rivals, Spurs, mindful of their enemy's eyes on the coveted Double which had not been repeated since Spurs' achievement under Bill Nicholson ten years before. Spurs also badly needed points to qualify for Europe the following season. Before the match had even started, the statisticians had a field day calculating the various permutations, which ultimately indicated that an Arsenal win or a goalless draw would give them the title, whereas a loss or any score draw would hand the title to Leeds. Alan Mullery epitomized the Tottenham resolve: 'Arsenal have got as much chance of being handed the title by Spurs as I have of being given the crown jewels. They are the last people you want to win the championship'.

On the day of the match the Arsenal players followed their usual ritual of lunching at the South Herts Golf Club and setting off on the team coach to meet their North London rivals. With his characteristic meticulous planning, Bertie Mee had allowed an hour for a half-hour journey, anticipating huge crowds. However, not even he could have imagined the mob of excited, desperate fans slowly pushing forwards to the ground. Ray still remembers the journey to White Hart Lane with a mixture of exhilaration and terror: 'I have never played in a match with so many people. People's faces were crushing up against the coach window. We were frightened, but at the same time bucked up by the fantastic support. There must have been more outside the ground than in'.

The referee, Teessider Kevin Howley, who was supervising his last League match before retiring, was obliged to abandon his car and struggle through the crowds. Inside White Hart Lane were 51,000 delirious North London supporters. McLintock's barking commands to keep a clean slate at all costs were largely inaudible in the din and even the referee's whistle was difficult for the players to hear at times. In the opening minute Jennings pulled off a brilliant save from George, then McLintock saw his shot career off a defender. Throughout the first half, Arsenal pressurized players and created moments of panic in the Spurs defence through Armstrong's deceptive corners and Radford's threatening long throws. Despite Arsenal's forceful commitment, it was by no means one-way traffic, with Chivers and Gilzean worrying the Arsenal defence and Peters going close with a rasping right-foot shot. However, Chivers kept getting caught offside and it seemed unlikely to be Spurs' day when Peters was denied a penalty when floored by a Wilson dive at his legs. Wilson was then injured at Kinnear's feet, with a scuffle involving six players breaking out as Wilson lay injured on the ground. In the sixty-first minute, Neighbour sent Knowles free on a left overlap. He, in turn, sent over a low cross which Gilzean fluffed from six yards out. Arsenal then turned the screw and Kinnear whipped the ball off Graham's toes to concede a corner. A few minutes from the end, the referee got in the way of McLintock as he was about to slam Armstrong's free kick into the net and went tumbling over, red-faced, to the cheers of the crowd. Arsenal desperately surged forwards, with Graham heading just over the bar. With four minutes to go, Joe Kinnear, the Spurs defender and now the Wimbledon manager, was robbed of the ball by George as he attempted to run out of the box. 'George then crossed the ball to Radford whose shot was parried by Jennings after a partial block by Kinnear. For a fraction of a second the Spurs were rooted to the spot as the ball seemed destined to run out of play on the left touch-line. However, the indomitable Armstrong rescued it and chipped over a perfect ball to Kennedy, who rose high to head the ball past Cyril Knowles to the left of Jennings and over the goal line via the underside of the bar. The Arsenal supporters erupted with a roar of relief which was echoed by the thousands milling outside the ground listening to radios. The goal seemed to recharge Spurs, and the Arsenal players were driven back by determined pressure. It suddenly dawned on the Arsenal side that if Spurs scored, the championship would still go to Leeds. The Arsenal goal for which Kennedy will always be remembered appeared at the time to be a mixed blessing: 'I knew I was going to score as soon as Geordie crossed it but immediately afterwards Tottenham came back at us. I started to think I'd done the wrong thing scoring. Those were the longest three minutes of my life'.

After a frenzied last-minute goal-mouth incident with Wilson clutching the ball as if his life depended on it, the referee blew the whistle. Before the Arsenal goalkeeper could move he was swamped by thousands of fans surging onto the pitch from the terraces. Fifteen minutes later some of the Arsenal players had still not reached the tunnel and Don Howe was convinced that McLintock and Wilson would be certain hospital cases and others of his squad would be ripped apart and injured before Saturday's Cup Final. The jubilant Arsenal hordes invaded the directors' and press boxes chanting and cheering. This astonishing scene was not witnessed by the nation, as mid-week matches were not covered by television. One of the first to congratulate the Arsenal side after the match was Bill Shankly, manager of their Cup Final opponents, Liverpool, who phoned the Arsenal dressing room before the team had showered. His canny words were: 'Congratulations on a tremendous performance. Now you may even give us a game on Saturday!' Condemned to yet another second place, Revie and his disconsolate Leeds players sitting at home generously acknowledged the Arsenal achievement: 'We have not lost the title with 64 points, Arsenal have won it and are true champions'.

After the game, most of the players went to the White Hart Pub in Southgate to celebrate and, despite the imminent Cup Final, were given the following day off training. The season had been so full of dramas for young Kennedy that the significance of the team's achievement was not fully acknowledged: 'I didn't appreciate really what we'd done. I just had a couple of drinks and then went home almost as if it had been any old match'. Charlie George, asked to comment on Ray's goal, said: 'He's so big it takes defenders five minutes to walk round him, never mind get the ball off him'. Peter Batt, in *The Sun*, reported Ray's championship-winning goal as follows:

> Ray Kennedy, the nineteen year old baby of the side, gave them the First Division Championship last night with one of the most dramatic goals in the history of the Football League. Kennedy was a two year old toddler when Arsenal last won the title in 1953. But he became a giant of a man in the eyes of tens of thousands of ecstatic fans at White Hart Lane. From the scenes which followed he might have been a hot gospeller like Billy Graham. For with the fervour of a religious ceremony the Arsenal hordes went crazy.

The analogy with Billy Graham was to prove a tragic prophecy, as the evangelist has also been diagnosed as having Parkinson's disease.

After the day of celebration Arsenal went back to prepare for the Cup Final. Their preparation was thorough; the grass at London Colney had even been allowed to grow in an attempt to replicate the lush Wembley turf. Mee sheltered the players from the press and television and he and Howe both tried to keep the players as relaxed as possible. Peter Storey, who had missed the Spurs match with a groin strain, was responding slowly to physiotherapy, but it would be touch and go whether Arsenal's hit man would be fit to play. The day before the game the Arsenal team went for a preparatory walk on the Wembley turf only to find that the wily old fox, Shankly, was there to pry. Although the final was to take place in glorious sunshine, rain was in the air that Friday, and before the game Shankly cunningly whispered in the Arsenal goalkeeper's ear: 'It'll be a nightmare for goalkeepers tomorrow, son.' Shankly, who was a past master at unnerving the opposition, had scored the first psychological advantage. Mee was to get his revenge the following day by keeping the Liverpool players waiting in the tunnel. The omens looked good for the Gunners, who had booked into the Grosvenor House Hotel on Park Lane, which had been a lucky venue for West Bromwich Albion three years earlier. On the day of the match, Arsenal arrived for their traditional lunch at the South Herts Golf Club. Most of the Arsenal players were quietly confident that they were about to write themselves into the football history books. Ray told the press: 'Raddy and I will run round Wembley three times on our own with the cup. That's the way it is with us two – togetherness'.

The teams for the 1971 FA Cup Final were:

Arsenal: Bob Wilson, Pat Rice, Bob McNab, Peter Storey (Eddie Kelly), Frank McLintock, Peter Simpson, George Armstrong, Charlie George, John Radford, Ray Kennedy, George Graham.

Liverpool: Ray Clemence, Chris Lawler, Alec Lindsay, Tommy Smith, Larry Lloyd, Emlyn Hughes, Ian Callaghan, Alun Evans (Peter Thompson), John Toshack, Brian Hall, Steve Heighway.

The referee was Norman Burtenshaw.

The twelve-strong Kennedy clan, led by Veronica, Martin and Trevor, had left Newcastle Station on the Friday and spent the evening before the game talking with Arsenal friends and scouts who were all staying together in another London hotel. Before the game, the Kennedys were able to walk round Wembley Stadium to savour the atmosphere before being ushered to VIP suites close to the Royal Box. Veronica remembers that Ray seemed excessively nervous.

The captains of the teams were unquestionably two of the strongest, most charismatic leaders in the Football League: McLintock, passionate, temperamental and fiercely competitive, but up until then jinxed at Wembley, and Tommy Smith, the Anfield Iron, born round the corner from the ground and prepared to give his life for a Liverpool victory. In front of a 100,000 capacity crowd, the two teams were introduced to the Duke of Kent. Kennedy, at nineteen, was the youngest man on the pitch, but immediately prior to kick-off he seemed calm and collected. The game opened cautiously. Storey scythed into the Liverpool attack, fouling Heighway within a few minutes of the start. As Liverpool built up a number of early raids into the Arsenal half, Rice and McLintock were also pulled up for brazen fouls on Toshack. Kennedy missed an early opportunity for Arsenal, putting the ball wide of the left post from an angled shot. Midway through the half and largely as a result of the calming influence of 'Stroller' Graham, Arsenal began to settle into their game, and soon the crowd were witnessing a tightly contested technical match sprinkled with niggly fouls. Kennedy again threatened, seeing a half-chance to run past the Liverpool defence, only to be beaten to the ball by Clemence. Minutes later he was nearly through again. Radford, who was proving to be the more threatening of the Arsenal strike force at this stage, incensed Tommy Smith with a savage charge on Clemence. A few minutes later Radford broke free to give Storey a half-chance in a movement which led to the first corner of the match. Storey, when not cutting down the Liverpool attack, was rifling long shots at the Liverpool goal, and George also blasted a fearsome shot just over the bar from twenty yards. Throughout the first half Liverpool remained dangerous on the break, especially on the flank, through the pace of Heighway. Tommy Smith also went close with a long shot. In the first half Arsenal gave away ten free kicks, the last of which nearly brought a goal from a spectacular shot from the Liverpool full back, Lindsay.

Through the second half the Arsenal defence remained resolutely secure, with McNab doing sterling work. Radford, having his first game for several weeks, provided Kennedy with a further chance which the youngster just pushed wide, acknowledging Radford's lay-off with his customary hand clap. Peter Thompson replaced the ineffectual Alun Evans in the Liverpool attack and immediately injected more penetration, and Kelly came on for the struggling Storey. Despite these tactical changes, very few clear chances were created by either side. However, to the impartial observers in the crowd it appeared that Arsenal had gained a slight advantage despite the mounting roar of 'You'll Never Walk Alone' from the Liverpool ranks.

Kennedy and Armstrong had further half-chances which on a good day both would have buried, and George Graham, having an excellent game, headed onto the bar from a Radford long throw, before the ball was finally scraped away by Smith. From the corner, Armstrong again found Graham's head and this time Lindsay was forced to clear off the line. Full time ended without score, but within two minutes of the first half of extra time Liverpool went ahead. Heighway, who had been threatening all match, finally broke the Arsenal defence and cut in sharply from the left. Wilson, seeing Toshack take up a good position in the middle, was torn between guarding his near post and anticipating a Heighway cross. The university graduate, who had not started to play football seriously until he was eighteen, sold Wilson, the schoolmaster, a perfect dummy and fired the ball inside the near post with a wonderful piece of skill. The Wembley Kop immediately broke out with 'We Shall Not Be Moved' and 'Show Me the Way to Go Home'. A few minutes later Wilson had to save brilliantly from Hall to keep Arsenal in the game. Even then Martin Kennedy was never in doubt that his son would be on the winning side, as everyone sensed that Arsenal would claw the game back. At this point, the Arsenal bench became aware of George's weariness and signalled for him to fall back a little, and encouraged Graham to push forward. This paid immediate dividends and, just before the end of the first period, Arsenal had equalized. Radford put the ball over his shoulder in a congested Liverpool penalty area and Kelly pushed it past Clemence with Graham following it through. Whether Kelly or Graham scored is still contested, even with the camera's eye of hindsight.

With five minutes remaining, a replay looked a certainty and Don Howe afterwards confessed that Arsenal would have settled for that in order to regroup and fight another day. After a wonderful season the young Kennedy had been somewhat over-awed, Armstrong had had an off day and George was out on his feet. At this point, George was pushed back up front and Graham came into midfield to bolster the defence. Immediately, almost as if to celebrate his reinstatement in the Gunners' attack, George linked with Radford and then from twenty yards, let fly a bullet of a shot which was even more unstoppable after a slight upward deflection off Lloyd, leaving Clemence with nothing more than a momentary blurred anguish followed by the depressing task of picking the ball out of the back of his net. George immediately collapsed backwards onto the hallowed turf with his arms outstretched in a joyous Messiah pose. Charlie George had scored the historic goal which gave Arsenal the Cup and League Double and rocketed him into the Arsenal Hall of Fame.

George was the antithesis of Kennedy; he was a local lad from Islington who had stood on the North Bank to support Arsenal as a child. His lank, untidy, shoulder-length hair contrasted strikingly with Kennedy's immaculate appearance, and there was a menacing streak in his personality which frequently spilled over into undisciplined aggression during a game. Although Ray did not like interviews, Charlie George's inarticulate responses to the press were as legendary as those of John Radford and, in contrast to Ray, the female sex seemed to hold little attraction for him as he stuck loyally to his long-term fiancée, Susan Farge.

Arsenal had proved all their critics wrong and became only the fourth club – after Preston North End in 1888–9, Aston Villa in 1896–7 and Spurs in 1960–1 – ever to have won a League and Cup Double, a triumph which stemmed from spirited team effort and a refusal to accept defeat. Frank McLintock's moment of glory had finally come. On that day, McLintock was shrewdly held back by Wilson before going up to receive the cup in order to allow him to savour his moment of triumph for as long as possible. Unfortunately, McLintock went up in a detached vacuum, drained of all emotion: 'I've never been able to feel that supreme thrill of winning the Double. Our Fairs Cup the year before had meant so much to me and winning the League earlier in the week must have drained me completely'. Ray also remembers the occasion with awe and incredulity, his major recollection being his initial disappointment with what he considered to be his own mediocre performance. The following day, the Arsenal team, granted the freedom of Islington, paraded their three cups through the streets of Highbury, greeted by a quarter of a million people. At the end of an unbelievable season in the Arsenal first team, Ray Kennedy had finished with a League and Cup Double and twenty-six goals to his tally.

At that point Ray could see no one stopping Arsenal for the next few seasons and felt that the team was likely to go from strength to strength. Although increasing affluence had enabled him to buy things such as a red Ford Capri, his feet remained firmly on the ground: 'I could have gone on the FA tour to Australia in the summer, but it meant five weeks away and after the season we've had I'm sure everyone understood when I said I wanted to go home instead. That's me, a quiet lad who couldn't think of a better way to spend summer than back home with the family. You'd have been wasting your time if you'd have been looking for me on the beaches of Europe or the night spots of London, that just wasn't me'.

Acclaim came from all directions. The press hailed him as a second Tommy Lawton or a Ted Drake but with more skill. He was considered the natural successor to Geoff Hurst in the England team and in common with the West Ham man and John Charles, Kennedy put brain before brawn. Don Revie, never one to praise players from the capital, enthused over Kennedy's potential. Ray was also awarded the *Rothman Football Yearbook* Young Footballer of the Year Award. A memorable picture of the era shows Ray resisting a desperate challenge from Everton's Howard Kendall, Kennedy's face radiating commitment and raw aggression. Brian Scovell, a journalist on the *Daily Mail*, remembers Ray in those days as a courteous young man who always welcomed the press with a joke or a cheerful greeting, an honest self-deprecating man prepared to admit his mistakes. Patrick Collins described his attributes rather differently: 'A big, raw, tubby fellow whose football was drenched in sweat and optimism, the straight man with thick muscular hairy legs. A battler who could run through brick walls and act as the second striker'.

Ray explains his meteoric rise as follows:

Arsenal picked me up and made me believe in myself again after I'd been finished at seventeen. In the '70–1 season, the senior players took all the pressure off me so it was easy. Much that I did that year was sheer instinct; my mind was not really in unison with my legs, and the hardest part of all was interviews. Raddy and I fooled defences because we could swap roles so easily in the middle of a game, each turning and spinning off the other. We were very similar in our way of playing, but I took more of the knocks. Raddy, Geordie and I were the work horses up front. We relied heavily on breakaways and a sound defence, often winning by the odd goal.

We stopped defences coming out and took pressure off our midfield. We'd cover every piece of grass on the park and, when the opposition defence came out, we'd hit them on the rebound. I was convinced at the time that if the squad was kept together we would sweep the board for years to come.

Also, in a more realistic, tragically prophetic statement to the press, he issued what was felt at the time to be little more than a self-protective modest understatement: 'I can't help thinking what will happen if the goals dry up. The lads tell me I'm not likely to be at my best until twenty-five or twenty-six years of age. But I can't see that. I'll be too slow by then. I think I'll be finished by twenty-six.'

During that first season, when Ray had begun to sense that football was a mirror of an indecent society rather than a romantic world of heroes and villains, he relied heavily on Frank McLintock's pastoral guidance, John Radford's friendship and Gordon Clark the chief scout's encouragement. Clark had been instrumental, through the Emersons, in bringing Ray to Highbury. When Ray complained to him that Bob McNab was always telling him what to do, Clark had replied: 'Don't let the others drag you down. You don't know yet how good you can be'. In contrast to today, senior players enjoyed and expected to advise the youngsters coming into a side. Ten-year testimonials for service to a football club were commonplace and, once a player arrived at a top club, his aspirations centred around how long he would be able to keep his first team place rather than where he would be moving in three years' time.

Despite their outstanding achievements, Arsenal's Double side has never captured the whole country's imagination in the same way that the charismatic Manchester United side of Law, Best and Charlton did. Adjectives such as boring, functional, defensive, solid, reliable and efficient were those most frequently heard to describe the side. These sentiments were largely shared by Martin Kennedy: 'We went down to see our Ray four or five times that year on a £5 train ticket. The first time I saw him play I could have cried. They were such a dour team. He had been totally moulded by the coaches into a different player. Ray told us that Don Howe used to mark the pitch into squares and each player was only allowed to move in a certain area of the field'.

The strength of the whole unit was much greater than that of the individual player, the level of technical ability was high, tactical preparation superlative and, whenever morale began to flag slightly, Mee was there to inject belief and determination. Although a number of the players had already gained or were to go on to savour international honours, in comparison with other great sides, the Arsenal Double side had a relative dearth of players representing their country.

Arsenal's success that season relied in no small part on the family atmosphere and a genuine sense of belonging which the club instilled into its players. Everyone had a desire to improve their game and settle only for the best. Furthermore, as the year progressed, despite their varying backgrounds, the players developed a communal respect on and off the pitch. Each began to appreciate the others' foibles and compensated for them. They rallied to one another's aid as in the Lazio affair. Within their midst was a bedrock of men with forceful and uncompromising characters. Only the most resilient survived the often brutal analyses in which every aspect of a player's performance was publicly scrutinized. In addition to the old heads in the side, a fair proportion of the team had risen through the youth ranks of the club, establishing patterns of friendship which artificially constructed 'bought teams' can never achieve. Their loyalty is so strong that Rice, Graham and Armstrong have remained with the club, and Bob Wilson and Frank McLintock maintain close regular contact.

Luck, of course, plays some part in every football success and Arsenal were blessed that year in having relatively few injuries. At the beginning of the season, Don Howe had altered the tactics at the back from Sexton's man-to-man marking to zonal play, with the defence pushing up whenever possible to catch the opposition offside. McNab masterminded this strategy, and Wilson, whose confidence grew steadily throughout the season, proved superb at reading and dealing with opposition crosses and through balls. This allowed Simpson and McLintock more freedom to play the ball forward from the back. Armstrong was the wide man, with Graham timing his runs from midfield to score vital goals. There was no doubt that the Double was won by getting the ball to Kennedy and Radford as early as possible; they then usually held the ball for the midfield to push forward or with darting runs pulled the opposition's defence from side to side, providing an opening for one another or Charlie George. These tactics are now emulated by many of the most successful of today's Premier League sides.

7 Sumo

Our youth was gay but rough,
Much drink and copulation.
If that seems not enough
blame our miseducation.
In shabby boarding houses
lips covered lips,
and in our wild carouses
there were companionships.

(JAMES SIMMONS)

BABY Janet was lavished with increasingly luxurious presents and was wickedly spoilt by her famous brother. The family remained extremely tight-knit. During that close season in 1971, Ray met one of his old classmates from Astley Comprehensive, Jennifer Lockey, who was now working as a telephone operator and singing in the evenings in working men's clubs. Ray remembered Jennifer as always having a high opinion of herself and being in the A form at school. Perhaps it was her self-confidence and spirit that attracted him. That summer Ray and Jennifer started courting seriously, much to the irritation of Ray's little sister.

Meanwhile, back at Highbury, rumours were rife that Don Howe wanted Bertie Mee's job, or at least a promise that he would get it eventually, and he had issued an ultimatum. Frank McLintock released a statement, purporting to represent all the players, expressing concern that the directors would even consider letting Howe leave the club. Predictably, a few days later, Howe, George Wright, the club physiotherapist, and Brian Whitehouse, the Arsenal youth coach, had all been head-hunted by West Bromwich Albion, and Arsenal's pre-season planning was thrown into disarray. The Arsenal board could do nothing except bemoan a lack of loyalty in their employees. Ironically, fifteen years later, after Howe had finally fulfilled his dream of becoming the Arsenal manager, the directors dismissed him. Following Howe's departure in 1971, Steve Burtenshaw was promoted to first team coach and Fred Street came in as the new physiotherapist. The other major close season change was that Sammels, who had been increasingly barracked by a faction of the Arsenal crowd, left for Leicester City.

Within the demi-monde of the boot room, sports psychologists are looked upon with a mixture of suspicion and disbelief. Nevertheless, most successful football coaches and managers instinctively use psychological techniques in motivating their squads. Most trainers will tell you that football is all in the mind and that inner confidence and a communal self-belief is often all that distinguishes League leaders from relegation strugglers. How else can one explain the sudden transformation of fortune so often seen at a club simply by introducing a new manager? Why else do some teams suffer from 'away-itis' or have bogey teams? The game cannot be divorced from life itself and an emotionally crippled personality is a diminished footballer. However, correcting behaviour problems in players often takes time, and time is something which coaches no longer have. The player with a flaw in his nature which cannot easily be ironed out is dispensed with either by putting him on the transfer list or by dropping him. Even the greatest players soon lose a hold on their ability to perform consistently once booze, horses or women become a compulsion.

Despite a down-to-earth, no-nonsense approach, Mee and the coaching staff at Arsenal were open to new ideas and had expressed interest in some of the psychological assessment scales being used to assess motivation in National League American football. At the beginning of the 1971 season, Mee and Burtenshaw contacted a sports psychologist at the Institute for the Study of Athletic Motivation in San Jose, California. The Arsenal players were asked whether they would be prepared to fill in a questionnaire, the purpose of which was to help the coaches to assist the players in attaining their maximum potential by highlighting their strengths and weaknesses. As a group, footballers tend to be extroverted, ruthless and tough; although motivation

to perform well is not a guarantee for success, it is certainly a
key ingredient. Each player was reassured that the information
gleaned would be kept confidential between manager and coach,
and would only be disclosed to the rest of the squad if the player
so wished it. The coaches were under strict instructions not to
use the results of the tests against the player even when angry or
in pressure situations. The whole of the Double side, with the
exception of Charlie George, consented to taking the test; this
may have been a shrewd decision on George's part for, although
the questionnaires gave considerable insight into personality,
they didn't assess an individual's talent or natural ability. Once
the results were published, Burtenshaw and Mee were amazed at
the concordance between the findings and their own judgements
of individual players. When I spoke to Steve Burtenshaw recently,
he was even more struck by their accuracy twenty years on. He
told me that Peter Marinello's assessment was so poor that,
irrespective of his skill, it seemed incompatible with any form of
success in the professional game.

Ray's assessment highlighted his determination and aggression
and, in particular, his ability to listen, learn and act on what he
was told. It also drew attention to his disinclination to take a
leader's role, his lack of self-confidence and trust, and his reluctance to integrate fully into the team if he felt his own interests
might be jeopardized. His results are outlined below:

DRIVE
This athlete is average in drive and ambition. His ability to set
goals for himself depends upon the circumstances of each
competitive situation. His willingness to compete and accept
challenges is typical of most athletes at this level. This person
derives only partial ego satisfaction from his participation in
sports.

AGGRESSIVENESS
This athlete is above average in aggression and feels it is
important to win. He does not like to be pushed around, feels
free to show anger easily at anyone who betters him, and may
try to get even. He releases his aggression readily and will not
allow other people to take advantage of him. This is a self-
assertive athlete who will make things happen and rarely will
back down from an argument.

DETERMINATION

Characteristically, this competitor is above average in determination and will stick with assigned drills and exercises and diligently pursue his goals. He is willing to endure the discomforts of practice and conditioning which are essential to athletic success. Because of this attitude, he is willing to put in extra practice in order to perfect his skills. He is a plugger, not often giving up, and will usually work hard without being monitored.

GUILT-PRONENESS

This athlete is above average in accepting responsibility for his actions. His non-defensive attitude allows him to admit his mistakes and contributes to open communication. He considers pain a part of the conditioning process and minor injuries will not prevent him from playing. This athlete rarely gives excuses for bad performances. When the characteristic combines with extreme sensitivity, he may be inclined to get down on himself.

LEADERSHIP

This person is below average in his desire to be a leader. He would rather follow than lead his team-mates and will refrain from assuming responsibility for them. He will avoid positions of leadership and will not make decisions for others. He does not insist on having his way and will readily follow a dynamic leader. He does not expect others to look to him for guidance or direction, and rarely will he be forceful in his self-expression.

SELF-CONFIDENCE

This athlete is average in his level of self-confidence and has moderate faith in his athletic ability. His confidence in meeting new situations and defeating more successful opponents depends upon the circumstances and/or the particular opponent. Any strong challenge to his self-confidence could cause him to experience indecisiveness and self-doubt. He will not frequently speak out; however, a strong test of a value that is important to him will cause him to exert himself.

EMOTIONAL CONTROL

This player is average in his level of emotional control, and for the most part is able to handle his feelings. However, when competitive stress runs unusually high, tension may interfere with his performance. His estimation of his ability and likelihood of defeating opponents will determine just how much his feelings intrude. Since he has only a moderate capacity to handle bad breaks or bad calls, they may diminish his self-control.

MENTAL TOUGHNESS

This athlete is average in this trait. Generally, he will be able to handle criticism and rough coaching, but excessively harsh criticism will cause him to feel hurt and abused. In these instances, he will seek encouragement from the coach or team-mates. He will be slow to recover from a crushing defeat or a major disappointment. There also may be situations where he feels left out of team interactions.

ABILITY TO RESPOND TO COACHING

This player is extremely receptive to coaching and accepts it as essential for personal and team development. He attempts to meet all of the coaches' demands willingly and eagerly and is confident that the coaches' decisions are correct. In this regard he may rely excessively upon the coach for guidance. He has a high regard for the team captain, and will respect his leadership as well. He is eager to learn from others and is most receptive to advice and suggestions.

CONSCIENTIOUSNESS

This athlete is below average in conscientiousness and is prone to break or bend team rules which are contrary to his desires. He will not completely appreciate the rights of others and it will be difficult for him to set his needs aside when they conflict with team needs. He will interpret even just demands to be a denial of his individual freedom. This athlete tends to accept only those rules which are made personally relevant to him.

TRUST

This competitor is below average in his capacity to accept others at face value and is on guard against real or imagined dishonesty from others. He has considerable difficulty in maintaining his faith in coaches' and team-mates' statements and is susceptible to being drawn into team factions which could contribute to disunity. In addition, he finds it difficult to trust because others have taken advantage of him in the past.

The notes for the coaches on how Ray should be handled said

that he would benefit from a structured training programme with specific goals, but this needed to be reinforced with praise and encouragement. It was stressed that the coaches should pay close attention to Ray's emotional state in order to build his trust, to relieve his guilt over a bad performance, to help him maintain his emotional control and to bolster his self-confidence.

At the time, Burtenshaw marked Ray's score as accurate with the exception that he felt that he had been given too high a score on leadership and self-confidence. Frank McLintock's profile was, in many aspects, different to Ray's, perhaps explaining their mutual respect for one another. Bob Wilson's assessment of Ray at this time also concurred closely with the psychological evaluation: 'Ray was immature emotionally, insecure and for such a skilful player had an alarming lack of self-esteem. He was constantly looking for self-assurance and never totally believed in himself. He was basically a gentle giant, but there was an underlying fearsome strength, an assassin's eye and a hard-man interior'.

Clem Cattini is the ex-drummer for The Tornadoes, best remembered for their instrumental hit 'Telstar'; he is an incorrigible Arsenal fan who for thirty years has supported the club and became close to many of the players in the early seventies. He adds another slant:

> Ray was a shy lad, a good listener who would need a pint or two before he'd tell a few gags. He was one of the boys though, never a loner, although he found it hard to strike up a relationship for any length of time with anybody. With Ray there were no half measures, but a lot of footballers are like that. There always seemed a bit of a barrier with Ray as if he couldn't trust anyone completely. It took me a long time to get to know him. He gave me the impression he was not that committed to football. We usually talked about music in which he had a wide taste – rock, soul, folk and light classics – he liked them all. Again, like many footballers, he didn't suffer fools gladly. He hated hangers-on, the types who kept patting him on the back, or, worse still, the little men who tried to provoke him after a game. He said to me once, 'You do the talking with what you do on the pitch. You can chat your way in and chat your way out just as quick'.

*

The 1971 season started well for Arsenal, despite the absence of Charlie George with a cartilage injury, with the Gunners putting three goals past Chelsea and then winning at Huddersfield. Kennedy scored in both games. This was then followed by three successive defeats and the emergence of an uncharacteristic sloppiness in the Arsenal defence. A sweet victory against Don Howe's new team at the Hawthorns then renewed confidence, but this was followed by a 5-1 thrashing at Wolves after Arsenal had led at half-time. Arsenal were now able to field six internationals, with Wilson and Graham representing Scotland, Rice and Nelson, Northern Ireland, Radford, England and Roberts, Wales. However, Storey, George and Simpson all lost form, and Radford, following an injury, was unable to fight his way back into the team immediately. In order to combat the apparent fall in standards, Mee bought Alan Ball from Everton for £220,000.

Ray's romance with Jennifer Lockey had blossomed and, after the 2–0 home win against West Bromwich Albion on 18 December, Ray drove back home to get married, arriving in the early hours on Sunday. The couple had obtained special permission to wed on a Sunday, and the ceremony took place at Holy Trinity Church in Seghill near Seaton Delaval. Ray wore a black velvet suit, a white shirt and a purple tie, and John Radford was his best man. Paul Davis, with whom he had shared a room at Mrs Baynton's, was also present, as well as the two families. Jennifer, explaining to the press why the marriage had occurred on a Sunday, said: 'I'm afraid a football match had to come before a love match'.

Martin Kennedy warned Jenny before the marriage that it was not going to be easy being the wife of a football player. Ray had bought a house next door to John Radford's in Barnet in preparation for Jenny's arrival. After their wedding the couple drove back down south and spent their honeymoon in a hotel in Doncaster before driving to London on the Monday. Jenny became more and more apprehensive about the move to London as she confronted the reality of leaving her own life and career behind. Ray, at twenty, was beginning to appreciate the extra demands and commitments which his wife would expect him to meet. However, his need to have emotional support of the sort his mother had so selflessly supplied was great, and his marriage met with the full approval of the club management, who liked to see their players settled.

Through midwinter, Arsenal put in a fourteen-match unbeaten run, closing Manchester City's lead at the top of the table to four points. By February, with Arsenal still in the FA Cup, there was talk of another Double year. In the quarter-final of the European Cup, however, they lost 2–1 to Ajax. Kennedy's ability to undo continental defences was again obvious when he scored Arsenal's goal. He had also hit the target in the two previous victories against Stromgodset of Norway and Grasshoppers of Switzerland. Arsenal returned home optimistic after their match against the Dutch champions, but surprisingly lost the home leg following a George Graham own goal.

Arsenal had beaten Swindon and Reading in the first two rounds of the FA Cup but were then involved in a marathon tie against the future League Champions, Derby County, with Ray finally putting the Gunners through in the second replay at Leicester City. The first of these games is remembered by some Arsenal fans for the brazen, palm-back 'v' sign made by Charlie George to the incensed Derby terraces after he scored his second goal. The second game was eventful in that, as a result of the power workers' strike, it had to be played on a Tuesday afternoon; more than 30,000 fanatics playing hookey from work to attend the match. In the next round Alan Ball put Arsenal into the semi-finals against Stoke City with a goal against Leyton Orient.

On 30 March, after seventy successive League appearances in the number ten shirt, Ray was dropped for the game away to Manchester City and, although he was to regain his place, he missed four more League games that season, finishing with thirty-seven appearances. He began to look increasingly jaded as the season progressed and only made the substitutes' bench for the semi-final against Stoke City at Villa Park. Charlie George wore the number nine shirt and Radford, back after suspension, had Ray's number ten shirt. Earlier in the season Peter Storey had been dropped to allow Alan Ball to come in, but he had now fought his way back to claim a regular first team place. Armstrong scored for Arsenal but Wilson sustained a cartilage injury. The bench elected to keep him on, which proved to be a disastrous decision when Simpson, over-compensating for his keeper's injury, scored an own goal. This precipitated a belated decision to pull Wilson off, with Radford taking the goalkeeper's shirt and Kennedy coming on. The game finished as a draw, and in the replay Alan Ball was allowed to lead the Arsenal team out at the home of his former club, Everton. Barnett was deputizing for Wilson in goal and the match turned on a knife-edge. Each side had scored a penalty before Radford saw Arsenal through to their second successive FA Cup Final with a controversial winner.

The Centenary FA Cup Final was played in the presence of The Queen and Prince Philip with Leeds United as Arsenal's opponents. Leeds were attempting to emulate Arsenal's achievement of the previous season and win the Double. Rather like the Spurs players in the last League game of the previous season, Arsenal were determined not to have their Double success undermined by a repeat performance. This was Arsenal's fifth appearance at Wembley in successive years. Ball, Radford and George were again preferred to Kennedy, who started the match on the substitutes' bench. The game proved to be a cautious defensive battle won by a 'Sniffer' Clarke header for Leeds from a Mick Jones byline cross. Kennedy had come on for Radford in the second half but had been unable to make any impact.

Although Arsenal had little chance of winning the League Championship, they denied Liverpool by drawing with them at Highbury. On the same night Leeds, needing only a point to take the title, lost 2–1 at Wolves, badly missing Jones, who had been injured in the Cup Final. This gave the title to the amazed Derby County team, who had already set off on their summer holidays. Arsenal finished in fifth place, six points behind the champions, their season ending on a low note with a 2–0 defeat at home to Spurs.

Ray had had a mild dip in his performance following his marriage. Despite this, he ended the season as Arsenal's leading League goal-scorer with twelve, and scored another five in FA Cup competitions; he had also obtained England Under-23 recognition. He remained a firm favourite with the Arsenal crowd, who appreciated his unselfishness, and his ability to go forward into the eighteen-yard area where it hurts and to carry on without complaining even when desperately hacked down by opponents. He was seen as a brave, industrious player who moved instinctively into good positions and invariably supplied the *coup de grâce* in crucial games. Every time Ray was floored, the heaving mass of the North Bank would rise furiously in

unison with the chant: 'You're going to get your fucking heads
kicked in'. Or 'You're going home in a London ambulance'.

The 1972–3 season saw the beginning of the break up of the
Double side. Mee was convinced that the deteriorating motivation could only be solved by an injection of new players into the
squad. The general view was that some of the younger players,
such as Charlie George, Eddie Kelly and Ray, had obtained glory
too easily and too soon for their own good, and that they were
now experiencing an anticlimax. A breathing space might have
helped, but such a luxury could not be granted. Ray and Sammy
Nelson joined Charlie George and Eddie Kelly in a protest
against what they considered inadequate remuneration compared
with the more senior players, who received loyalty bonuses.
George, who had for some time been an increasing headache for
the manager, was put on the transfer list. He had been flitting
between the reserves, the substitutes' bench, the first team and
back again, and his hatred for Mee had grown so much that
the manager was reluctant to walk in front of George in case he
attacked him. George seemed unable to obtain the guidance he
needed to get back on the right road. Lacking confidence and
maturity, his game plummeted.

Ray was also getting into more and more difficulties. He
commented: 'Soccer is becoming more and more defensive. People
are marking me more and more tightly, with more and more
defenders coming back. Raddy and I usually have five on us. I
feel fine in myself. I go out there believing I can do well but it
doesn't make any difference, I've lost my way and simply can't
get going.' He was eating boxes of crisps, drinking gallons of
lemonade and ten pints of beer each weekend, and rapidly
ballooned to fourteen and a half stone.

His weight gain was not noticed by the coaches. When he
stood on the scales each week in training, he would simply knock
off any weight he had gained the previous week, shouting out
that his weight was stationary. Ken Friar told me that once this
deception had been detected, the practices at Highbury were
changed so that the coach would read the weight of each player
rather than relying on the player's honesty to call out the correct
figure. Ray's experience at Highbury has left him with a persistent
phobia for scales. Before Ray, Mel Charles had also fooled the
Arsenal coaches for a time by hosing himself all over to mimic

profuse perspiration and then jogging round the pitch once
rather than the statutory five times.

Jenny was also becoming more and more unhappy and asked
if they could go back to live with Mr and Mrs Allen, where Ray
had previously been in digs before buying the house in Barnet.
Crazy antics were occurring off the pitch too, with Ray driving
his car between bollards on the way home to try to reduce his
level of frustration. Ray did his socializing and made his friends
in North London, away from the club. In the Arnos Arms, in
Arnos Grove, he met Malcolm Sale, a Spurs fan, who now owns
a company making parts for Westland Helicopters. Malcolm
remembers this about Ray:

> You would never have thought Ray was a top football player.
> He was so unassuming, he just became one of the lads. On
> Wednesday nights in the summer we used to go and have a
> game of football in the park. Ray used to join in although he
> didn't take it too seriously. We could never get the ball off
> him and he would seem not to be trying and then would
> suddenly fire a pinpoint pass forty yards up the pitch.

Terry Felton, a car mechanic and Gunners fan, was another of
Ray's friends from the Arnos Arms. He told me that the gang
went on a trip to Calais one day on the hovercraft; half-way
across the sea became exceptionally rough and Ray was vomiting
his heart out. On arriving in Calais the group were greeted as if
they were football hooligans and were not allowed to buy
drinks. On the way home on the coach, Ray started to have a
playful scrap with a friend; both of them ripped their trousers,
and the two miscreants had to hurry home, clutching what
remained of their tattered clothes, thankful for the darkness. Both
Sale and Felton remember Ray as a generous, good-natured,
agreeable friend who enjoyed a drink in the pub, but never had
an alcohol problem. Terry Felton told me: 'If Ray had a vice, it
was women. He couldn't lay off them. We'd go to clubs and he'd
always end up taking one home.'

Ray's long-standing claustrophobia increased with his unease.

> I was travelling by underground one day when the train made
> an emergency stop in a tunnel. In no time at all I was in a real
> panic. I was hot, sweaty and frightened. I couldn't stand the

thought of having to get out and walk along the tunnel. I
won't take hotel lifts even if it means walking up ten flights of
stairs. Arsenal's trips into Europe were a nightmare for me and
I would close my eyes when the plane took off.

Bob Wilson remembers a coach trip through the Dartford Tunnel
with Ray crouching on the seat with his eyes closed, asking him
to tell him when they got through. Yet on a football pitch,
encircled by thousands of critical eyes and exposed to a deafening
roar, he was in total command. Lifelong panic attacks and phobic
reactions are commonly reported by patients with Parkinson's
disease.

Frank Harrington wrote in *Reveille*:

Ray's secret problem ever since he came into the game is a
lack of confidence, strange for a man with a build like a heavy
weight boxer. Even now with the fame and success that has
come his way it is still there sneaking inside his guard. Ray
told me that when he goes out onto the field he can feel his
confidence slipping a little, a loss of belief that he is able to do
what is needed. He had lost the confidence to go at defenders
to take them on and was worried about losing the ball.
Kennedy had started to have a battle to convince himself that
he was good enough and that if he lost the ball it wouldn't
matter. He was constantly fighting with himself not to take
the easy way out and push the ball on to the next man.

Ray now concurs with this opinion. 'I became scared to take
opponents on and my work rate dropped.'

About two months into the season, Mee made what was later
regarded as one of his greatest errors when he bought Jeff
Blockley, a big central stopper from Coventry City, for £200,000;
he was supposed to replace McLintock eventually. McLintock,
at thirty-two, was furious since he considered that he still had
plenty of football in him, as did his team-mates. Mee later
justified his action:

Every club suffers a let down after winning the League. I faced
this the season after we had won the Double. I bought Alan
Ball at Christmas but it was too late. The problems really were
in the first three months. The thing is, when you're young and

you've done it all, what do you do for an encore? If you are Jack Nicklaus or Lee Trevino you go on and do it again. It is easy enough perhaps for one man to capture that sort of drive, but how do you instil it into eleven men? One way which I employed was to buy new players and make the others fight for their places. I bought Blockley because I didn't want a situation occurring here as Leeds had in trying to find a replacement for Jack Charlton. The game had reached a stage when success or failure is measured by the results of each match. If you lost, it was a real crisis for three or four days or until your next win. There was no comfort in failure at all. You had to win and keep on winning. The spectators demanded it.

Shortly after Blockley had arrived at Highbury, Steve Burtenshaw told him to get the ball off Ray in training. Ten minutes later, Blockley, red-faced, was still trying to get a kick, while the rest of the Arsenal squad stood by killing themselves laughing.

Despite their success, Arsenal were still criticized, especially in the north, for their failure to entertain. Perhaps, as a result, a brief flirtation with a continental form of Total Football occurred in the 1972–3 season, in which the players were expected to ape the successful Dutch team and acquire greater flexibility. Defenders were made to attack and strikers defend, though everyone behaved like midfielders. This change began promisingly with a win at Leicester and a 5–2 annihilation of Wolves. There was rising excitement and purrs of approval from the Highbury crowd. However, it was not to last and, after a couple of defeats and a 5–0 thumping by Derby County, the system was abandoned for the tried and tested doggedness.

Between October and November, Ray missed eight Arsenal games as a result of a further drop in form and mushrooming weight gain comparable to that sported by playmaster Jan Molby in the present Liverpool side. (Molby is now perfecting a style of football which is so visionary that there is no need even to move.) Not for the first time Ray's guardian angel, Frank McLintock, came to his rescue: 'I had a talk with the lads in the '73 season when things began to go wrong. I talked especially to Raddy and Ray and Peter Storey. Only Storey came up to me afterwards and said, "How about your own form, then?" The others took it in a good spirit'. Some of the senior players,

including Frank McLintock and George Graham, had little respect for Steve Burtenshaw and discipline slipped somewhat after
Don Howe's departure. McLintock then took it upon himself to
go and talk to Bertie Mee about Ray, telling the manager that
there was a young lad who, in McLintock's opinion, was top
class, but who was only playing to sixty per cent of his capacity
because of his weight and lack of fitness. Mee fined Ray £200, a
considerable sum in those days, and McLintock felt somewhat
bad about this afterwards. However, it got Ray going again, and
by the end of November Arsenal were back to their mean long
ball game with Radford and Kennedy up front. With their fierce,
hard-to-beat formula back in operation, they won the next fifteen
games and were pursuing Liverpool for the title.

Despite regaining his number ten shirt and playing in thirty-
four League games that season, Ray continued to feel insecure
about his first team place. The talent, which had been ever-
present in the Double season, returned only in sporadic flashes.
Although Arsenal were again riding high, Ray began to feel that
things were not going quite right and a disillusionment with
football in general began to creep in. He began to yearn to have
the ball at his feet for a little longer rather than being hooked
into the stereotyped chase and run, long ball game, which
seemed to be the only way Arsenal could win. At times he felt
like walking out on football, and it was only Frank McLintock's
long hours of counselling, telling him how he could be the best
centre forward in the land, that kept him going. The modern
game of obsessive tactical pre-match planning and the emphasis
on winning at all costs was not totally to Ray's liking, but like
the other players he was forced to conform or flounder.

Charlie George, who loved Arsenal through and through,
finished the season with only eighteen League appearances. Only
defenders Storey, McNab and Rice of the Double side held their
places consistently throughout the season. Alan Ball, despite all
his fiery determination, failed to bring honours back to Highbury.
Coming second was developing into a disturbing trend, with the
1972–3 League title going to Liverpool with Arsenal runners-up.
Ray's League total of goals had slumped to nine; both John
Radford and Alan Ball claimed higher tallies.

Arsenal, however, did have the satisfaction of beating Liverpool 2–0 at Anfield on 10 February, with Bill Shankly again

having the opportunity to admire Kennedy's strength and resilience. After a somewhat fortuitous quarter-final win against Carlisle United 2–1 in the fifth round of the FA Cup, Arsenal then beat Chelsea in a replay at Highbury 2–1, with Kennedy scoring. In the semi-final Arsenal were paired with Second Division Sunderland, and were confident of reaching their third successive FA Cup Final. George Armstrong, who had been out of the first team for a long stretch before Christmas, re-joined Ray in the team in November, and both had firmly re-established their places by the semi-final. Kennedy and Armstrong had been Sunderland supporters as boys and were well aware of Sunderland's strengths, which included Dave Watson, Dennis Tueart and Billy Hughes. Nevertheless, Ray predicted a 3–1 or 1–0 win to Arsenal and Leeds to win the other semi-final against Wolves. On the day, Sunderland were inspired, and Bob Stokoe's men won 2–1 despite a Charlie George goal. In a year when the form books were turned upside-down, the Wearsiders went on to win the Cup against odds-on favourites Leeds thanks to an Ian Porterfield goal and some spectacular goalkeeping from Jim Montgomery.

Despite his indifferent form in the League, Ray had gained further England Under-23 honours and been forced to lose seven pounds in a week by rigid dieting before he left with the squad for the Three Nations tour of Denmark, Holland and Czechoslovakia in May. Ray had just a few months to persuade Alf Ramsey that his credentials, so evident in the 1970–1 season when he was tipped as the obvious replacement for the ageing Geoff Hurst, were still valid for the Munich World Cup Finals.

On his return to the North-East, however, his weight again rose to above fourteen stone as a result of binge eating in response to domestic unhappiness. He was finding it increasingly difficult to cope with the responsibilities of marriage. Speculation began that Bob Stokoe was interested in taking him home to play for Sunderland. In public at least, Ray continued to blame his drop in form on tiredness and a reaction to the success of the Double season, pointing out that Charlie George and Eddie Kelly, the two other young members of the side, had also run into difficulties. By the beginning of the next season, Ray had managed to lose ten pounds and seemed to be starting out with fresh enthusiasm, although he complained that the continual battle against his weight was making him 'as weak as a kitten'.

Discontent was growing in the Arsenal dressing room with increasing friction between Bertie Mee and Frank McLintock, and finally, at the start of the 1973–4 season, McLintock, now aged thirty-four, was transferred to Queens Park Rangers, where he enjoyed four more good seasons. This move effectively dismantled the Arsenal Double team.

Morale generally remained low in the Arsenal dressing room, with many of the senior players continuing to resent the departure of Don Howe and lacking respect for Steve Burtenshaw. After two early season home defeats and an alarming 5–0 humiliation at Sheffield United, Burtenshaw resigned to make way for Bobby Campbell, who moved from Queens Park Rangers, which he had helped Gordon Jago to bring up from the Second Division. Ray was again commanding a regular first team place up front, usually in partnership with John Radford. Although six of the Double-winning side were also still playing regularly, without McClintock the fire had been extinguished. In what proved to be a disastrous season, Arsenal lost in the League Cup to lowly Tranmere in the second round and went out to Villa in the fourth round of the FA Cup. The defeat at Tranmere, however, allowed the young Liam Brady to come into the side and establish himself as one of the most gifted midfield players the North London club has ever had on its books.

In November there was further speculation that Kennedy might be transferred, this time to Newcastle, with Irving Nattrass moving to Arsenal. A month later the papers reported that Aston Villa had made enquiries. Despite holding down a regular place, Ray did not score a goal for Arsenal from 6 October to mid-January. The supporters were not to know that this could be explained by Ray's increasingly troubled relationship with his wife. By February the couple had separated; Jenny left their Barnet home and returned north. Ray confirmed the split in a press statement:

> My game has gone downhill since I got married but has started to pick up again now I am back in bachelordom. I missed my wife at first but I am over that now and feel that I am better off without her. I was too young to marry. I knew

after the first week that I was wrong. She put too much pressure on me. However, all this business about the marriage break up coming into the open worries me especially because Arsenal is in such difficulties at present. I had to worry about my wife and about us being relegated. I had tried to keep the split a secret until the end of the season so that I could at least concentrate on one thing at once.

He also laid a considerable amount of the blame for the couple's difficulties on Jennifer's family, who he felt had been over-demanding and greedy. Ray had started to binge again on crisps and chocolates, and his partnership with John Radford was going downhill. At this time he also began to be drawn into that death trap of many a promising football career, the London club life.

Revealingly, not long after the couple had separated, Ray's form began to pick up again, when he scored five goals in the last six games of the season. Two of these came against his favourite opponents, Chelsea, in a 3–1 away victory on 13 April. He then scored the winner at Anfield against the Cup winners, Liverpool, with Arsenal again proving to be a thorn in the Merseysiders' side. In the final game of the season against Queens Park Rangers, Brady scored his first goal for Arsenal, and Ball broke his leg in what was Wilson's farewell appearance. Little was Ray to know that this would be his last appearance too.

Unbeknown to him or his Arsenal colleagues, secret negotiations had begun between Bill Shankly and Bertie Mee immediately after Liverpool's victory in the FA Cup Final, and further talks had occurred at the time of Liverpool's last match of the season at Spurs. The deal, however, was put on hold temporarily, as Arsenal were keen to secure a replacement before letting their talented twenty-two-year-old striker go. Ray went on holiday to Crete and, on his return, the papers were full of Arsenal's interest in Manchester United's Brian Kidd. Ray assumed it would be John Radford who would be obliged to move should the transfer go through, particularly in view of Ray's impressive return to form towards the end of the season, which had enabled him to finish with twelve League goals, only one behind leading scorer Alan Ball. On 11 July a telegram arrived for Ray at his parents' home in Seaton Delaval telling him to phone Bertie Mee urgently.

Mee informed Ray that Arsenal had received an offer for him and that they had a replacement lined up. Initially, Mee would not divulge the name of the club and Ray was mortified at the possibility that he might leave the club which had brought him such success and for which he had full respect. Under pressure, Mee eventually told him that it was Liverpool who were interested in signing him. Ray begged time to talk it over with his parents before making a decision.

On coming off the phone Ray was incredulous that Arsenal would let him go: although he was only too well aware that his form had slipped since that first glorious season, he had commanded a regular first team place from the autumn of 1972. At first Ray did not want to move, determining to fight his way back into the side even if Brian Kidd moved to Highbury. Arsenal had his loyalty still and he could not conceive of playing for anyone else, even Liverpool. However, Martin Kennedy was in no doubt that Ray must leave Arsenal and told his son that he felt that he had achieved all he would where he was and that if he was to attain even greater success he must move on to Liverpool. After mulling over the offer for twenty-four hours, Ray decided to sign and the following day he drove to Merseyside with his father. To his surprise, on arriving in Liverpool he saw newspaper headlines everywhere saying that Shankly had resigned. Ray's immediate reaction was that this must have been caused by some dispute between Shankly and the board relating to his signing. He was also concerned that, should Shankly go, his position at Liverpool would be compromised even before he arrived. Shankly had admired Kennedy for some time and the matches at Anfield had always seemed to bring the best out of him: his goals scored in the previous season had robbed Liverpool of the chance of the Double. At Melwood, Ray met Shankly, who told him that he would have to apply himself if he was to be a success at Liverpool, avoid drinking and watch his weight. The plan was that he would replace Toshack and form a partnership with Kevin Keegan. After meeting the chairman, John Smith, Ray's signing went through for a record Liverpool fee of £200,000. Ray told the press:

I hope the Kop will take to me. I want to show them here that I am more than just a strong player. In my last season with

Arsenal I played every game, but things were changing with all sorts of departures and I didn't seem to be part of the new style. Liverpool or Leeds United were the only two clubs I would have wanted to join.

Shankly was characteristically enthusiastic:

There is no doubt that Kennedy will do a good job for Liverpool. He is big, brave and strong. His signing means that we now have the greatest strength that we have ever had. We are so strong that you need to have a couple of international caps to get into the reserve team. Kennedy will cause plenty of trouble to defences. He fights all the way and he was at the top of my list of wanted men. It's been a momentous day, but it shows I am not running away. Maybe it will be said that one of the last things I did at this club was to sign a great new player.

News of the transfer was greeted with disbelief at Arsenal. The general view was that although he had had a lean patch with a loss of hunger for the game, if given time and a stable team, Ray would return to his best form. Kennedy's move, while ultimately proving right for him, was a tragic loss for Arsenal. Even now there is not an Arsenal contemporary who has a bad word to say about him. Bertie Mee's assessment of Ray is a kindly one:

Ray was not the most rapid on two legs but he had an intuitive mind and learned very quickly. He was excellent in the air, remarkably composed on the pitch and had a wonderful first touch with his left foot. His vision was as good as any player I have managed. I had no problems with him until the last year. He was involved in a lot of very hard games, and Radford and he took a lot of punishment. He was easy to handle, quiet, unassuming, malleable, never a raging extrovert or leader of the pack. For a successful team one needs a blend of characters with mutual respect. In our Double year we had the flamboyance of Graham, the leadership of McLintock, the bread and butter of Armstrong and the quiet application of Kennedy. For a long time Ray felt that he owed his break in that first season to Charlie George's injury, but this was not true, as he would have

forced himself through in any event, he was such a good
player.

Ray's team-mates, interviewed twenty years after his departure
from Highbury, to a man enthused over his playing abilities:

FRANK McLINTOCK:

Ray was a terrific player who never stopped running and who
had a great first touch. He could hit balls at all sorts of angles
and was extremely strong. He was never a great tackler, but
he could see openings for first time balls quicker than the rest
of us. On the pitch you couldn't get Ray to be aggressive.
Someone would kick him and he would get up and laugh. He
wouldn't even give other players any verbals. Off the pitch,
however, he could start a fight in an empty house and to
handle him you had to show that you really cared, gain his
respect and then he'd listen and do almost anything for you.

GEORGE GRAHAM:

Ray played a vital role in the Double team. He had an
outstanding partnership with John Radford and the two of
them were the mainstays of the championship team. Ray will
always be remembered by Arsenal fans for his goal at Spurs in
the same way as Michael Thomas will be for his goal at
Anfield in 1989. He had an incredible all round versatility. He
was a quiet man, a typical Geordie with an unusual sense of
humour. I remember his calm, cool controlled play. After the
Double he went back a bit and I wasn't surprised to see him
go.

GEORGE ARMSTRONG:

Ray will be remembered as one of the all time greats of the
Arsenal Football Club. We were bitterly disappointed when he
left and thought it would be the end of him. He was strong,
resilient and never rattled. You knew that when the ball went
to him you would have a few seconds to get into position. I
used to run all day chasing balls to the dead ball line and just
turn and knock the ball across knowing that Ray would be
thereabouts. As a man I always found him warm-hearted,
generous and giving. Everyone had confidence in him that
first season even though he was only nineteen. He was a quiet

man with simple pleasures off the park. In some ways he was a split personality and in that last season before he left he started getting increasingly irritable and aggressive. He threw the odd punch in training, even at his friend John Radford, and got progressively harder to handle. In that first season I used to take Ray home a few times and his dad always thanked me for looking after him. Ray took a hell of a lot of battering from hard teams like Leeds. He always gave me the impression football was not everything for him. I would rate him as a better player than Kevin Keegan, who lacked Ray's natural ability for the game.

BOB WILSON:

Ray had a lot of ability and was not a determined plodder. He seemed to me to become increasingly unhappy after the Double season and he used to throw out his belly like a Sumo wrestler. He told me once there was nowhere to go after the Double season. Ray needed a guru to get the best out of him. He was regarded here as a bomber pilot, but there was much more to him than that.

CHARLIE GEORGE:

Ray was one of the most underrated players at Arsenal. He was strong and scored a lot of goals. He was a quiet, amenable fellow, a nice gentle man. When we were in the youth side we got on very well together.

PETER STOREY:

Ray Kennedy was a great player, easy to find in the midfield and he would hold the ball up to give people time to come up.

JOHN RADFORD:

Ray had a nice short backlift to his shot and didn't need a great deal of room to release his explosive power. I couldn't believe it when he left and felt it was a great shame to have broken up our partnership which had wobbled slightly but which I was sure would come together again with a little time.

JON SAMMELS:

Ray had great vision. If you made an angle to receive a pass he would always give it to you. He was a nice big affable lad who was popular with the guys. He was the best centre forward I have played with or against.

PAT RICE:

Ray was terrific in the air and had a great first touch. For a big fellow he had unbelievable skill. I was always struck by his wonderful temperament. He was a man to himself, always helpful. It was a privilege for me to play with him.

While sorry to leave his team-mates and the club, which he still regards as the best in the League, Ray's departure from Highbury allowed him to express some of the factors which had contributed to his disenchantment over the past two years:

Arsenal should never have let Don Howe leave for West Brom. Don't let's kid ourselves, when we took the Double we weren't an attractive side. But Don got us working and fighting for each other. It was all basic football – the long ball down the middle with little midfield build-up – but it worked. When Don left, the best was still to come for that Double side. He would have brought out the skill and Arsenal would have flourished. Instead we became a club stale with success – new coaches, new stars, chop and change all the way. Take big John Radford and me, we were mates, shared rooms on away trips and would run our hearts out for each other. The new men kept changing the pairings, me and Charlie, Charlie and Raddy, never the same. They should have kept us together and we would have come good again. Why they let Frank McLintock go and then bought Terry Mancini I'll never understand. I felt like walking out on football in the 1972–3 season. I got on OK with Steve Burtenshaw but some of the older players resented him. Then Bobby Campbell arrived and more changes were made. Bobby used to stop me eating chocolates on the team coach.

Ray's team-mates and the supporters assumed that Ray had got fed up with being kicked about as the target man who took all the punishment and that his precocious success had spoiled his appetite for further victories. They also felt that he had become increasingly a marked man, whereas in the Double season he had burst on the scene as a complete unknown. The reality, however, was somewhat different. Ray was unhappy in his home life and was unsettled by the constant changes which were occurring at Highbury. He had felt the departure of Howe more keenly than most and, without the paternalistic guidance of his mentor, Frank McLintock, he floundered even more. His sensitivity also led him to complain about the Arsenal support, claiming that the majority of fans looked for points to criticize rather than getting behind their team. At the time of his departure he really believed that the majority of the Arsenal supporters had never really understood what he was attempting to do and that their cruel barracking of Sammels, Blockley and, latterly, McNab, effectively curtailed these players' careers at Highbury. 'At Arsenal people go to a match, rather than to support their team. You feel isolated on the pitch. You might have a few friends in the stand, but the rest are weighing you up game by game.'

Although there was undoubtedly considerable truth in this, twenty-five years on he is still respected by Arsenal supporters and still acclaimed and toasted on his trips to London. Hunter Davies in his essay 'Selling Spurs Short' empathizes with the players' grievances, but counters with the fans' viewpoint:

In calm moments I know only too well that nothing that the most abusive supporter can shout on the terraces, or the nastiest stirrer write in the Spurs fanzine, or the directors mutter into their whiskies, will ever equal the pain and despair the players themselves suffer. They know and feel the agony better than we do, and have to live with it seven days a week. We can go home on a Saturday, kick the telly, switch on the wife and settle down with a Holsten Pils, be sick and get it over with for another week. They can't escape . . . so should we have more pity on the suckers? Do they not bleed when we carp and criticise. Of course they do, and they hate us for hating them, thinking as loyal supporters our duty is to offer blind unswerving support. Hard Cheddar. We fans do not pay our hard earned money to be kind, to contemplate politely in the calm moments, to consider carefully the feelings of the players and the manager. They have chosen to be up there. No one forced them and they get well rewarded. They must be prepared to be shot at like politicians and rock stars . . . If they are to avoid total crucifixion, top players must learn to handle media attention with circumspection and come to accept that the large majority of supporters are as fickle as the weather.

This love-hate relationship between supporters and the media on one side and players and the manager on the other continues to rage, reaching its nadir recently when Graham Taylor and some of the England players astonishingly hit out, during the European Championship, at some of the critical excesses of the media which had led to headlines such as SWEDES *v* TURNIPS after England's defeat at the hands of the host nation, Sweden, in 1992.

Ray considered that the blame for the demise of many a young starlet in the capital could be laid on the doorstep of the cliques of cannibalistic hangers-on who sucked players into an underworld of pimps, male and female groupies, fly-by-night confidence tricksters, petty criminals and the gutter press. Players away from their family roots were particularly susceptible to these influences, especially when not even given rudimentary instruction on how to handle this aspect of their lives. They were cosseted, institutionalized and discouraged from thinking independently during working hours, but away from the ground, with the absence of a moral guardian, players were vulnerable to all sorts of destructive influences. Nowadays a start has been made in educating apprentices on how to handle themselves in front of the media and at social engagements and most have their own agents to help with fiscal matters. As Ray prepared to leave his alma mater for a new life on Merseyside, he also had some acerbic off-the-cuff reflections on London life:

London was OK, but the people didn't strike me as genuine. Perhaps it was my northern upbringing but I am suspicious of people who want to get to know you because of who you are. The Arsenal players were always being invited to this and that do because so and so would be there. I'm a quiet sort of bloke and not much of a mixer. We used to go to functions, with one Arsenal player put on each table. There were always those little men who thought they were clever with words who tried to belittle you. But I learned to play them at their own game and I had a regular patter of Who do you work for? How much do you earn? What car do you drive? I've seen so-called top company directors disgustingly drunk, stumbling around with their trousers down.

Meanwhile, the city of Liverpool reeled in shock, incredulous at the unexpected resignation of Bill Shankly, Mr Liverpool, the man who had made Liverpool Football Club what it was and what it would continue to be. More than any other English city, the passions of Liverpudlians ebb and flow with the trials and tribulations of its two football clubs. Shankly devoted his life to Liverpool Football Club and, through his unshakeable confidence, had restored civic pride in a city increasingly ravaged by urban decay and demeaning poverty and unemployment. His obsession had been so overriding that he had been able to take his wife out on only two occasions throughout the many years he had been in the city. One of his classic quotes was: 'Of course I didn't take my wife to see Rochdale as an anniversary present. It was her birthday. Would I have got married during the football season? And anyway, it wasn't Rochdale, it was Rochdale reserves'. Shankly, the man of the people, worshipped by his players and the fans, would now for the first time be able to devote more time to his beloved wife and family.

In July 1974, in an atmosphere of inconsolable loss, Ray Kennedy entered this former gateway to the British Empire, now a city associated since the war in the public consciousness with the bleakest poverty, worst unemployment and gravest social problems in Western Europe. Despite this stark reality, the people of the city of Liverpool remained arrogant, proud and convinced that their city had the finest buildings, the world's best pop groups, the best gags and, without a doubt, the best football team.

8 Imago

Heard a siren from the docks
Saw a train set the night on fire
I smelled the spring on the smokey wind
Dirty old town, dirty old town.

(EWAN MACCOLL)

ON 12 July 1974, as the civil war in Cyprus hit the headlines, a press conference was called by Liverpool Football Club. After introducing Ray to the newspaper men as the most expensive buy in the history of the club, John Smith, the Liverpool chairman, got up and read out the following statement: 'It is with great regret that as Chairman of the Board I have to inform you that Mr Shankly has intimated to us that he wishes to retire from League football'. The news was greeted with incredulity in the city. Shankly justified his decision somewhat unconvincingly by saying that he had become tired and feared that the persistent pressure was beginning to damage his health. He also expressed a desire to spend more time with his long-suffering wife, Nessie. He told the press:

> I am not saying staying would kill me, but football management is like a minefield and I thank God for steering me through up until now. I may be retiring from football, but I am not retiring from life. If the new man here wants help I will stay on for a while. If not, I'll go. It will be a clean break. When I've had a rest there will be plenty of things I can do in

the game. People say I'll be bored without football. I'll wait and see.

Later he said his decision was 'like sending myself to the electric chair'. All the football world reeled in shock. At first the Liverpool faithful thought it was so implausible that they regarded it as another publicity stunt by the great man.

Ray Kennedy's signing was completely overshadowed. Shankly, ever the ready communicator, afterwards told the press: 'Kennedy has been brought in to provide additional striking power. All his experience has been in the top flight and he fights all the time, home and away. He can do the donkey work and take the knocks. He'll add to the greatest playing strength Liverpool have ever had'. Ray commented: 'This has kept the pressure off me. Shankly hasn't bought many bad players, has he? I know the Kop are expecting great things of me but I hope they'll understand if I tire a bit towards the end'.

The roots of both Liverpool and Everton Football Clubs can be traced back to the same source. In 1876, the then new chapel of Saint Domingos was consecrated in Breakfield Road in Everton, and two years later St Domingos Football Club was founded. Within a year, in order to widen its appeal, it had changed its name to Everton Football Club. By 1884, the club had moved to Anfield Road, and four years later it became a founder member of the Football League. The owner of the ground was a Unionist, conservative brewer and former Lord Mayor of Liverpool called John Houlding, known locally as 'King John of Everton'. However, after an acrimonious dispute over rents, a group of malcontents, together with the team, decamped to the other side of Stanley Park, taking with them the name of Everton Football Club.

Houlding was left with a ground, but no team. However, with the help of John McKenna, an Ulsterman who had worked himself up from errand boy to successful businessman, a new team was formed which joined the Lancashire Association League. McKenna had close contacts in the divided city of Glasgow and the first Liverpool team fielded eight men with surnames beginning with Mc; there was not a single Englishman. Liverpool won the League from Blackpool on goal average. The trophy and the Liverpool District Cup, another of the season's successes, were stolen and the club was obliged to pay £130 to replace them.

However, encouraged by their victories, McKenna, now secretary of the new club, re-applied to the League for entry and, following the resignation of Accrington Stanley and their more illustrious neighbours, 'Brutal Bootle', Liverpool were admitted to the Second Division in 1893. Their first League match ended in a 2–0 away win against Middlesbrough Ironopolis. The season concluded on a high note, with the club finishing as champions and being promoted to the First Division. The following season they were relegated, but by 1895 they had become First Division champions. Liverpool Football Club went on to win five League Championships before Shankly took over the reins in 1959, but they had never won the FA Cup.

The first derby game against the local rivals, Everton, ended in a 3–0 defeat in front of a crowd of 44,000 supporters. Unlike the Glasgow clubs, Celtic and Rangers, no strong denominational ties divide the two Merseyside teams, although for a considerable period of time Everton was identified with the Catholic support and Liverpool with the Protestants. In truth, however, Houlding could be said to have founded both clubs, and his strongly conservative influence still pervades the Anfield and Goodison board rooms. When Houlding died, he was carried to his grave by players from both clubs and their historical links and the close geographical proximity of the teams explains the amicable rivalry which has always enabled Liverpool and Everton supporters to stand next to one another harmoniously on the terraces.

Continuity and consistency were early priorities, and the club's supporters still revere honest endeavour and grit. Throughout its history, Liverpool Football Club has relied heavily on Scots, Welsh and Irish players for its success, and there was also a period when a number of talented South Africans were recruited. It developed a knack of signing players from the lower echelons of the League and turning them into internationals, as well as developing home-grown players to provide the backbone of the chauvinistic loyalty essential for success. Kevin Keegan, even in his prime at Liverpool, felt insecure of his place: 'At Liverpool the greatest fear was to be sick or injured. However big your name there was never a guarantee you'd be back in'. Unpredictable touch players have often had trouble at Liverpool, as the club holds dependability above all other football virtues. Ian Callaghan and Tommy Smith, products of the Shankly school, were role models for future Liverpool players. Shankly's motto was always: 'If you're going to fight for something, fight 'til you drop'.

Liverpool's play was honest, resilient, solid under siege and without airs and graces. Possession was a crucial part of the Liverpool game. Shankly would say: 'Never pass to a red shirt in one direction when there are two in the other; support the man but look to the ball. If you lose the ball work twice as hard as the opposition to get it back.' This approach led to the constant pressurizing of opponents, and at times gave the impression that there were twice as many red shirts on the pitch as whomever they were playing.

Bill Shankly's reign had lasted fifteen years. In his third year at the club, he won the Second Division title and then went on to take the First Division Championship three times and the FA Cup twice. He also brought the UEFA Cup to Liverpool. For ten years his team was never out of European competition; they contested a European Cup Winners' Cup Final and a European Cup semi-final. From being just another run-of-the-mill side, he had transformed Liverpool into the most consistently successful club in the land, and such was his influence that club archivists now divide their chronicles into pre- and post-Shankly eras.

Bill Shankly was born in the Ayrshire mining village of Glenbuck, the second youngest of ten children. His reputation as a player at Carlisle, Preston North End and for Scotland was as an uncompromising, never-say-die wing-half who had a number of intriguing duels with Sir Stanley Matthews during their overlapping playing careers. Football was in Shankly's veins, and on retiring from the game he went straight into football management. When he was called to Anfield in 1959, he had already been in charge at Carlisle, Workington and Huddersfield Town.

On his arrival at Liverpool he found apathy, complacency and decay. The Liverpool directors were in the habit of interfering with the manager's team selection; Shankly's pre-condition that he be allowed to pick his side without interference from management was granted largely due to the foresight of Eric Sawyer, one of the Liverpool directors. Sawyer summarized his views on football management as 'like running a shop. It needs attractive premises and first class products. It is no good having a nice shop, however, if you don't have the right stuff on display'.

Over the next few years Shankly's relationship with the board remained uneasy even after he had brought unprecedented success. His general view of directors was that most of them knew nothing about football and were only interested in enhancing their own images. He was also fond of relating the story of an Everton director who had been overheard after a Merseyside derby saying, 'I don't think much of that Leishman', when Leishman hadn't even been in the Liverpool side! Shanks could be equally withering about referees: 'The trouble with referees is that they know the rules but not the game'.

Despite the decrepit state of Anfield, Shankly detected he had been put in charge of a sleeping giant: 'I could sense the potential amongst the crowd, the people were desperate for success. Liverpool is a city of a million people, all with a deep love for football'. He immediately dispensed with twenty-four of the playing staff and started his rebuilding programme by signing two Scots: the colossus of a centre back, Ron Yates, and the mercurial striker, Ian St John, both of whom would play vital parts in the transformation of the club. Like almost all Shanks' signings, they were made to feel that they were joining the greatest club in the world, even though at the time Liverpool were languishing in the Second Division. Such was his optimism and self-belief that the players found him irresistible. When Emlyn Hughes, another inspirational Shankly signing, was hunted down at Blackpool, he was brazenly asked 'Do you want to play for a football team, son?', implying that Blackpool was no more than a park side compared with Liverpool. Shankly's ambitions knew no bounds: 'I want to build a team that is invincible so they'll have to send a team from Mars to beat us'.

Although there were major changes in the playing staff, Shankly kept faith with most of the ground staff, which included former Liverpool players Bob Paisley and Ronnie Moran, Reuben Bennett, a dour Scot in the Shankly mould, Tom Saunders and Joe Fagan. This cabal was to be the think-tank which would lead Liverpool to its future glories. However, the first job of the coaching staff and the apprentices was to clean up Anfield and the training ground at Melwood, which were in an appalling state of decrepitude. Shankly made it clear from the start that he was the boss, that cliques were taboo and undying loyalty was expected. By 1962 Liverpool was back in the First Division. One wag wrote on the wall behind the Kop 'What would you do if Jesus came to Liverpool?' and then underneath had written 'Move St John to inside left'.

Shankly was a phenomenal motivator and man-manager. Failure did not exist in his book, and he was able to reduce even the most impressive opposition to a pile of useless crocks in the pre-match team talk. Generations of players testify how he was able to imbue them with a sense of invincibility. When the opposition arrived Shanks would frequently stand eyeing them up for signs of weakness, and it was Shanks who made sure that the intimidating 'This is Anfield' plaque was at the top of the players' tunnel to remind the opponents where they were and what they would face once they ran onto the pitch.

Although Shanks had a tough guy exterior, he had a deep love and sympathy for his players and, as a result, he preferred to keep a fixed side which everyone knew and expected. He hated to face players who had been dropped, knowing, as an ex-player, the pain this could produce. To Shanks, everyone was the greatest player in the world until they had a bad game. Defeat was a word which he never condoned. After the 1971 FA Cup Final in which Ray had played for Arsenal, Shanks, on returning to Liverpool, addressed the crowds as if his team were the real victors: 'We lost the cup, but you the people won everything. It's not managers who make football players, it's their mums and dads. My team play for you, the greatest public'. Shankly had the foresight to see that a new team was developing in front of his eyes which would go on to great things.

It was rumoured that when Liverpool did lose, Shanks would slope off home and clean the cooker. In many ways, he was a simple man, with simple pleasures. He had a distaste for flying and often became apprehensive on European trips, fearing that the gods would conspire against the team. As time went by, he became increasingly superstitious and ritualistic. On one trip to the United States he refused to adjust his watch the whole time he was there, attempting to carry on as if Greenwich Mean Time were in operation.

Shankly's natural communication skills endeared him to the media, and he always seemed to have an original and disarming quote or anecdote to catch the headlines. His larger-than-life personality, his unchained arrogance and hyperbole struck a chord with the armies of unemployed Scousers to whom football was the most important thing in their lives outside their family. His eyes betrayed a comic streak and his gravelly voice fired a volley of caustic, witty one-liners which turned him into a media star. So many of his pithy aphorisms remain in the folklore of Anfield. Children who never saw his teams can recite his sayings like nursery rhymes:

> 'The two best teams in Liverpool are Liverpool and Liverpool reserves.'
> 'I'm a people's man, a players' man, you could call me a humanist.'
> 'I don't drop players, I make changes.'
> 'Football's not a matter of life and death. It's much more important than that.'

Shankly will be for ever remembered for his chastisement of a police officer who kicked a Liverpool scarf thrown from the crowd onto the perimeter at Wembley. Shankly picked up the scarf, put it round his neck and said, 'You shouldn't do that, that's somebody's life you just kicked'. He was an inveterate gambler, and his heroes were Tom Finney, who he said could wriggle through the eye of a needle, the cowboys of the Wild West, and James Cagney, on whom he modelled himself. His happiness stemmed from a deep-felt desire to provide the people of his adopted city with hope and jubilation. Despite his later triumphs, Shanks never lost the common touch:

> The socialism I believe in is not really politics. It is a way of living. It is humanity. I believe the only way to live and be truly successful is by collective effort with everyone working for each other, everyone helping each other, and everyone having a share of the reward at the end of the day. It is the way I see football and the way I see life.

The rules and rituals of the club, which largely continue to the present day, were firmly in place by the time Ray arrived. Everyone had an important role, from tea lady to manager. Dirty linen was washed inside the club, not in the newspapers. Any player who did not give his all every time he pulled on a red shirt did not last long. Liverpool Football Club respected craft, skill, industry, combativeness and consistency, and was suspicious of capricious flair and flamboyance. These are values that are implicit in the British game and were propounded by Mee, Howe and McLintock during the Double year at Arsenal. However, at Liverpool under Shankly they were developed to a fine art.

After Shankly's resignation, the Liverpool board made the decision to promote Bob Paisley, Shankly's loyal lieutenant for so many years, from the boot room to the manager's post, a move which at least had the advantage of ensuring consistency. Paisley and Shankly were like chalk and cheese, but both men shared a deep love, dedication and understanding of the game of football.

Bob Paisley was born in Hetton-le-Hole, had worked briefly down the pit and then as a bricklayer, before winning an FA Amateur Cup medal with Bishop Auckland in 1939. Just as the war broke out he moved to Merseyside and Liverpool Football Club for a wage of £5 a week, and played with both Matt Busby and the Liverpool legend, Billy Liddell. He made thirty-three appearances in the Liverpool 1946–7 Championship-winning side. Like Shankly, he had a reputation as a tireless and dour wing-half. After scoring a crucial goal against Everton in the 1950 FA Cup semi-final, he was left out of the Wembley side, losing, in a 5–4 vote from the board, to Bill Jones, the grandfather of Rob Jones, the present Liverpool defender. This scar never healed, but he bore the club no lasting grudge. On retiring, in 1954, after more than three hundred appearances, he joined the Anfield back room staff as a physiotherapist.

Paisley had tried hard for several weeks, before and after Shankly's resignation, to persuade his friend to stay on. He disliked the limelight and regarded himself as part of the Anfield furniture. After diffidently accepting the manager's post he perceptively remarked: 'I hope the team will do the talking for me. This job is like being given the helm of the *Queen Mary* in a force ten gale'. Paisley came under immediate pressure from all sides, but at least he knew that the boot room was firmly behind him. His dry humour got him through those difficult early days. Nevertheless, each team selection was scrutinized by the board, media and supporters. Within a few weeks, however, it soon became clear that, despite his inarticulate, often indecipherable, monosyllabic mumblings, Paisley was a shrewd, knowledgeable tactician and possessed the ruthlessness to survive in management. Whereas Shanks's mouth sometimes overtook his brain, Paisley's decisions were deliberate and considered. Throughout his period at the helm he kept diaries documenting every match.

At the first team meeting Ray was bewildered by the apparent organizational chaos. Paisley was nervous, talked of 'what's-its' and 'doings'. At the end of the meeting Ray, nonplussed, turned to Tommy Smith, the Liverpool captain, for guidance. Ray later teased Tommy that, compared with Arsenal, Liverpool was a pork pie and pop outfit. This infuriated Smith; nevertheless he and Ian Callaghan warmed to Ray, and took him under their wing. Ray also remembers Chris Lawler as a great support in his early days at the club.

In private, he was beginning to brood more and more on why Arsenal had sold him: 'I keep asking myself why Arsenal let me go. Surely I was a better long-term bet than either John Radford or my replacement, Brian Kidd'.

Ray made a promising start on the close season tour of Germany in August 1974. However, in the match against Kaiserslautern, he was carried off with bruising of his knee ligaments after being upended by the German defence. Following this incident, an angry mêlée broke out and Keegan was sent off after being misidentified as the instigator of trouble instead of the offending Cormack. Before his premature departure, Kennedy had scored in the eighth minute, and Liverpool went on to win 3–1.

Ray had managed to lose a stone and was down to thirteen and a half stone; his team-mates had nicknamed him 'Razor' because of all the weight he was expected to cut. He attributed his successful battle against the bulge to a new-found inner contentment:

> I am the lightest I have been since the Double season. At Arsenal I had the target man role, I was told to hold the ball and lay it off, all strictly method stuff. But at Liverpool there is much more free expression and I love every minute of it. I am not trying to knock Arsenal. That was their style and they were a good club to me. But I never really settled in London, it was too big and impersonal for a northerner. In Liverpool I am more settled and really at home.

Shankly commented: 'I've seen him in training and he looks good. He reminds me of Rocky Marciano'. Shortly after Ray had signed for Liverpool his estranged wife contacted him and, by Christmas, they were back together in their own home in Ainsdale.

Ray made his League debut in the fifth game of the 1974–5 season, at Stamford Bridge, which had been one of his favourite stomping grounds when he was at Arsenal. A low cross, flicked up off Droy's boot, went over the keeper's head and Ray loped in to nod in the easiest of chances. Bob Paisley, although still keen to stay in the shadows, was beginning to stamp his authority on the team selection, and had brought Ray in for the Anfield favourite, John Toshack. This decision was rewarded by a superb piece of vintage Kennedy leadership which kept constant pressure on the Chelsea back four. He was well supported by Phil Boersma, who had walked out on Liverpool the previous season just before the Cup Final with Newcastle because he had not been selected. Boersma scored the other two goals in the Liverpool victory, and Kevin Keegan, who was under suspension after being sent off in the Charity Shield, looked like he would have to fight hard to regain his place. After the match Paisley commented: 'At Anfield the crowd make demands on how we should play which is not always the best thing. We are looking to balance our play more and add variety'.

After his first match, Ray predicted that the team were strong candidates to win the League and Cup Double on the strength of their squad. At his home debut, before 37,000 fans, on 7 September, he was again on the score-sheet with an eighty-seventh-minute goal in a 5–2 drubbing of Spurs. However, after this game, the team wobbled a little, unexpectedly losing one or two League games before Christmas and going out to Ferenc-varos, the Hungarian side, in the second round of the European Cup Winners' Cup. After the game, the Magyars' manager not unreasonably observed, 'I thought Liverpool had very few ideas up front'. This was particularly galling after the first round had been won with a record 11–0 victory over Stromsgodset Daman; Ray was one of only two Liverpool outfield players not to get his name on the score-sheet against the Norwegians. After the Stromsgodset match, the Norwegian goalkeeper, Thun, had woken to headlines of THUN-DERSTRUCK.

Liverpool finished as runners-up in the League to Derby County, and seemed to have successfully come through the difficult transitional period following Shankly's resignation. For both Paisley and Kennedy, the season had been a learning process and, in retrospect, the manager considered his first season in charge as one of relative failure, with the club going out of both the League and FA Cups in the fourth round. However, he was beginning to learn each player's strengths and weaknesses and to master the pressures of being the man in charge. He quickly realized that he could not be a 'Mr Nice Guy' and survive as Liverpool manager, and he soon determined always to be guided by what he thought was best for the club and the team rather than by compassion.

Early headlines were encouraging for Kennedy:

5 October 1974, Carlisle United 0 – Liverpool 1
TWINKLETOES KENNEDY

> Kennedy substituted seven minutes from the end after aggravating his knee injury commented afterwards 'My goal was a bit lucky but just what was needed to take a bit of pressure off us. I played the ball to Phil Boersma who shot. The ball was deflected. It came across to me. I brought it down, it then started to run on before I just managed to toe it in'.

16 October 1974, Liverpool 4 – Bristol City 0
CITY SHOT OUT OF THIRD ROUND REPLAY OF LEAGUE CUP BY HEIGHWAY AND KENNEDY

> Although Keegan failed to score he is clearly developing a close understanding with Kennedy. Kennedy said afterwards 'The partnership between us is getting better. We are working for each other, feeding off each other. Kevin is sharp and lively and I am the target man, but he can also be used as the target and sometimes takes the pressure off me'.

However, after these entries in Ray's scrapbook, it goes silent for the rest of the season.

Although he made sixteen successive appearances in the number ten shirt before Christmas, and played a total of twenty-three games that season, both he and Boersma lost their places with the resurrection of the Keegan-Toshack partnership. Toshack had almost gone to Leicester City, but had failed a medical; he returned to Anfield furious and determined to regain his place. It was clear that Ray was going to have to fight hard if he was to establish his own place in the team. His pairing with Keegan had been generally disappointing, which Ray explained away: 'I used to bring the ball down whereas Toshack always flicked it on and as a result my game's suffered'. Some years later, Ray learned that Keegan had told the management he found it difficult to combine well with him.

After moving to Liverpool in 1974, Ray began to notice that his right hip would push forward involuntarily when he walked, causing him to move in an unusual way and occasionally feel off balance. His right foot would sometimes scuff the floor and his right arm and leg felt tired and tense.

After a year or two these feelings seemed to pass, but he continued to be exceptionally weary. After matches he was too exhausted to do anything and he would slump motionless and speechless on the bench. Curiously, he was always able to perform adequately for the full ninety minutes of the game and was rarely substituted. In training he was aware of considerable incoordination and asynchrony in carrying out star jumps, in which the right arm has to be raised as the left leg is kicked out, followed by rapid alternation to right leg kick and left arm raise. At times he felt leaden, stiff, awkward and stooped.

By February 1975 there was already speculation that Ray might be transferred to Spurs and, in March, after being taken off against Sheffield United, he demanded an interview with Paisley to clear the air. 'Why is it always me? I am not the only one who is playing badly,' he said.

Paisley retaliated: 'He did nothing to justify my confidence in him. He didn't play, he didn't even get started. If Ray wants to play for Liverpool he can, but I only want those people who want to do well for this club'.

If Ray was having his ups and downs, then his old club was doing little better. Nick Hornby, a lifelong Gunners' fan, summarizes the Highbury season in his book *Fever Pitch*:

> I stopped going in the 74/75 season because Arsenal were dire: George, McLintock and Kennedy had gone and were never properly replaced, Radford and Armstrong were way past their best. Ball couldn't be bothered, a couple of the young players (Brady, Stapleton and O'Leary were all playing) were having understandable difficulties settling into a

struggling side, and some of the new purchases simply weren't up to the mark. (Terry Mancini, for example, a bald, cheerful and uncomplicated centre half, seemed to have been bought for the Second Division promotion campaign that was beginning to look inevitable.) In seven years Highbury had once again become the unhappy home of a moribund football team, just as it had been when I first fell in love with it.

Bill Shankly, who was still a regular visitor to the training ground at Melwood, confidentially approached Bob Wilson, who by then was working full time for television, and said, 'Tell me Bob, was my signing of Ray Kennedy the biggest mistake in my managerial life?' Shankly was beginning to fear that those who had sniggered that Liverpool had bought a spent force were proving to be correct. Nevertheless, he never let his reservations show to Ray and would say, 'Keep at it, son. You'll make a great player'.

Rapid integration into the set-up at a football club is crucial for the survival of a player. The atmosphere in the Liverpool dressing room was a mixture of barrack room and playground. What communication existed took place in the form of continuous mickey-taking which at least had the effect of keeping everyone's feet on the ground. Reputations counted for very little in the club, and prima donnas were not allowed to get above themselves. A player who was not 'one of the boys' or failed to conform to the group ethos, which was often based on values more appropriate to an adolescent than an adult world, found life difficult. Sensitivities or idiosyncrasies were not tolerated, and each player was forced to succumb to the ritualistic 'put-downs' which ultimately led to group bonding and camaraderie. It was made crystal-clear that no one individual was bigger than the club.

Ray, with his cheeky sense of humour, soon became one of the boys, but he had early difficulties in fusing his individuality with the style of the team, and for a time felt marginalized by the coaches and some of the players. The way of doing things and behaving at Anfield was quite different from that at Arsenal. Ray considered it, in many ways, to be amateurish, anarchic and confusing. Arsenal did things with style and aplomb: smoked salmon and chocolate cake were served on trips to away games, and much attention was paid to the players' personal appearance, with suits and ties being mandatory for away games. Nevertheless, by the end of the season, he felt he had made a reasonable impact.

The 1975–6 season began for Ray as the last had left off, with Toshack wearing the number ten shirt. The pressure for places was becoming even greater with the emergence of a local boy, Jimmy Case, now challenging for a first team place. In fact, Ray played only four more games for Liverpool wearing the number ten shirt. He regained his place briefly in mid-August, scoring twice, once against Leeds United in a 3–0 victory and then hitting the winner against Sheffield United. After a poor game against his bogey team, Ipswich Town, in which he missed several chances in a 2–0 defeat, Ray found himself back in the reserves, along with Terry McDermott, Paisley's expensive signing from the previous season. By October, the newspapers were predicting that Bill McGarry would take Kennedy to Molyneux to partner the Wolves striker John Richards for a bargain £75,000. Ray's career seemed to be spiralling downwards, uncannily parallelling that of his Arsenal Double team-mate, Charlie George.

Ray considered Charlie George to be the 'closest thing to George Best' in the game at the time. Arsenal tried to mould him by punishing him and sometimes dropping him from the side, but this was counter-productive. Although George was superficially full of himself, Ray always felt that he was insecure and needed encouragement. After the success of Arsenal and the efficiency of Highbury, many players found it difficult to settle down at other clubs, however successful they were.

In the autumn of 1975, Ray was summoned to Bob Paisley's office. The two had always been able to talk freely to one another, and Paisley told Ray that he had formed a firm impression that he had lost his sharpness and drive to play up front and that he would like him to consider playing in a deeper midfield role. Ray simply replied, 'Would you put us there, boss?' In his heart he felt Paisley was just doing this because he did not want him in the first team. However, this astonishing decision did not stem from desperation or divine intuitiveness on Paisley's part, but was influenced by his chance meeting with one of his old mates from the North-East: 'One of my old friends told me that before Ray went to Arsenal he had played much deeper. I then knew I could back my instinct and see if he could recapture his spark'.

Whereas another player would have rebelled against the indignity of this change, Ray's professionalism and ability to adapt saved him now. At Arsenal he had always felt that he had not been able to express himself enough, but his inhibitions and modesty prevented him from ever feeling able to suggest a change in playing role himself. His metamorphosis took place in the reserves. After four or five reserve games, Ray's progress in midfield looked promising. Following a cartilage injury to Peter Cormack, he was back in the first team, deep on the left against Middlesbrough on 1 November 1976. Within a few weeks, despite intense competition from Callaghan, Hall, Case and a recovered Cormack, Ray made the number five Liverpool shirt indisputably his and his alone for the next six years. A transformation was taking place as remarkable as any witnessed in the modern game.

After an empty year, cuttings began to reappear in Ray's scrapbook:

November 15 1975, Newcastle United 1 – Liverpool 2
LOCAL LAD STUNS NEWCASTLE by Jackie Millburn

> With one minute left and United looking the more likely to score, Liverpool produced a victorious K-plan; Kevin Keegan started the move when he broke like a greyhound from midfield and stroked a perfect pass to the onrushing Kennedy. The big lad looked up, picked his spot and left Newcastle's Mahoney sprawling on the deck as his shot flashed home.

SMASH AND GRAB KENNEDY by Len Shackleton

> This was definitely not a candidate for soccer's Hall of Fame . . . indeed the only player who'll want to remember it is North-East born Ray Kennedy . . . Keegan and Heighway were the stars, but Ray Kennedy had settled well into his new role and added a new dimension to the Liverpool team.

28 February 1976, Derby County 1 – Liverpool 1

> Ray Kennedy saved Liverpool a point of immense value with an out of the blue equalizer three minutes from the

end to rob his old Arsenal pal Charlie George of the glory of being match winner. Liverpool strung six passes together and nineteen-year-old Fairclough crossed the ball low to Kennedy who had pushed up from midfield to get the vital touch and turn the ball into the net.

By now established in his new role, Ray was able to reflect on his ups and downs at Anfield:

When I joined Liverpool I found it hard to motivate myself playing up front. John Toshack is much better in that position than I am. When you play up front it is a case of waiting for service from the people behind you and then trying to get in the shot. Sometimes it was frustrating. Now I am more involved. The boss has told me to be more aggressive and put more bite into my game. I have had my problems up here. At one time I wasn't doing my stuff. Maybe I was fed up doing the running for other people.

Such was his enthusiasm for his new role that the boot room began to tease him that he regarded himself as a winger in the Steve Heighway or Peter Thompson mould, but Paisley shrewdly bolstered the left side of the defence with Joey Jones. Ray said, 'Early on it wasn't easy for me. I tended to neglect the defensive part of the job and let people get past me. Now the boss gets on to me about getting stuck in. It also took a bit of time to get the angles and positioning right'.

Liverpool vied for the championship all season with the charismatic Queens Park Rangers side that had beaten them 2–0 at Loftus Road in the opening game of the season. Everything came down to the last game against Wolves. At half-time Liverpool were surprisingly losing to a Steve Kindon goal, and Wolves were fighting every inch of the way for their First Division survival. With less than a quarter of an hour to go, Keegan equalized. If the score remained the same, this would have been enough to take the title to Anfield. However, with a characteristic late flurry, Toshack and Kennedy scored two goals. No sooner had the last goal gone in than the whistle blew and the euphoric Liverpool fans poured onto the pitch, mobbing their heroes and forcing Ray to the floor under a pile of bodies. The old firm of Keegan and Toshack had scored twenty-eight goals and taken Liverpool to another championship born out of only five defeats. Behind them, however, a second midfield strike force was emerging in Case and Kennedy, who finished the season with six goals apiece.

Although Liverpool had gone out of the FA Cup in the fourth round against Derby County, the season ended with wins against Hibernian, Real Sociedad, Slask Wroclaw, Dynamo Dresden and Barcelona, which took them to the final of the UEFA Cup against FC Bruges. In the first leg of the final at Anfield, Liverpool were 2–0 down at half-time but fought back to win 3–2, with goals from Kennedy and Keegan. In the second leg in Belgium they held on for a one-all draw to take the Cup.

Ray was enjoying his football again. He told the press: 'I much prefer this new role. It was how I played as a youngster. I always liked to drop back a bit.' At the end of the season Bob Paisley joked with Ray: 'A lot of people laughed at you and me, but we've got the laugh on them now.' In private, however, Paisley was amazed at the versatility and flexibility which Ray had shown in taking up the new role. Shankly's belief in his last signing was fully restored:

> Ray Kennedy was born to play. A natural, great ability and an obvious Liverpool player who could be moulded. I knew he could play anywhere. He might even finish up as a sweeper. When players of his class become available you buy them and then think how to use them. Look at the man's assets, a left-footed player – they are always more accurate than right-footers. He had experience of playing at the front so he knows what life is about in the box. He's a strong man who has got the habit of slipping markers and sneaking in on the blind side – terrible habit that – terrible number of goals he'll score. The other thing is he was twenty-three when he signed – great age to buy a player – St John, Yeats, Thompson, they were all twenty-three. Kennedy plays in no man's land in a world of his own, but he has given the team balance. His style reminds me of Matt Busby's. Aye, Ray Kennedy is some player.

Although Shankly did not convey his thoughts directly to Ray during his frequent visits, Reuben Bennett did. Bennett, who had been Shanks' side-kick, was the opposition assessor in the boot room and had been the chief coach when Shanks arrived. He was a tough, competitive Aberdonian who had been goalkeeper for Third Lanark and a PE instructor in the Forces. In the five-a-side games, which were the bread and butter of football training at Liverpool, he would goal-hang, waiting for the other players to slip him a pass and allow him to score. One day, for a joke, Tommy Smith switched Bennett's boots to a pair with revolving studs so that once the game had started he was unable to move, frozen, facing away from the goal, as the studs swivelled round like chair casters. One day, when he was having tea with 'Benn' after training, Ray was told, 'Shanks and I never knew why you didn't knock on Mee's door and ask for Charlie George's wages'.

Within a few remarkable weeks, Ray had been converted from a jaded, failing striker to an accomplished midfield dynamo. He had returned to the role first given him by his games teacher, Rob Bryden, at Astley Comprehensive School. Kennedy, now nicknamed 'bag of bones' by his colleagues, had put five years of struggling frustration behind him, and was finally fulfilling the potential predicted of him during that first season at Arsenal. His relationship with Jenny had also greatly improved.

Only five months after the switch in position, Paisley came in and asked him if he wanted to play for England. Although there had been some speculation in the press that he might be called up, Ray thought that the manager was joking. However, by the end of March 1976 he had gained his first full England cap against Wales and scored his first goal at international level. People were already predicting that he would be in Revie's squad for the Argentina World Cup Finals. An interview after the game reflected his growing confidence:

> Our manager Bob Paisley came to me one day and said, 'You're going to play in the midfield in future. You'll do better when facing the ball'. You don't argue with a man like him. The goal I scored tonight is going to make other people sit up and take notice. My form since I switched roles can't be a fluke. I mean, I wouldn't be playing for Liverpool if it was, would I?

At the end of the season Ray displayed his customary loyalty to his roots:

> My career takes me all over the world, but do you know where I would be by choice this weekend? Not in Los Angeles

but Seaton Delaval, near Whitley Bay. I love the place. There is nowhere in the world as warm as the North-East. The minute my career comes to an end I'll be back home. Although I am perfectly happy with Liverpool I still have my dreams and wake up regularly thinking I've played a match in red and white Sunderland stripes at the ground I visited as a boy.

9 Where's St Etienne?

> Our broken heritage:
> Forced to this city by hunger from Ireland's villages
> We were first vagrants then vassals
> We lined up like strays in a home, eager
> To be picked out for just one day's labour
> Our religion kept us from ship-building, our class
> and accent tied us slum-bound yet true
>
> (STEVE EDWARDS)

THE 1976-7 season began with considerable doubts as to whether the team would be able to emulate the previous season's successes. Paisley made a characteristic pre-season Liverpool transfer, bringing the Liverpool-born former Evertonian, David Johnson, back to Merseyside from Ipswich for £300,000. This move was partly motivated by Kevin Keegan intimating that he was keen to play overseas. Real Madrid had already approached the club with an attractive offer for the player. However, an agreement was struck with the Liverpool board that Keegan would be allowed to leave the club only at the end of the season, after Liverpool had completed their campaign for the crown they considered they had deserved for some time – Champions of Europe.

Liverpool Football Club was unusual at that time in having two university graduates in their squad, Brian Hall and Steve Heighway, known affectionately as little Bamber and big Bamber after Bamber Gascoigne, the moderator of the then highly popular television programme, *University Challenge*. Much was made of this by many football people in order to establish a kind of middle-class legitimacy for the game. Football, like the Labour

Party, was trying to shed its cloth cap image. Whenever the two players' names were mentioned in the press they were prefaced by 'university graduate'. The biographies of professional football players, by and large, reinforce the stereotype of a working-class, urban youth, of humble origins and limited opportunity who, from an early age, is singled out from his peers by his technical gifts at controlling a football. Players were fellows whose brains were kept in their feet and who spent most of their time gambling or hanging around snooker halls. Steve Heighway's story, however, contrasted markedly with this. Born in Ireland of English parents, he graduated from Warwick University with a Bachelor of Arts degree in economics. Educated at a small prep school with no organized games, he did not watch a football match until he was ten years old. The grammar school he attended was rugby-dominated, but in his fourth year he decided to take up football and began to support Sheffield United. Bob Paisley claims that his two sons were the first to spot Heighway when he was wreaking havoc for Skelmersdale against South Liverpool. Paisley later said that Heighway was the most talented amateur he had ever seen. Heighway signed professional forms for Liverpool at the suspiciously late age of twenty, and went on to represent the Republic of Ireland before he established a regular place in the Liverpool side. In his first full season with the club in 1970, he was so naïve about the ritualistic team regulations that he frequently found himself in trouble. When he first walked out at Anfield, he astonished his fellow professionals by inquiring heretically, 'Which end is the Kop?'.

Idealistically, he proclaimed, 'Soccer is fun, a game which should be enjoyed'. Unlike most of his team-mates, Heighway had other alternatives, but was attracted to the game by its increasing respectability, his desire to do something he enjoyed and the improving financial rewards. When he missed what his team-mates considered to be an easy goal, Tommy Smith took him to task and told him that it was all very well for him to play for fun, but that miss had just cost the rest of his team-mates their badly needed bonus. Despite this sacrilegious attitude, Heighway ex-celled at football; he had the ability to go past players on the outside with his high-kicking, scintillating speed. His goal in the FA Cup Final against Arsenal in their Double year remains in Liverpool supporters' minds as one of the finest goals ever scored by a Liverpool player. Heighway was a social misfit, regarded by his team-mates as a stuck-up intellectual and a bit of a weed. As a result, he had to absorb continual mental and physical abuse. When the playing cards came out in European hotels, Heighway would go sightseeing, a pastime indulged in by very few professional footballers, whose lack of interest in inanimate historical objects is encapsulated by Nobby Stiles' remark: 'Give me a gurgling baby any time rather than the Mona Lisa'. It is rumoured that an England player on tour in China on being taken to the Great Wall remarked, 'I've bent balls round better walls than that'.

Hall's and Heighway's wives also adopted a somewhat superior middle-class attitude by going to matches casually dressed in slacks, whereas all the other wives paraded around in the latest fashions, dressed to kill. It was some time before Mrs Hall and Mrs Heighway realized that, in contrast to themselves, Saturday afternoon was the highlight of the week for many of the other players' wives who were there to support their men. Even twenty years on, the middle-class revolution has failed to material-ize, at least with respect to players, the vast majority of whom are still sons of skilled or semi-skilled manual workers.

Ray, who later considered Heighway one of the most graceful, courageous and skilful footballers he had ever played with, but at the time was baffled by the man, would often ask: 'What are you doing in the game, Steve?'

At that time there was also another outcast in the Liverpool dressing room, but of a very different kind. Howard Gayle was black, born and bred in Liverpool 8 and a highly talented player. However, he was an angry young man, and the racial jibes designed by his team-mates to bring him into the fold were unacceptable to him, and led to frequent confrontations. Unlike Heighway, who had the intellectual machinery to cope with alienation, Gayle's career at Liverpool never really took off despite one unforgettable appearance as a substitute in the European Cup semi-final against Bayern.

Liverpool began their defence of the League Championship in commanding form, losing only two of their first sixteen games — and those only by a single goal — to Birmingham City and Newcastle United away. Kennedy continued in excellent form with glowing newspaper coverage:

11 September 1976, Derby County 2 – Liverpool 3

ONLY A BIT OF VENOM NEEDED

Once Ray Kennedy, not always one of Liverpool's most conspicuous players, planted his oak tree frame in the centre of the Baseball Ground all others were twigs by comparison. From a Keegan free kick, Kennedy's side footed volley over the keeper's head stunned Derby after only six minutes. Liverpool had not won at Derby since 1961, but this was a marvellous way to break that run and with the victory they moved back to the top of the First Division after an enthralling, entertaining and open game which was a fine advertisement for all that was good in English football.

After the match Bob Paisley commented: 'Ray still lacks venom on the pitch. If he could find that he would be world class. He is too gentle at times'.

20 November 1976, Arsenal 1 – Liverpool 1

RAY'S STING

Ray Kennedy kept the Liverpool machine clear at the top of the First Division with an equalizer two minutes from time at Highbury. It was clear that the Liverpool team were well in charge after the break with better organization and desire to play for one another, but they were still unable to give Paisley his first win against the Gunners. However, Kennedy's superb midfield contribution was sufficient to enable Liverpool to get a point against his former club. Keegan, however, was everywhere after the interval, weaving intricate patterns that frequently threatened and a Toshack goal was disallowed on seventy-two minutes. Phil Thompson, with an interception and powerful run to the edge of the Arsenal penalty area, slid the ball to Kennedy whose shot, lacking power, bobbled in front of Rimmer and bounced over his arms into the net. Liverpool's reputation of never being beaten until the final whistle was reinforced.

Although Ray was now fully established in the Liverpool set-up, he was still adapting to his new position and would oscillate from match to match, sometimes pushing forward, neglecting his defensive role and scoring, and on other occasions playing a classic midfield role, but not scoring. The Liverpool coaches were working hard on trying to weld these two playing styles.

Even the greatest sides have off days and Liverpool's came in mid-December at Villa Park when, despite a goal from Kennedy, they were thrashed 5–1, all the goals coming in the first half, including two from Andy Gray and one from Brian Little. This was Liverpool's worst defeat in many years, but they remained top of the League. Three days later, away at Upton Park they lost again, 2–0, to bottom club, West Ham, and the prophets of doom were beginning to shake their heads that it would not be Liverpool's season. The club had already gone out of the League Cup against West Brom, and their FA Cup run after Christmas got off to a faltering start with a goalless draw at Anfield against Third Division Crystal Palace. In the replay, however, they scraped home 3–2 at Selhurst Park. The next two rounds of the Cup were negotiated fairly smoothly, against Carlisle and Oldham Athletic, both at Anfield. In the quarter-finals, with a fourth successive home draw, they saw off Middlesbrough 2–0. Hopes of an all-Merseyside final disappeared when they were drawn against Everton at Maine Road, Manchester. In a fierce, unrelenting derby battle the first game ended two-all, but in the replay, again in Manchester, Liverpool went through to the FA Cup Final 3–0 winners, with Kennedy scoring the third goal with a header from a free-kick move started just outside the box. Liverpool would contest the FA Cup Final that year at Wembley against the hated enemy, Manchester United, the glamour team that never won anything but continued to voice their superiority. While the city of Liverpool floundered on its reputation for militancy, neglected by big business, with mounting poverty and unemployment, Manchester, its cosmopolitan neighbour, was slowly starting to recuperate from the death of the cotton trade and regain some confidence.

After the hiccoughs at Christmas and their erratic away form, Liverpool continued to head the League as a result of their home record. During a tough April battle with Ipswich Town at Anfield, Kennedy again played a crucial part in squeezing through a 2–1 victory. Liverpool had already reached the FA Cup Final and, in this game, were called upon to test all their reserves of stamina in a bad-tempered affair against fellow title contenders.

Heighway was carried off with a bleeding right eye before half-time and even the indestructible Tommy Smith was knocked unconscious in a clash with Paul Mariner. In a further incident before half-time, David Johnson was concussed in a head-on collision, following which an incensed Liverpool fan ran onto the pitch. In the second half Liverpool were able to play more football. Tommy Smith eluded two Ipswich attackers and sent Case away with a superb pass: Case ran on and squared the ball to Ray Kennedy, who struck the ball beautifully with his left foot into the net. Following a second goal by Johnson, Liverpool took the game by the scruff of its neck, with Keegan and Kennedy stroking the ball around contemptuously before Ipswich got a consolation penalty. A week later in a dress rehearsal for the FA Cup Final against Manchester United at Anfield, Keegan headed them into the lead after fifteen minutes and the Kop was in ecstasy. Although the score remained at one-nil, the Manchester United defence looked frail and hopes rose for an FA Cup victory.

Paisley at this time made one of his most important signings, bringing Alan Hansen from Partick Thistle for £100,000. Hansen was to establish himself in the centre of the Liverpool defence and become indispensable for the next thirteen years, his play being distinguished by his unruffled composure and positional sense. He was to prove, if anything, more difficult for Liverpool to replace than either Dalglish or Souness.

Much of the traditional urban landscape associated with the birth of professional football in this country remains unscathed in Liverpool. North-east from Lime Street Station, heading away from the river with its grand imperial waterside buildings and the showpiece, Albert Dock, you enter Everton, a devastated industrial wasteland, featuring vandalized post-war council blocks, back-to-back terraces with children kicking footballs against lamp-posts, crumbling churches with Fenian graffiti scrawled all over the walls and sordid alehouses. From Arkels Road, Edith Road, Scerries Road, St Domingos Grove, Bagnall Street, Baltic Street and Robarts Road, men leave their houses, converging like the Lowry picture, fusing in an ever broadening stream to flow up Walton Breck and Oakfield Roads to the people's citadel.

On 22 January 1900 British troops fighting in the Boer War

engaged in bloody battle. To relieve their besieged colleagues at Ladysmith, the British Tommies had to scale and take the hill called Spion Kop. This they succeeded briefly in doing, but at the expense of 2,000 lives. The Boers immediately recaptured the hill, but such courage was shown by the British troops that it has remained in folklore as a historic military engagement. The Spion Kop at Liverpool Football Club came into being, in 1906, as a mound of cinders and mud built behind one goal, which was later covered with concrete. Military survivors from the King's Regiment based in Liverpool, returning to the city from South Africa, stood on the slope to watch their team wage war against the opposition and named the bank the 'Spion Kop' in memory of their dead compatriots. In 1928, the Kop was rebuilt with a massive cantilever roof and an awesome capacity of 24,000. The Kop, a cathartic temple, the nexus of Liverpool, where the city's red-scarved, shirt-sleeved male population expresses its hope and shame, has an unassuming exterior jutting out from behind a brick wall. Once inside, however, the towering Gothic stairs go deeper and higher to the top of a huge expanse of terracing which seems to fall endlessly down towards the goalposts. On match day, the primeval echo from its claustrophobic roof is filled with menace. Here, in this cathedral of working-class communion, the life blood of Liverpool Football Club flows – the touch paper of the crowd's triumph or dejection. For more than half a century, the competitive harshness of waterfront life has expressed its passion in a cacophonous, intimidating Celtic roar. Since the Mersey sound swept the world in the sixties, Kopites have interlarded their eucharist with tribal hymns, including their national anthem, 'The Tommy Boy', and Rogers and Hammerstein's chart-topper – sung by Liverpool's own Gerry Marsden – 'You'll Never Walk Alone'. Here on this greasy, uncomfortable terrace with the air rancid with beer, onions and stale farts, an incensed entanglement of fervent flesh rocks and rolls, sways and sinks, cursing and quipping with an ever-changing repertoire of wicked one-liners, plummeting forward with a routine of spontaneous synchronized clapping or draping emblazoned red emblems for the world's media to digest.

During Ray Kennedy's time at Liverpool, the Kop was still the most innovative, knowledgeable and witty support in the land. On one occasion, the Leeds United keeper, Gary Sprake, threw the ball accidentally into his own net; on his visit to Anfield, he was greeted with strains of Max Bygraves' song 'You Need Hands'. Following the revelation that Tommy Docherty was having an affair with the Manchester United physiotherapist's wife, Mary Brown, the Kop greeted him with chants of 'Knees Up Mother Brown'. Even when Liverpool were having a bad day, the Kop would remain good-natured, expressing their vexation with the abstract chant 'We all agree Tiswas is better than Swap Shop', references to two children's television programmes. Liverpool fans are reputed to be the most generous in the League, applauding opponents' skill and raising their team, when down, to even greater deeds. On one occasion, Joe Corrigan, the Manchester City goalkeeper, was hit by a flying object from the Kop and the chant immediately went up to the police 'Get the bastard out', a gesture acknowledged by Corrigan once he had come round. Liverpool support through the sixties and seventies was always worth a goal start.

Many a future Liverpool player has himself stood on these terraces with his father or brother; Phil Thompson, who watched the defeat of Inter-Milan, is one of the more distinguished. In the wake of the Hillsborough disaster in 1989 and following the publication of the Taylor Report, a Member of Parliament may have had Anfield in mind when he wrote: 'A nasty, cold, windswept ground where crowds are herded together on concrete terraces, where lavatory facilities are minimal and dirty, catering facilities virtually non-existent and where, in short, people are treated like animals and not surprisingly act like animals'. The large majority of Liverpool fans do not behave like animals. The people of the city have maintained a humanity temporarily submerged in much of Thatcherite-inspired yuppie England. The overspilling of sorrow and the magnitude of grief in the aftermath of the Hillsborough disaster could probably not have occurred in any other English city. Even when sandwiched between the most foul-mouthed, evil-smelling Hogarthian figures, there is a feeling of human warmth and compassion. Liverpool and football are inextricable. It is hard to imagine Liverpool without a Kop. People come to football for the atmosphere as well as the game, and if that is lost the executive boxes will lie empty.

On 14 May 1977, with 10,000 Scousers locked out of the

ground, 55,000 fans cheered Liverpool to their second successive League Championship against West Ham United. However, in contrast to the previous season, when supporters had been dancing and singing all the way up the M6 motorway back from Wolverhampton, the celebrations after the goalless draw were quite muted, as if victory were a *fait accompli*. Success was beginning to be considered a divine right, and two more important hurdles were yet to be overcome if the club was to achieve an unparalleled treble.

Manchester United were in the process of building a new attacking team in the wake of Best, Law and Charlton, and boasted among their strike force Steve Coppell, Gordon Hill, Lou Macari, Sammy McIlroy and Jimmy Greenhoff. However, their defence was highly suspect and had conceded sixty-two goals during the League season. Meanwhile, the Kennedy and Lockey families were preparing to head south to watch them play in the FA Cup Final; Martin Kennedy joked that they should be given season tickets for Wembley.

Bob Paisley's team selection was influenced considerably by a tactless dictate from the Football Association which announced that if a replay of the Cup Final were necessary it should be played on 27 June, five weeks later, in the middle of Wimbledon and well into the close season. This would have meant that the players, who had had a gruelling season, and many of whom were involved in international duties in May and June, would have to be kept in full training almost to the start of the next season. This crass decision influenced Paisley's choice of an uncharacteristic three-man attack instead of his best formation of four midfielders with Keegan and Heighway up front. Ian Callaghan was therefore relegated to substitute, with David Johnson spearheading the attack and the luckless David Fairclough missing out altogether.

In the dressing room before a big game each player reacts differently, but the bigger the game as a general rule, the quieter the dressing room. Ray was renowned for always seeming at his most relaxed just before a game. Ray Clemence tended to go quiet and Terry McDermott would clown around. Paisley and Docherty led the two teams down the tunnel to the Wembley roar.

Liverpool got off to a good start with Keegan and Kennedy

probing relentlessly in midfield, but Johnson, in the squad for the injured Toshack, could not capitalize on the chances, and against the run of play early in the second half Stuart Pearson drove a low shot past Clemence to give United the lead. Paisley said afterwards that it was the sort of shot that the Liverpool goalkeeper usually trapped with his foot. Immediately on resumption of the second half, however, Jimmy Case rasped a blinding shot into the left-hand corner of Alec Stepney's goal to equalize, and it seemed odds-on that Liverpool would go on to win. A few minutes later, a shot from Macari which was going wide ricocheted off Greenhoff's trunk and into the net. Despite Kennedy hitting the woodwork twice in the dying minutes and Liverpool always looking the classier side, it was the dreaded enemy, Manchester United, who seized the trophy. Although Ray had been denied a second League Championship and FA Cup Double by a whisker, he felt more satisfaction on that day with his own performance than he had when Arsenal had won against Liverpool in the Cup. In any case, the prize he now valued beyond all others, the European Cup, was still within his grasp.

The road to the European Cup Final in Rome had begun in the previous autumn at Anfield against the Northern Irish club, Crusaders. What was thought would be a walkover proved to be a difficult encounter against a well-drilled defence, but a penalty by Phil Neal and a goal by John Toshack gave the Reds a 2–0 cushion for the second leg. One of the Crusaders' players lost a contact lens during the game and Bob Paisley told him to concentrate on looking inside the Crusaders' penalty area, as the side had rarely advanced beyond that point during the whole game. In the return game at Seaview, one of the Crusaders' officials came into the Liverpool dressing room and offered the players a glass of whiskey before the match, in an effort to improve the Crusaders' chances. Liverpool destroyed the parttimers 5–0, with two goals from David Johnson and one each from Keegan, Heighway and substitute Terry McDermott.

In the second round Liverpool were drawn against the Turkish champions from Trabzon, a small town on the Black Sea, close to the Russian border. For many years Liverpool had chartered Aer Lingus for their European trips; a plane was flown over from Dublin to Speke to collect the team. However, on this occasion even the usually imperturbable Barney Croughan, the regular captain, was unable to transport the side because the air strip at Trabzon was too short. Because of the length of the journey the team were obliged to fly out two days early and stay one night in Ankara before travelling on to their destination on a Turkish Airline flight. The team visited a local night club that evening and one of the belly dancers appeared to take a shine to Ray, tweeking his cheek and asking him to buy her a drink. Jimmy Case and Tommy Smith, who had been with Ray, left discreetly, chuckling to one another, telling Ray that the only gentlemanly thing to do was to oblige. The ingrained discipline of the Liverpool side, however, prevented Ray from landing himself in embarrassing difficulties. The following day, on beginning the descent into Trabzon, he turned even greener than usual when flying once he saw the tiny runway that was built on the edge of a cliff and ended with a brick wall separating it from the mountain road.

The hotel the players were put in was a flea pit, the food was unpalatable and the Turkish press were so omnipotent that they were able to change the time of the kick-off so that Miss Turkey, who had been invited to meet the players before the start of the game, could be filmed and then shown live to passengers on the domestic flight to Istanbul which was due to take off at the official kick-off time. The pitch was as deplorable as the hotel, and even the ball was described by Paisley as a pig's bladder. In front of thousands of people watching the game in the foothills of the Anatolian mountains, some throwing stones, Liverpool went down to a hotly disputed penalty. The damage could have been greater but the long experience of the club in the Shankly era had taught the Liverpool side never to retaliate however much they were provoked in away matches in Europe. In the second leg at Anfield against an increasingly frustrated and physical Turkish outfit, Liverpool ran out easy victors with goals from Johnson, Keegan and Heighway. Both Ray and Phil Thompson needed medical treatment before the game.

This brought Liverpool into the quarter-finals and the beginning of serious competition against a club generally regarded as one of the best in Europe, the French champions St Etienne, who had unluckily lost by a single goal in the previous year's European Cup Final. To minimize boredom and dietary problems,

Liverpool set out on 1 May 1977 for the away leg in their Aer Lingus BAC 111, affectionately called the Fisher-Price toy by the Irish crew. On this occasion the pilot was 'The Rat', Dick O'Keefe, rather than Barney, the Liverpool team's favourite. As usual the plane had been blessed and carried the lucky shamrock.

Beatrice, one of the air hostesses on the flight, remembers the group of players she had to look after at the back of the plane, which included Ray Kennedy, Ian Callaghan, John Toshack, Jimmy Case and Joey Jones, as natural, unassuming, polite and undemanding. During the flight not a drop of alcohol passed the Liverpool players' lips and not one of them made a pass or lewd suggestion to the hostesses. The Liverpool coaching staff expected the players to behave in a responsible way, and the players were by now well versed in the European pre-match routine. Endless card games whiled away the time until the plane landed at Chartres.

St Etienne had not lost a match on their own ground for four years. If Liverpool had Keegan, then they had Dominique Rocheteau, the *enfant terrible* of French football. In fact, Liverpool were without Keegan, and Toshack was injured. Despite these setbacks, they held the Frenchmen to a single goal and returned to Anfield confident of victory. Liverpool had had their chances in the game with Phil Thompson missing a relatively easy header and Heighway hitting a post.

The return leg at Anfield on 16 March turned out to be one of the most memorable European nights ever at Anfield, and one of Ray's fondest playing memories during his time with the club. The atmosphere before the game was electrifying. The Kop was bursting at the seams, whipped to a competitive frenzy by the massed 7,000 French army facing them who chanted 'Allez les verts' to the tune of 'Ave Maria'. A rich cacophony of terrace noises and chants filled the air. Liverpool got off to a tremendous start with Heighway's short corner after two minutes finding Keegan, who brilliantly angled the ball over the French keeper into the net. Despite relentless pressure, Liverpool could not break down the French defence again. Immediately after half-time, what Liverpool had feared most happened, with a break-away French counter-attack leading to Barthenay scoring a brilliant long-distance solo goal against the run of play. With the away-goal rule in operation, Liverpool now had to score twice to clinch victory, a task which, despite all their pressure, looked beyond them. In the fifty-ninth minute, with Liverpool throwing caution to the winds, Kennedy scored one of his most important goals for the club from a flick on from Toshack after a Callaghan centre. With fifteen minutes left, Paisley played his last desperate card by sending on spindly-legged, redheaded 'supersub' David Fairclough, nicknamed 'The Bionic Carrot'. Emlyn Hughes recalls: 'Although Davie was at times impossible to play with his appearance gave us all life'. With six minutes to go, Kennedy played a beautifully weighted long pass down the left to catch the French defence off balance. Fairclough brought the ball down just inside his own half and advanced towards the French massed defence with Emlyn Hughes screaming at him to pass. Oblivious to all around him, Fairclough, with his lightning turn of pace, launched himself at the French ranks, beat three players and shot low past Curcovic, the Yugoslavian goalkeeper, to clinch a sensational victory.

In Anfield folklore, this game is compared with the victory against Inter-Milan. Liverpool's 3–1 win at Anfield in 1965 in the first leg of the semi-final of the European Cup, against the European champions from Italy, is still regarded as perhaps the Reds' greatest achievement. Unfortunately, the second leg in Inter's San Siro Stadium was lost 3–0, with two highly contentious Italian goals.

After Fairclough's goal people were hugging complete strangers in a frenzy of sheer joy, finally believing that their side was now capable of going the whole way. Afterwards, the French, some of whom sported green Beatle wigs, mingled happily with the jubilant Liverpool supporters in the waterside pubs and bars, and a close, affectionate bond grew between the two groups of supporters, so much so that some of the Frenchmen travelled to Rome to watch Liverpool play in the final.

Over seven seasons Fairclough was only on from the start in eighty-eight games, but came on as substitute in sixty-one more. In games in which he started, he often seemed to lose his way and drift out of the action, perhaps because his style of play did not fit with that of the rest of the team. He was also accused at times of having a low work rate. Nevertheless, when coming on late as substitute, he saved the side on numerous occasions and scored fifty-two goals.

However, the more knowledgeable Kopites and the opposition credited the success of the Liverpool side against St Etienne to Ray Kennedy. After the game Ray remarked: 'I know I have my critics, but I like to think I've good vision as I can hold and shield the ball and pass it accurately. Towards the end at Arsenal I was getting sick of being hacked down. I always seemed to be working and running, but never having ball satisfaction'.

Ray, happy in his life and enjoying his football, had regained his desire to beat an opponent fairly, which was the thing that had always given him pleasure in professional football. Paisley would compliment him on some of his telling passes and after the St Etienne match commented: 'Ray is now confident and enjoying his game. He is excellent at winning the ball by interception which is just as valuable as tackling in the European game'. Part of this renewed confidence Ray owed to Bob Harris, now the *Mirror* sports editor, who had rung him up one day and advised him that he must start believing more in himself if he was to achieve his potential.

The semi-final against FC Zurich turned out to be something of an anticlimax, with Liverpool returning from Switzerland with a 3–1 first leg lead, with two goals from Neal, one from the penalty spot, and the other from Heighway. Ray, who had set his sights on a European Cup medal, recalls never being so nervous before any other match. Back at Anfield in the second leg, Jimmy Case scored twice and Keegan got a late goal to take them through to the European Cup Final, 6–1 on aggregate, where they were to play the formidable German champions, Borussia Mönchengladbach, in Rome on the Wednesday after the FA Cup Final. Undeterred by the defeat by Manchester United at Wembley, thousands of Liverpool supporters left directly from London to travel overland to Rome. To the Wembley valediction 'See you in the Vatican' came back the response 'In the bar or in the lounge?'.

As the fans headed for Dover, the dejected Liverpool side left Wembley to take a train back to Merseyside. If the FA's decision had been a stroke of bad luck, then on the return journey fate was on the Liverpool management's side. A special train taking fans back to Liverpool broke down in front of the team's train and gradually, during the protracted wait at Watford Station, the mood of the team changed from one of utter dejection to renewed hope, catalysed by a grotesque Clemence jig across the platform. With the help of liberal sprinklings of alcohol and a good meal followed by a round of jokes, despair was replaced by defiance. By the time the train drew up in Lime Street, the players were relaxed and motivated for their destined role as champions of Europe. This crucial change of mood is what turns football games, and is reminiscent of the dressing-room episode at Anderlecht which swung the Fairs Cup for Arsenal.

On arriving in the Eternal City, Liverpool were in confident mood. They had the edge psychologically over their German opponents, having beaten them in the Fairs Cup in 1973. However, the opposition was skilful and disciplined, and had Allan Simonsen, the Danish international, as their danger man in attack. Uli Steilike was a quality sweeper, the ageing Heinckes was still a force and Bonhof had been an influential presence in the German 1974 World Cup Final team. However, there was a view in the Liverpool camp that the Germans were vulnerable to big target men like Toshack, and here Paisley played a master tactical stroke by convincing the Germans that Toshack would be included in the side. In fact, the big Welsh striker had been out of the team since the St Etienne game due to injury and had no chance of playing. The front runners were to be Keegan and Heighway, with Callaghan restored to midfield, the formation Paisley rued not having played against Manchester United. The full Liverpool team on the night included Clemence, Neal, Jones, Smith, Kennedy, Hughes, Keegan, Case, Heighway, Callaghan and McDermott.

On that summer evening in the Olympic Stadium in Rome, with long shadows shrouding large areas of the pitch, the Liverpool team were greeted by an incredible 25,000 Scousers. After expending their giros on the Cup Final some had pawned all their worldly possessions – including domestic cookers – to get to Rome. Liverpool supporters do not fit the Moynihan stereotype of pot-bellied drunken oafs, but evenly represent the congregation of the city, with businessmen from the Wirral, priests and scallies from the Dingle and huge nuclear families from Kirkby. To the Liverpool team, it felt like playing at home as they were greeted by the chants of 'Champions, champions'.

They got off to a competent start and were soon on top. Bob Paisley described the first Liverpool goal in his autobiography:

The first goal was a coaching showpiece. Kevin Keegan, who was giving that great professional Bertie Vogts a dog's life, had the German selling programmes to the crowd – so far had he pulled him away from where the build-up was taking place. He was a key defender and he didn't realise what was happening until it was too late. Borussia were spreadeagled and Ian Callaghan won the ball in midfield and pushed it out to Steve Heighway on the right. Cally followed on down the flank, pulling the Germans even wider and allowing Steve to cut inside and play the ball into Terry McDermott's path. It was a perfect example of Terry's awareness, anticipation and running and he scored magnificently.

Liverpool went in at half-time a goal up, with Paisley warning them about being over-confident. Shortly after half-time Simonsen latched on to a back pass from Case to Neal and scored a superb goal to equalize. Liverpool then wobbled as the Germans stepped up their game, and it was left to Ray Clemence to keep them in the match with a superb save from Uli Steilike. A few minutes later, however, Liverpool gained a corner. The disciplined Germans picked up all the big men as usual, with Kennedy acting as a decoy. Fatefully for them, they failed to notice Tommy Smith coming in to score one of his few goals with his head.

Tommy Smith, supposedly in his last professional game for Liverpool, the man to have next to you in the trenches, who improved under pressure and without whom Liverpool had never won anything since Shankly, had done it again. Afterwards he joked that it was 'a header worthy of Dixie Dean', vowed not to wash his hair ever again and considered having a brass plate fixed into his head.

Liverpool regained their confidence. When Bonhof floored Heighway, the travelling Kop bayed for a penalty. By now the Germans were increasingly dejected. Keegan, who had completely outfoxed Vogts, was brought down in the box and this time a penalty was awarded. Neal had already planned that if he had to take a penalty he would hit it low in view of the German goalkeeper Kneib's great height. He also knew that the keeper would have seen his penalty in the semi-final when he drove it hard to the left. This time, with Ian Callaghan, the old campaigner of thirteen seasons in Europe, hiding his face, Neal blasted the ball low to the right with the keeper diving left. On that unforgettable night in Rome, Liverpool became only the second English club to win the European Cup, in what Bob Paisley later declared to be 'the greatest night in the history of Liverpool Football Club'.

Although Ray had brought out a superb save from Kneib, the German goalkeeper, and had a reasonable game, a pattern had been appearing gradually throughout his career. He was beginning to be regarded as a semi-final man because his best performances never seemed to occur in the showpiece games. Ray himself justified this by claiming that he found it difficult to raise his game for what he described as 'glamour games'. The real challenge is to get the team there in the first place. However, an alternative explanation might have been that Ray was a victim of success phobia, a syndrome in which top-class athletes, despite brilliant performances in the past when out of the limelight, may fail to deliver the goods on occasions when it matters. One explanation for this is that a player might, in fact, have difficulty accepting his own outstanding abilities and, as a consequence, might fail to cope with the responsibility which success brings.

After the game Sir Stanley Matthews came into the Liverpool dressing room to congratulate the players. Ray remembers the pleasure he had in displaying his medal and saying, 'Seen one of these before Sir Stan?'

That night the streets of Rome were filled with good-humoured Scouse arias. Some of the supporters even found their way to the team's hideaway celebratory buffet and were allowed through in droves to devour sumptuous spreads in seconds. Eventually the players slipped away to unwind in their own cliques, joining up the following morning to take their revenge on the press by throwing them in the swimming pool. Probably the only sober man that night was Bob Paisley, who was determined to savour every moment with a clear mind.

In the cafés around St Peter's Square the joke was going round that every time Kevin Keegan went up to the bar, Bertie Vogts' guardian angel got up and followed him. Keegan's performance had been one of his greatest for Liverpool and was to prove to be his last, with his transfer to the German club FC Hamburg scheduled to take place in June. Ironically, since his transfer from Scunthorpe United six years earlier, Keegan had had his worst season for Liverpool, possibly related to his father's death and the thoughts of a move to Europe at the back of his mind. For the first time, the Kop in their anxiety had taunted him with gibes of treachery and had grown increasingly impatient with his uncharacteristic, erratic play. However, Keegan is now remembered at Liverpool as one of their greatest players, his assets being his lightning reactions, infectious enthusiasm, boundless energy and courage. His telepathic partnership with John Toshack was as effective as the one that Ray had enjoyed with John Radford at Arsenal. In many ways Keegan was ahead of his time: his single-minded philosophy that he must use football to get what he wanted out of life is now *de rigueur*. Although this view was shared to a certain degree by most professional players, Keegan's calculated self-aggrandizement tended to distance him from the others at Liverpool. After Keegan's transfer, Paisley stated that, in his view, any player who had left the country should not be considered for England international honours. This was not meant to be a threat, but was really an expression of a mounting concern in the game that the best players would be creamed off by the attraction of larger salaries in Europe.

Throughout this phenomenal season, which had seen Liverpool go to the wire in three major championships and finish victorious in two, only seventeen players had been used, with Clemence, Neal, Hughes and Kennedy ever present. Ray, with his new slimline look, had become an integral cog in the Red machine, yet his play remained enigmatic and baffling to the Liverpool supporters. His approach was too scholastic, lacking any sense of impetuosity or frenzy. The more extrovert, brighter Liverpool talents such as Heighway and Keegan continued to capture the headlines, and Ray's driving force, which often lay behind the best Liverpool moves, was underplayed and frequently unrecognized. At times it seemed that he was living in another world, or at least another game, building his own moves methodically, yet effortlessly, so often playing the right ball at the right moment between baffled defenders and then slipping unnoticed into the box for a return. He would appear languid and disinterested for long periods on the fringes and then would suddenly intercept a crucial ball and flash a telling cross to the right side into the onrushing path of McDermott. By this stage in his career, he had comprehensively married his skill to his physical presence, but his power was only rarely used as a warning device as he wove patterns on the pitch. Ray's remoteness was often misconstrued by the Kop as indifference and his positional sense was so refined that he rarely needed to put in a tackle in order to construct his game plan. His speed of decision-making was impressive and helped to supply the front-runners with much of their ammunition. Then, when a goal-scoring opportunity presented itself, he would appear from nowhere.

10 The Iron Curtain

So many of her sons drowned in the slime of trenches
So many of her daughters torn apart by poverty
So many of her children died in the darkness
So many of her prisoners slowly crushed in slave ships
Century after red century the Mersey flowed on by
By the waters of Liverpool we sat down and wept

> But slaves and the poor know
> better than anyone
> How to have a real good time
> If you're strong enough to speak
> You're strong enough to sing
> If you can stand up on your feet
> You can stamp out a beat

So we'd been planning how to celebrate
The great red river of Liverpool
As our team rose to a torrent
That would flood the green of Wembley
We'd been planning how to celebrate
The great red dream of Liverpool
For Dalglish held the cup in his left fist
And the Championship in his right –
By the waters of Liverpool we sat down and wept

Our scarves are weeping on the gates of Anfield
And the great singing ground is a palace of whispers
For the joy of the game, the heart of the game
Yes the great red heart of the great red game
Is broken and all the red flowers of Liverpool –
By the waters of Liverpool we sat down and wept

(ADRIAN MITCHELL)

R AY and Jenny were looking forward to the birth of their first
child in July 1977. After the four years of unhappiness which had

led to Jenny's departure, their marriage was coming together again with the imminent arrival of the baby. Jenny's life, however, continued to be difficult, with Ray needing a lot of emotional support and encouragement. Often he would arrive home in the early hours of the morning with a pocketful of 'groupie' women's telephone numbers. The Liverpool schedule was so busy at peak holiday time and there were so many team trips abroad that married life was disrupted. Like most professional players, Ray regarded the periods between matches as preparation time for the coming threat of the next game and restricted himself to the basic pleasures of 'booze and birds'. As Jenny's confinement continued, Ray became increasingly keen for the child to be born a Geordie. However, training started again at Liverpool on 12 July, and he was concerned that he might not be able to get up to Seaton Delaval at all that year because of the home internationals and then the Latin American tour to Brazil and Argentina with England.

Janet, his little sister, now aged ten, was as keen as always to see her famous brother and was constantly asking her parents when he would be coming home. By now she was aware of his success and got a particular thrill when the boys at school told her that he had played well in a game. However, like most football families, she was already becoming suspicious that people wanted to be friendly with her just to get tickets for games. Her image of her brother was idealistic; he was away for most of the year and, when he was there, there was always a great fuss with plenty of presents. She never had any doubt, however, that Ray adored her and temperamentally the two were similar. As soon as big brother arrived home he became extremely protective towards her.

At the end of July, Cara Kennedy was born on Merseyside weighing 7lb 13oz. Ray was present at the birth on a hot summer's day. He remembers hoping that their first-born would be a girl. The nurses had left a blue nightdress on Jenny's bed; Ray replaced it with a pink one. During his wife's labour, the droning sound of a lawn-mower drifted through the open window, creating a surreal image in his mind. Cara is Irish for friend and was a name Ray had heard and liked on one of the Aer Lingus flights. Following Cara's birth, Martin and Veronica were frequent visitors at Ainsdale.

Ray was thrilled and delighted with Cara and, on reporting for pre-season training, he had a new spring in his step. By hard work in the close season he had kept his weight steady at twelve and a half stone. He had taken to wearing a plastic bin liner under his shirt when training to purge himself of sweat. On the traditional after-training journey by coach from Melwood back to Anfield, he would feel faint, as Ronnie Moran refused to have the windows open. Moran and Joe Fagan continued to keep Ray on his toes, knowing that he was one of those unfortunate players who could very easily go to seed.

Training started at Melwood around ten in the morning with gentle jogging and, after a salad lunch, the players would do some ball work. Gradually it would be stepped up after Thursday afternoon and into the next week with circuit work, in which there would be one stretch and seven jogs, then two stretches and six jogs and so on. The players would also do some mild weight training. After two weeks, they would have their first practice game and then, at the end of July, head off on the pre-season tour to Germany. During these tours, where everything down to what the players ate was meticulously planned, behaviour before matches was always impeccable. The players then returned for the Charity Shield, 'a day out at Wembley' but a bit of a farce because of the meaninglessness of the outcome. On this occasion it was played to a dreary goalless draw against Manchester United. Once the season started in earnest with games on Saturdays and Tuesdays, most of the training took place on Wednesday and Thursday mornings. On Tuesday afternoons and Friday mornings there would be five-a-side games and, if the side was doing badly, they would be brought back for more fitness work on Sundays and Mondays. The Holiday Inn, now the Moat House Hotel in Paradise Street, was the meeting place on Fridays before a match. Training at Liverpool was always designed to make football players and not athletes, a philosophy which has become increasingly threatened as more and more clubs are prepared to sacrifice skill, flair and basic technique for force, power and fitness.

Flushed with the success of his Rome goal, Tommy Smith decided to play on for a further season at Liverpool. At the end of the season he would move on to join John Toshack, who had been appointed player-manager at Fourth Division Swansea City. Smith and Callaghan took Ray under their wing at Liverpool, taking over the paternal role Frank McLintock had vacated.

Tommy Smith was born just off the Scotland Road, a stone's throw from Anfield, in one of the meanest parts of the city; as a child, he had no alternative but to act tough. He passed his eleven plus from St John's Road Catholic School and was later to forsake a scholarship in architecture to pursue his childhood dream of football. Much of his early apprenticeship was served playing against youths even larger and rougher than himself at the Lee Jones Boys Club; at fifteen he was full grown. After being spotted playing for Liverpool Schoolboys, he was drafted straight into Liverpool Reserves. Smith recalls that he was treated like dirt on his arrival at the club, with some of the senior pros doing everything in their power to break him. However, within two years, he was playing regularly in the first team, where he remained for fourteen successive seasons.

Tommy Smith was a far better player than he was often given credit for and, after captaining the England Under-23 team, many considered it a travesty of justice that he gained only one full England cap. This lack of international recognition always galled Smith and compounded the hatred he felt towards Emlyn Hughes, who had not only taken over the Liverpool captaincy, but had also been honoured with more than fifty international caps. By the beginning of the 1977 season, Smith and Hughes were barely talking to one another, although on the pitch one would never have guessed it. A story circulates in Liverpool that after a home match Smith invited the whole team to a night club in which he had business interests and everyone was allowed in free. When Hughes arrived, however, Smith instructed the door to demand the standard entrance fee.

Smith's reputation as the hardest man to play in the Football League since the war lives on, and the opposition would normally steer clear of him whenever they could. Although Smith later admitted that his tough guy image was in many ways more bark than bite, few were allowed to take liberties with him. It was common knowledge that his nickname was 'Beans on Toast', referring to his pock-marked complexion, but no one, however big, called him this to his face and remained vertical. Even the Leeds United hard men, Giles, Bremner and Hunter, treated Smith with respect, and George Best, who revelled in demeaning the so-called hard men, was rather more circumspect with Smith. Soon after his arrival at Spurs, Ossie Ardiles, the diminutive and skilful Argentinian midfielder, confronted Smith in all his ferocity. After the game Smith explained his philosophy: 'They can't expect to come here and play fancy flickers. That tackle was to say to him this is a man's league — and he didn't like it. I think Spurs ought to buy a good stock of cotton wool for such poseurs. He can't expect not to be tackled just because Argentina won the World Cup'. Tommy dished out shit all day and, if given an inch, he would take a mile. If the victim took what Smith gave him on the chin and retaliated, Tommy could live with him. The capacity to cope with denigration is the way footballers and managers assess that disproportionately revered attribute called 'bottle'. As well as physical intimidation, Smith employed verbal bullying to put off opponents, deriding them with insults. He was combative and fearless on the pitch, and possessed innate powers of leadership. For the Liverpool team, he was a motivational spirit; honest and straightforward, he was a player who was at his best when the chips were down.

When I contacted him and explained that I was writing a book about his team-mate Ray Kennedy, he immediately offered his full assistance, despite being in severe pain from two knees worn out prematurely by the constant punishment they had received on the field of play. The morning after the Liverpool Supporters' Club had held their dinner at Anfield for Ray in November 1990, Tommy and I met at the Moat House Hotel close to the Pier Head. He was full of praise for Ray's natural ability and told me that he always included Ray in his best-ever Liverpool team:

> At Arsenal Ray was a tough player and we used to kick lumps out of one another. I remember having stand-up arguments playing against him, but that was what went on in those days. On the pitch Ray was a cool customer who controlled his temper and the ball brilliantly. He could open tin cans with his left foot and had an uncanny ability to appear where least expected. He had the effect of taking the pressure off the rest of us. A pure left footer can be a liability in a team because they always go the same way, but Ray could put the ball anywhere and had a useful right foot. At Liverpool he brought strength to our midfield and would open up defences with his deceptive blind side runs.

In his autobiography, *I Did it the Hard Way*, Smith wrote:

Ray Kennedy came to Liverpool disillusioned with Arsenal. I never really knew why. At Arsenal he used to look up to Frank McLintock a lot and when he left Ray was none too happy. Some players need other players to give them the extra will to win. McLintock was Arsenal and when he left the team seemed to fall apart ... When Ray arrived at Anfield he was overweight and had lost interest in the game. When he had sorted out whom he could trust he used to confide in Cally and me and take his cue from us. Once Liverpool had switched his position he became one of the best midfielders we've ever had.

When we talked, Smith had some even more revealing observations about Ray's character off the pitch:

Ray could blow up very easily and, whereas with me my reputation would defuse things, with Ray there would often be a flare-up. He got into more problems off the pitch than I did and seemed sometimes to make his own difficulties. One day before a particularly tense match, on the way from the Holiday Inn to Anfield, Ray had been tormenting himself and started on me. I said to him 'Ray, it's Smithy you're talking to not Phil Neal or Alan Kennedy, don't cross me and I won't cross you. If I don't like you, I'll tell you, and as a matter of fact I like you, so don't mess around'. Later he apologized and I told him he had to control what he was doing and stop picking on his friends. Those were the only harsh words the two of us ever had. In those days the older players were expected to take care of the younger ones like Ray. We saw it as part of our job. Off the pitch Ray was erratic and I used to call him 'The Susser', because he was always sizing people up and would take a dislike to a particular person, but he wouldn't say it to their faces at first and then suddenly he might blow up with aggression.

Ray was unpredictable in everyday life, going fifty different ways at once, and I sometimes had the frightening feeling that he might do something really stupid. When he arrived in Liverpool, he behaved like Jack the London lad, generous as hell, always with a few quid in his pocket and definitely one of the boys. However, he never seemed to be relaxed, he was always worrying about something and could never sit still. He would flick his fingernails a lot when you were sitting talking to him. Yet in most ways he was a typical footballer. He would do silly things, have late nights, go on binges and then get in trouble at home, but he was no different from the rest of us. Show me a footballer who doesn't go out now and then on the town and I'll show you a bad footballer. It's the standard way of relieving tension.

Despite his down-to-earth attitude Ray enjoyed the good life and liked to be involved in the action, especially with the girls. He also enjoyed being acknowledged by the public.

At Liverpool, what goes on at the club and what goes on away from it are two very different things and Ray was a prime example of this split. Ray needed a lot of understanding. He seemed to need someone to take control of his life for him, to give him sympathy and while he was here that was provided by Jenny and Liverpool Football Club.

Tommy Smith's wife, Sue, and Jenny were close friends. Jenny would sometimes confide that everything had to be 'spot on' when Ray came home, with the house tidy, Cara changed and his adoring wife made up ready to receive him. Unless life was organized with military precision, there would be scenes. Smith's view was that Ray's wife was one of the nicest people in the world and the two of them seemed very well suited.

It is in some senses surprising that McLintock and Smith, both charismatic captains, have never become top football managers. After dabbling in management, McLintock is now involved with the media and is a players' agent, while Smith has business interests and writes a regular column in the *Liverpool Echo*. After hanging up his boots at Swansea, Smith returned to Anfield to coach the apprentices. He would often tell them that, although few would make it as professionals, at Liverpool at least they would have received the best of all possible starts to their career. In the end Smith resigned because of constant disagreements with Ronnie Moran. The only job good enough for Tommy would have been Paisley's and he wasn't prepared to wait. Perhaps both Smith and McLintock were a bit too outspoken and blunt to negotiate the narrow tightrope between players and their paymasters.

At Liverpool, all the players in the first team squad are equally important and are treated with respect as human beings, not as purchased commodities. Ray knew that if he continued to do a good job he would be rewarded. Equally, he was quite clear that if he stepped out of line or let the club down he would soon be on his way. The club kept its players sweet by sorting out contracts amicably and, through the caring family atmosphere, fostering friendships, and providing a calming influence and stability. Liverpool restored Ray's childhood joy of playing the game for its own. The club's success hinged on buying good players with resilient characters and ensuring that their feet stayed on the ground. Players were taught not to get too high if they won because they'd get too low if they lost; an even keel and a steady side were always the target.

For several weeks before Keegan's transfer, Paisley had shrewdly been lining up a replacement, and the switch was so smooth that Keegan was barely missed. Paisley had settled on the twenty-six-year-old Celtic star, Kenny Dalglish, already a centurion in his goal tally and an established Scottish international. Ironically, he had had a trial at Liverpool as a schoolboy and been missed by Shankly. Dalglish was to score in his first three League games for Liverpool. King Kenny, or 'The Supreme Being', as he was known by the Kopites, was in Ray's opinion the greatest forward he had ever played with or against. Single-mindedness, professionalism and an ability to blend into a team and yet show sensational individual skill characterized his career. Off the pitch, Dalglish was a solitary man, superstitious, blunt and uncommunicative, but a devoted husband and father who was to show his true mettle years later in the wake of the Hillsborough disaster.

The third Jock, after Hansen and Dalglish, arrived midway through the 1977–8 season. After an abortive start to his career at Spurs when he had fled, homesick and disillusioned after constant clashes with Eddie Bailey, the Spurs coach, Edinburgh-born Graeme Souness had resurrected his career as the star of a useful Middlesbrough side. On arrival at Anfield, 'Souey' was already a highly ambitious man who adored the good life and refused to settle for second best. His love of fast cars and women, flashy suits and jewellery earned him the nickname 'Champagne Charlie', but basically he was dedicated and industrious, and believed in working and playing hard. On the pitch he was strong and uncompromising, an enforcer, with the reputation that he would cripple his grandmother if it meant winning a game. He had vision, excellent ball control and a fearsome shot, attributes which led John Roberts, now sports writer with *The Independent*, to label him 'Tommy Smith with a Rolls Royce engine'. In common with Smith, he possessed significant powers of leadership. Although he had the reputation of being somewhat precious, arrogant and obsessed with his own physique, Souness could be thoughtful and considerate when a colleague was in distress. Ray got on well with all three of the newly arrived Jocks, although away from the club they did not mix in the same circles.

In the 1977–8 season Nottingham Forest, under the leadership of Brian Clough, emerged as a major force in the English game. Liverpool started well enough, going seven games without defeat. Then, after their first loss of the season at Old Trafford, Liverpool went to Highbury, with Ray warning his old Arsenal team-mates that Liverpool were always at their most dangerous when required to prove their pedigree. Without the injured Emlyn Hughes and Tommy Smith, Liverpool held Arsenal to a creditable goalless draw. After victories against Chelsea at home and Leeds away, Liverpool drew against Everton at Anfield 0–0. A disastrous run of three successive defeats then followed, including their first at Anfield for forty-six games, when they lost to Aston Villa 2–1. By the end of November, Liverpool were sixth in the League and five points behind the leaders, Notts Forest. After Christmas, an even more calamitous six weeks ensued when Liverpool lost four League games and went out of the FA Cup 4–2 to Chelsea. This collapse, which effectively put paid to Liverpool's ambition for a third successive League title, left Bob Paisley declaring:

> Hard work must now be the order of the day. I have always said we have no divine right to win anything and we all knew that after last season's successes in Europe the challenge would be fiercer than ever. I've still got the best squad of players in the country once we get things sorted out.
>
> We'll not change our approach to the game and we're not going to relinquish what we've got. The fact that people are calling it a crisis only goes to show the standard we have set.

From 11 March to the end of the season, Liverpool did not lose another game, winning nine of their last twelve matches. Unfortunately, Notts Forest kept winning as well, and took the title comfortably with a seven-point cushion, with Liverpool as runners-up.

Kennedy's season had been a model of consistency, the Sunday tabloid sports writers invariably giving him a score of seven out of ten, whereas other members of the squad would oscillate between scores as low as five and as high as nine. Portman Road continued to be his bogey ground, and the fiery little Scot, Archie Gemmill from Notts Forest, one of his most difficult opponents. It had always been the small men like John Giles and Archie Gemmill who had given Ray trouble. The Kop had grown to expect a gritty, resilient, workman-like performance from him in the boiler room, where so many of Liverpool's ball-winning and defence-splitting moves took place.

During the season Ray had been singled out by the Clothes Manufacturing Association as one of the nattiest dressers in the country, and nicknamed Ray 'Machine Gun' Kennedy, the pin-striped wizard. These were the days when professional footballers were showing the rest of the country how to dress – a shabbily dressed footballer was as rare as a well-dressed politician.

Liverpool went all the way to the final in the League Cup, beating Arsenal in the semi-finals. After an early goal by 'Supermac', Malcolm Macdonald, had been cancelled out by Dalglish, Ray got the winner at Anfield and the Reds held on to a goalless draw in the second leg at Highbury. In the Wembley final they came up against Nottingham Forest again, and the game ended in a dreary goalless draw. In the replay at Old Trafford, late in the game Phil Thompson was alleged to have uprooted O'Hare in the penalty box and John Robertson came up to score, denying Liverpool for a second time that season. Larry Lloyd, one of the few players to leave Anfield and go on to even greater success, had a fine game in the middle of the Forest defence.

Defence of the European Cup remained Liverpool's only chance of honours. Having received a first round bye, the Reds crushed Dynamo Dresden 5–1 at Anfield, with Toshack scoring a hat trick, and went to Germany for the replay that was expected to be a formality. However, the Germans were unrecognizable from the first leg and appeared so supercharged that the boot room wondered if they had been given stimulants. Although in the end they only went down 2–1, the force and physical presence of the opposition frightened the Liverpool team out of their wits. This game is still talked about in the Liverpool boot room as one of the best performances ever played against Liverpool in Europe. In the quarter-finals Liverpool were drawn against Benfica, the Portuguese side that had twice won the European Cup. In the Stadium of Light, in front of 70,000 fans and in torrential rain, after going a goal down, Case and Hughes put paid to the Eagles of Lisbon's unbeaten record of more than forty games. In the return leg, Liverpool cantered home 4–1 to win 6–1 on aggregate.

Liverpool were then drawn against Borussia Mönchengladbach, the team they had vanquished in the previous season's final. The Germans took the first leg 2–1 with a last-minute free kick from Bonhof, giving them hope for the return at Liverpool. However, on coming out to the intimidating roar of the Kop, the Germans immediately seemed nervous. After only seven minutes, Kennedy levelled the tie when, unmarked, he headed in a centre from Dalglish. Kennedy then laid on a second goal for Dalglish and dummied brilliantly before providing a third for the belligerent Case. Souness – deputizing efficiently for Callaghan – McDermott and Kennedy had all been superb in midfield but Udo Lattak, the German manager, singled out Ray Kennedy as his man of the match, reaffirming him as a semi-final specialist. In fact, Paisley had nearly taken Ray off at half-time because of a mild groin strain after what he considered to be one of the big Geordie's best-ever first half performances.

Liverpool were in their second European Cup Final, which this year was to take place at Wembley, giving the Merseysiders what their opponents FC Bruges considered to be virtually a home advantage. The Belgians, though the underdogs, had beaten Panathinaikos, Atletico Madrid and Juventus on the way to the final, and were a useful side with a sprinkling of Dutch, Danish and Austrian internationals. They had, however, lost to Liverpool two years earlier in the UEFA Cup Final, giving the Reds an important psychological advantage. In contrast to the previous year's final, the game proved to be a dismal bore, with the Belgians, deprived of two of their key players, packing their defence and rarely advancing into the Liverpool half. The game watched by 92,000 came briefly to life in the sixty-fifth minute when Heighway, substituting for Case, passed to Souness, who split the Belgian defence with a pass to Dalglish, who then coolly lobbed the ball over the keeper to score. In the last minutes, Thompson saved the young Alan Hansen's blushes by forcing the ball off the Liverpool line after a casual error by the usually cool and reliable Scot. Although the game had been an unimpressive spectacle as a result of their opponents' negative approach, Liverpool had changed the course of English football history in retaining the European Cup. Their success could be attributed to a unique blend of skill, stamina and teamwork born out of fourteen years in the maelstrom of European competition. Paisley called Ray Kennedy his 'Euro King', commending his strength at the back and his versatility in attack. At twenty-five, Ray had now won three League Championships, one FA Cup medal, two European Cup winners' medals, one Fairs Cup and one UEFA Cup medal, and gained eleven full England international caps.

On 11 May 1978, the victorious Liverpool team arrived at Allerton Station in Liverpool on a windswept, grey and rainy evening. The players and their wives then transferred to an open-topped bus for a tour of the city where half a million Liverpudlians were waiting to greet them. As the bus meandered through Liverpool the players sipped champagne and occasionally disembarked to greet friends. This led on more than one occasion to them being mobbed by the rapturous supporters. Fans had climbed trees, telegraph poles and lampposts to get a better view of their heroes. On Scotland Road, a man lay down in front of the bus and had to be dragged away. In Mather Avenue, a cricket match came to a halt as the players dashed to catch a glimpse of the European Champions and, on Queens Drive, a young woman appeared in a négligé to the ribald comment, 'I know they were worried about overspill . . . but this is ridiculous'. Even Evertonians were out on the streets. The statue which stands above Lewis's store in the city centre was bedecked in a red and white scarf. A huge banner near Lime Street proclaimed 'Dalglish scores more than Casanova' and another read 'Kenny's from Heaven'.

Ray was now an established celebrity in Liverpool. His standard of living was continuing to improve and he was increasingly at risk of succumbing to the easy-street syndrome where whatever he wanted was potentially there for the taking. However mature one is, continual acclaim on the pitch can lead to a corruption of the mind and the emergence of the familiar 'Don't you know who I am?' syndrome, with a slide into an artificial fantasy world of high life and moral temptation. Ray kept his feet firmly on the ground. He adored Cara, his daughter, and any indiscretions related to the opposite sex were kept away from the family home.

During the week, when he was not training at Melwood, Ray would often go home and sleep, he was so tired. Although Cara slept badly when she was a small child, Ray felt his exhaustion could not be explained just by this. He enjoyed shopping with Jenny, and the two of them would often go to his friend Ian Kidd's Southport restaurant for lunch or wine-tasting sessions. At this time, Ray was driving a sponsored Lada car.

Towards the end of the season, after eight years at Anfield and ninety-two goals, John Toshack had moved to Swansea City as player-manager. Once Keegan had arrived on the scene, Toshack's Liverpool career had blossomed, and he is remembered for some wonderful, intuitive headed goals and brilliant flick-ons which were to earn him forty caps for his native Wales.

The odds of two clubs representing England coming together in the first round of the European Cup must be long, but that is exactly what happened in the 1978–9 season. At the City Ground, Nottingham Forest again thwarted Liverpool's ambitions by winning 2–0. Liverpool's powerful midfield had a quiet day and Forest played a cunning long ball game. Liverpool also contributed to their own downfall by attempting to attack relentlessly, as if the match were an FA Cup tie, and were caught on the break by a second goal. In the return leg at Anfield, Forest blotted out the Liverpool strikers and, despite the Reds' territorial superiority, held on for a goalless draw. After two years of unchallenged ascendancy in European competition, Liverpool had been dumped in the first round by Clough's upstarts, and their dreams of joining Real Madrid, Ajax and Bayern Munich as the only teams ever to complete a hat trick of European Cup wins were shattered. So impressed was Paisley by the Forest performance that he went out immediately to lay money on them to win the Cup. Six months later he was rubbing his hands when Trevor Francis scored the Nottingham winner against the Swedish side Malmo in the final in Munich.

The following season Forest were to emulate Liverpool's triumph by retaining the European Cup with a 1–0 win over Kevin Keegan's FC Hamburg. Although many of Clough's team were not known to the general public Forest were a complete team made up of experienced and talented footballers who replicated Liverpool's technique of non-stop pressurizing football. With Peter Shilton in goal, they had one of the greatest keepers in Europe, and their midfield included two highly competitive, fearsome Scots, Kenny Burns and Archie Gemmill. The side also contained the little Scots winger, John Robertson, who provided so much of the ammunition for their goal-scorers, Trevor Francis and Ian Bowyer. In defence they had the stylish, leggy Viv Anderson, the first black player to gain a full England cap, and still playing Premier League Football for Sheffield Wednesday.

Further embarrassment was to follow when Liverpool went out of the League Cup against Second Division Sheffield United. However, their season was far from over, as the League campaign had begun with six straight wins and eleven matches without defeat before Everton edged them out by a single goal at Goodison Park. In the League, Liverpool's attack had been devastating and, on 4 September, the newly promoted Spurs side, with their Argentinians Ricardo Vila and Osvaldo Ardiles, felt the full weight of Red power in a 7–0 drubbing of the London side. After a miskick by Case, Dalglish opened the scoring in the game after eight minutes, and twelve minutes later 'The Supreme Being' deflected a Case shot over the line for a second. On twenty-eight minutes, McDermott crossed to Kennedy, who headed into the net off a defender. Shots from Case, Ray Kennedy and Alan Kennedy were miraculously saved by the Spurs keeper, Daines, but early in the second half Johnson, on as substitute for Hughes, scored a fourth with a fifteen-yard drive from a Dalglish cross. Dalglish and Ray Kennedy then interreacted in a brilliant move to allow Johnson to score again, making it 5–0. Heighway, who had plagued the Spurs defence all night, was fouled in the box, which enabled Neal to score the sixth from a penalty. The final goal is still regarded by many at Anfield as one of the best ever scored by a Liverpool side. In a move involving Ray Kennedy, Johnson and Heighway and

stretching the length of the pitch, McDermott finally headed in
on the far post at seventy-six minutes.

The goal glut continued with Liverpool scoring five against
Derby County and six against Norwich in front of capacity home
crowds of 50,000. Even away from home, the double Scotch of
Souness and Dalglish was wreaking havoc on opponents' defences
and, when they were not scoring themselves, it would be
Dalglish's strike partner, Johnson, or Souness's midfield partners,
Ray Kennedy and Terry McDermott, who were hitting the
target. Four goals were put past Manchester City at Maine Road,
and four were also notched at Norwich and Bolton. Liverpool
moved effortlessly to the top of the table and by early in the
New Year it was clear that no one was going to catch them. The
whole team had got into the habit of getting stronger and
stronger as the season progressed. During this phase of his
career, Ray never tired of playing however many games he was
asked to compete in.

The season finished with Liverpool and Nottingham Forest
changing roles. Forest were now the European Champions and
Liverpool had retaken the League, with Forest eight points
behind, finishing as runners-up. Liverpool's championship statistics included the best-ever defensive record. Ray Clemence had
kept a clean sheet in twenty-seven of the forty-two games, and
Liverpool had conceded sixteen goals throughout the whole
season; only three teams scored more than a single goal against
them. The full record was:

Home: P21 – Won – 19, Drawn – 2, Lost – 0
        Goals for – 51, Goals against – 4

                                          Total Points: 68

Away: P21 – Won – 11, Drawn – 6, Lost – 4,
        Goals for – 34, Goals against – 12

The season had confirmed that Keegan had been successfully
replaced by Dalglish, Toshack by Johnson and Callaghan by
Souness.

Liverpool advanced smoothly in the FA Cup, reaching the
semi-finals without conceding a goal against Southend United,
Blackburn Rovers, Burnley and Ipswich Town. In the semi-final
they met Manchester United who, two seasons previously, had
denied them the League and Cup Double. In a game which they

should have won easily and in which Terry McDermott missed a penalty, Liverpool were eventually saved by a late Alan Hansen equalizer for a 2–2 draw. However, in the replay at Goodison Park, Manchester United, who had been beaten 3–0 and 2–0 in the League, were again to prove Liverpool's downfall in the Cup, with Jimmy Greenhoff scoring United's winner.

Throughout the season, Paisley used only fifteen players, with Sammy Lee and David Fairclough playing no more than a handful of matches between them. The season was also to see the departure of Emlyn Hughes to Wolves; his old adversary, Tommy Smith, had already gone to John Toshack's Swansea at the start of the season. The twelve 'regulars' in the side were: Ray Clemence, Phil Neal, Alan Kennedy, Phil Thompson, Ray Kennedy, Jimmy Case, Terry McDermott, Alan Hansen, Graeme Souness, Kenny Dalglish, David Johnson and Steve Heighway. Many of the more long-serving and obsessive supporters at Liverpool regard this side as the best that has ever represented the club and the midfield of Case, Kennedy, Souness and McDermott as the finest ever seen in Europe. As one supporter said to me, 'It was like an iron curtain stretched across the pitch, nobody, however good, could get past the four of them!' All four were strongly task-orientated, with ferocious shots and great competitiveness. However, each had his own additional gifts which, when united, produced an impregnable defence and a superb ball-winning machine.

Terry McDermott was a Scouser born in Kirkby who played football at school with John Conteh, ex-boxing World Champion. As a nine-year-old he used to watch Liverpool from the Kop but, after signing professional forms with Bury, he made his reputation with Newcastle United. When he started out as an apprentice, he was so skinny that the coaches built him up with a raw egg, cod liver oil and malt diet. McDermott arrived at Anfield a few months after Ray and, for much of 1975, both were languishing in the reserve side regretting their transfers. McDermott was underestimated at Liverpool. When he first arrived at Anfield, Paisley complained that he tended to doze off and lose concentration in a game and that he was too nervous, but with regular training this improved. He had a brilliant first touch and was a superb passer of the ball, frequently finding Ray Kennedy out on the left. During his Anfield career he scored many spectacular goals and his worth was appreciated by his fellow professionals, if not as much as it should have been by the fans or the England selectors. His playful temperament would also help to lighten the atmosphere in the dressing room. He made more than three hundred appearances for Liverpool and scored seventy-five goals.

Terry McDermott on Ray Kennedy:

Ray and I were both stuck in the reserves for a while and we both wanted to get away. We were quite close and used to change next to one another. One day I remember John Smith, the Liverpool chairman, coming round as usual to wish us well before the game. He would always ask us about the family and one day Ray, fed up with what he felt was an insincere routine, replied to Smith, 'My house has burnt down, the wife's run off and the kids are critically ill, otherwise I'm great'. If I remember rightly John Smith just answered, 'Oh, good!'.

I played on the opposite side of the park to Ray and we both hated the Kemlyn Road flank. If I played there in the first half and they were moaning, I'd warn Ray at half-time and we would have a laugh. There was one man with a loud voice who we both could hear and who would shout at Ray, 'Get going, you lazy sod'. Ray was a player like Chris Waddle, who always gave the impression of looking as if he was tired out and not that interested.

Ray was a smart dresser at Liverpool and very into money because he enjoyed the good life. Off the pitch he could be niggly, especially after a few drinks. His size was frightening. Ray and I went up to Newcastle once and went into a club. I stayed downstairs and Ray went up. Five minutes later a fellow came down with blood streaming from his nose; Ray had hit him. In practice matches he'd sometimes lose his rag and I remember him even having a go at Phil Thompson in an England training session.

After Ray had left Liverpool I kept making my usual runs into the box, expecting the ball to be there as it always had been, but it never came. I missed him and was soon on my way too.

Ray Kennedy on Terry McDermott:

He was the joker in the pack and you couldn't take him too seriously. In the dressing room he was always trying to flog things. Emlyn Hughes got to know Red Rum's trainer, Ginger McCain. At that time he was just starting off, literally keeping horses in his garage. One day the two of them came into the changing room and asked us all if we wanted to buy a share in one of McCain's horses. There was a unanimous 'No'. Later Terry and Emlyn went to inspect their horse with McCain. On arrival at the meadow McCain whistled to his steeds, all of which came running except one. Hughes then asked which of the horses was theirs and McCain pointed to the one lying down listlessly at the bottom of the field, which was called Simmering. The joke in the dressing room was that Terry had the front end and Emlyn the back. On its first outing, Simmering burst its intestines and had to be destroyed!

Terry was so nervy he couldn't sit still. He would drive Tommy Smith wild with his squeaking and restlessness. When Terry and I were both struggling in the reserves they used to call him Terry 'Gone Off', after the German star Reiner Bonhof. In Europe Jimmy and I used to chase Terry and make him give us his passport. He had had his hair cut too straight in the photograph and looked like a German spy. One day Jimmy and I chased him to his room. He locked the door on us, but we said we wouldn't go away until he let us have the passport. After a few minutes Terry slid it out under the door.

Graeme Souness was born in humble circumstances in an Edinburgh prefab. He was the playmaster of the four, straight-talking, reliable, and arrogant on and off the field of play. More than any of his midfield colleagues, he hated to lose. He was a great ball winner and an accurate passer who scored fifty-six goals for Liverpool in three hundred and fifty games and won thirty-seven caps for Scotland. He also had a sense of humour, particularly when relaxing after a game. One day when Terry McDermott came to training with a cold sore on his lip, Souness arranged for imitation stick-on cold sores to be provided for the rest of the team. Among his colleagues, Souness had the reputa-tion of being the one who would always be there to help them out if they were in difficulties and he would never shirk his responsibilities, however difficult or distasteful.

Graeme Souness on Ray Kennedy:

> Ray was very underrated at Liverpool. He was never spectacu-
> lar but had a good attitude and was very dependable. He was
> a hard worker although it didn't always show to the fans, and
> when he was on the park there was always the threat of goals.
> Some of the fans saw him as a work horse which was unfair,
> and others said he was lazy, which was nonsense. He had a
> great eye and was good at closing people down so he didn't
> have to run that much. We were the best midfield ever. He
> and Jimmy Case had the closest relationship I have ever seen
> between two footballers. Ray was also one of the people I got
> on well with during our playing days.

Ray Kennedy on Graeme Souness:

> I had great respect for Graeme. He was a good professional
> and very, very tough, but he had to be. When Graeme joined
> Liverpool it was the 'icing on the cake' for our team. It was to
> make my job that much easier. Graeme roomed with Kenny
> Dalglish, but he was always a man alone and I never mixed
> that closely with him socially.

Jimmy Case, like McDermott, was another local lad who was
encouraged to play football by his mother. On coming to
Liverpool as a nineteen-year-old, he insisted on finishing his
electrician's apprenticeship at Evans Medical, Speke, which certainly hampered his progress and led to a frenetic life style. At
Springwood Primary School he played football with John
Gidman, the Manchester United, Everton, Aston Villa and England international. Ian Callaghan came to the school to present
medals to the two youngsters. As a schoolboy at Toxteth High
School, Case was missed by Tom Saunders, the schoolmaster
turned Liverpool scout. Despite being somewhat underdeveloped
physically, he joined a dockers' Blue Union Club in Liverpool and
did so well playing against full-grown men that he advanced
quickly to the spawning ground of South Liverpool FC, where
he was finally spotted by Saunders. At Liverpool, he first played
as a striker before moving to a wide midfield position and,
although he never gained international honours, he was voted
European Young Footballer of the Year by the Italian sports
writers. Case was aggressive, industrious, a good passer and had

a devastating shot. He gained a reputation as the Liverpool hard man, following in the football steps of Tommy Smith, usually playing in the role of an old-fashioned inside forward. Like Kennedy, Case was something of a European specialist, thriving on man-to-man marking. He scored forty-five goals in two hundred and thirty-six appearances for Liverpool.

Jimmy Case on Ray Kennedy:

> When I came into the first team, Ray had already been there and done it all. Of all the first team players at the time he seemed to be the one from whom I could learn most and I asked specifically to share rooms with him on away trips. We became best mates and are to this day.
>
> On the pitch we had a good relationship. I remember once I had the ball on the far right and out of the corner of my eye I could see Ray with his hand on his chest as if to say 'I want it here'. I just let go with a cross field ball and he brought it down in one move, headed towards goal and slammed it into the net.

Ray Kennedy on Jimmy Case:

> I have always picked my friends very carefully, and Jimmy Case and I built our lives round one another at Liverpool. The way we worked it out was that if the two of us stuck together we would be a stronger force than if isolated. Each of us would be there to help the other out in difficulties and Jimmy was able to calm me down in difficult situations. We were an explosive mix and when we went out together something always seemed to get out of control. On European trips we liked to explore restaurants and taste good wine and would often go off on our own.
>
> I remember some funny things involving Jimmy on the pitch. One time he was taking a corner, and he fell over and hit the ball with his face. Another time we got set for a free-kick move with Jimmy taking the kick out on the right. Jimmy's kick came flying past us all, straight to their full back, who passed it to their centre forward, who scored from our free kick. We had some laughs about that later.

Bob Paisley, in his autobiography, was to name the 1978–9 side as the best championship side he had been associated with in

forty years at Liverpool. Significantly, they had clinched the
League title for their boss on 8 May, the day that commemorated
Paisley's fortieth anniversary with the club.

11 Jimmy Case

Let me tell you the story of a poor boy
Who was sent far away from his home
To fight for his King and his Country
And also the old folks back home

They put him in a higher division
Sent him off to a far foreign land
Where the flies swarm round in their thousands
And there's nothing to see but the sand

The battle started next morning
Under the Arabian sun
So remember that poor Scouser Tommy
Who was shot by an old Nazi gun

As he lay on the battlefield dying, dying, dying
With the blood gushing out of his head
As he lay on the battlefield dying, dying, dying
These are the last words he said

Oh I am a Liverpudlian
From the Spion Kop
I like to sing, I like to shout
I go there quite a lot
I support a team that play in red
A team that you all know
A team that we call Liverpool
To glory we will go

(KOP CHOIR)

THE 1979–80 European campaign proved to be almost a rerun of the previous season. Nottingham Forest were the new holders of the European Cup and, after meeting them in a difficult first round game the previous season, Liverpool were hoping for an easy tie to settle them back into European competition. However, the draw could not have been worse, for Liverpool were set to play against the tough and skilful Georgians, Dynamo Tbilisi. In the first leg at Anfield, with both Ray Kennedy and Alan Hansen unavailable through injury, Paisley was forced to select a makeshift midfield with Jimmy Case on the left, Colin Irwin and David Fairclough. Fifteen minutes before kick-off, the Georgians came out and fearlessly put on a show of superb passing skills in front of the Kop. The game proved to be a battle, with the Liverpool midfield struggling against Shenegliya and Gutsaev. The Liverpool camp at the end of the game felt fortunate to have finished with a slender 2–1 advantage.

The return leg proved to be one of the most gruelling and testing ties ever played by a Liverpool side. The Russians refused to allow Barney and the Aer Lingus plane onto Russian soil and insisted that the flight should first stop in Moscow, even after Liverpool had chartered an Aeroflot flight to take them from Speke. Liverpool were accommodated in a seedy hotel and awakened at 4 a.m. by rowdy, subversive Dynamo fans. Ray had recovered from his knee ligament injury and was back in the side. Liverpool hung on to their slender lead for fifty minutes, but were then hit with three second half goals. On the night, Liverpool looked outmoded and were literally outclassed.

After the game Paisley uncharacteristically criticized his squad, saying that individually the team were worth very little. While the customary post-match speeches were going on, downstairs the London press were already slating Liverpool's performance. Liverpool were toasted by their hosts with sour champagne and caviare. David Johnson, who had never tasted the Caspian delicacy before, came over to Jimmy Case and said, 'Stay clear of that black jam, it tastes of fish'. After the speeches were finished, Jimmy and Ray went downstairs. On spying the press, Case saw red and went over to the table where they were sitting. He cleared the table of glasses and then went up to each of the journalists in turn saying, 'I don't like you, I don't like you, I don't like you, you're all right, I don't like you'. Before he knew it, Jimmy had been hit full on the chin by Ray and the two had a set-to by the door, with Ray warning Jimmy that he was out of control. They went back, apologized and bought the press fresh drinks. After about thirty minutes, however, Jimmy's anger flared up again, and he raged that if the journalists didn't believe what he was telling them he would gouge their eyes out. This time,

Ray hit him solidly in the solar plexus and carried him out of the room on his shoulder, saving his mate from front-page notoriety and inevitable punitive disciplinary action from the club. Once Jimmy had come to his senses, they went off for a drink together.

Jimmy and Ray were always ready to help one another out, and were frequently involved in schoolboy intrigues. At Arsenal, Ray had been introduced by Frank McLintock and George Graham to 'Fat' Stan Flashman, king of the ticket touts and now the beleaguered chairman of Barnet Football Club. Flashman in those days would always be available to relieve the players of their unwanted tickets, and many by this means derived a welcome, though illegal, injection to their wages. When Ray lived in London, he had visited Flashman's home in Whetstone and had tea and cake with Flashman and his Scottish wife, who was as thin as her husband was rotund. Flashman often rang him up to see if he could supply tickets. On moving to Liverpool, Ray kept the contact, and Flashman would send his congenitally dumb messenger up north to collect Ray's tickets. Before the FA Cup Final against Manchester United, Ray had collected the complimentary tickets from six players to sell to Flashman. The handover took place at St George's Hotel in the centre of Liverpool, where a room had been hired by Flashman. Ray went in with the tickets while Jimmy guarded the exit and prepared a quick getaway by car. A fee of £33,000 had been agreed by the two parties, but on counting the money, Ray found it was £2,000 short. Flashman signalled to his mute accomplice and pulled out a wad of notes from his pocket to make up the missing amount. Ray remembers being terrified that they had been set up and would be mugged as soon as they stepped out of the room. Ray and Jimmy left hastily by the back door to drop off the loot at each player's home. Although the practice of selling tickets for pecuniary gain has come under increasing surveillance, it remains common.

Ray remembers:

> Jimmy and I had a lot of fun together. At Ipswich we climbed through an open hotel window and turned Ray Clemence and Phil Neal's beds upside down. Because they had their room keys with them they couldn't work out how it had happened. On another occasion we crawled along the veranda and set up a lamp standard so that we could switch it on and off from

outside their room. When the two of them got into bed and the light started flashing on and off they couldn't believe it and kept blaming one another.

On a pre-season tour of Switzerland, Germany and Austria, after the first game in Basel, Jimmy and Ray met one of Jimmy's acquaintances, who introduced them to some American girls working in Switzerland. Ray immediately hit it off with one of them and asked Jimmy for all his spending money for the night. On arriving at the girl's flat, Ray was astonished to find the living room full of dental plates and sets of teeth, and learned that his companion was a dental nurse. Later, on the tour in Austria, Ray and Jimmy came down the tunnel at half-time and saw the girl, standing with her suitcase, talking to John Smith, the Liverpool chairman, and asking if she could meet the players. Ray and Jimmy beat a hasty retreat and sent her some chocolates after the game.

Football takes players to strange places. Before Ray and Jimmy knew it, trouble would brew up, with fights and dangerous liaisons with women. Small-time businessmen and people who have never quite made it would incorporate them into their fantasies or use them as 'The Face' to promote their interests. Brushes with the criminal fraternity were also common, and Liverpool players living in the city itself were always at risk of being burgled or having their car scratched. Many of the hangers-on would seem as nice as pie at first, but not infrequently Jimmy and Ray ended up being used or ripped off in some way.

In the League Cup, after cruising into the semi-finals, Liverpool were again eliminated by Nottingham Forest, largely as a result of a superb piece of goalkeeping by Shilton. The 1979–80 League season had also got off to an uninspiring start, with a goalless draw against Bolton Wanderers, only two victories from the first seven games, and defeats at Southampton and Nottingham Forest. Ray continued to be troubled with a niggling knee ligament injury and missed some of the early games. The poor start to the season was blamed by many on his absence. He was flattered by these comments, but had his own interpretation for the poor start:

I've watched our last two games and they've been pretty boring. The players have stopped moving for each other.

People are saying Liverpool are breaking up at last. That will come sooner or later but this isn't it. When this side is on song I reckon it's the best in my time here. It's got everything. None of the present leaders of the League bother me. At the moment we are idling in second gear.

Ray's assessment was to prove correct, and Liverpool went through to mid-January without further defeats. Anfield remained an impregnable fortress; the team spirit was revealed at Norwich on 9 February when, with nine minutes to go, Justin Fashanu scored the goal of the season to put the Canaries back on level terms three-all, but Liverpool, never beaten until the final whistle, scored twice more, through the efforts of Case and Dalglish, to win 5–3.

Alan 'Barney' Kennedy, bought from Sunderland in 1978, had by now established himself as the regular left back and, by daring raids down the flank, was occasionally rewarded with crucial goals. Ray never considered his namesake, also a Geordie, to be qualified to play for Liverpool, despite his superb commitment and fighting spirit. In Ray's opinion, Alan did not have the natural skill and ability to hold down a regular place. When he first came into the side, Ray had to help him by covering back and reinforcing the left defence.

He took five years off my career. Whenever I wanted a short ball, he'd hit it long. If it should have been long, I'd get a short pass. Alan had no nerves and not much brain, which was why he was lethal at penalties. I didn't dislike him, but we didn't gel on the pitch.

As the season built to a head in March, with Liverpool contesting the League and FA Cup, Ray and Jimmy Case found themselves in much deeper trouble than in the Soviet Union. Liverpool, after defeating Everton 2–1 in the League, had gone away for a few days' break to the Bryn Howell Hotel near Llangollen. Since the New Year, Ray had been fighting, with some success, a return of the frustration and loss of enthusiasm which had blighted his later career at Arsenal. This was in part due to his increasing disenchantment with the England international set-up, where for the last two years he had been a regular in the squad, but was almost invariably passed over when the team was picked. For the first time he had begun to dread training at Melwood, and had to force himself to get up in the morning. This had come to a head earlier in the year when he had confronted Bob Paisley and, with his customary frankness, told the manager that he felt like quitting. Paisley had Ray's trust, and cunningly was able to convince him that he was just going through a bad patch and it was all in his mind. Ray now says:

> My mind kept going back to Arsenal in the season after the Double, where I couldn't swallow the success. Instead of getting stuck into my game at that time I'd got stuck into food. Piles of it, crisps, chocolate and stuff, you name it and I ate it, and why? Although I didn't realize it at the time, I was lonely. On the pitch it had all been too easy, but off it I couldn't cope. At Anfield I'd begun to feel like that again, but Bob Paisley saved me for the second time.

Ray was looking forward to a few days' relaxation in the Dee valley, and the hotel had a reputation for excellent food and wine. Jimmy Case had been fishing with Albert Lloyd, the owner of the hotel, on a number of occasions. On the first evening most of the players rushed down to dinner, but Ray and Jimmy took longer and, when they did come down, they spent time enjoying their meal over two bottles of Chablis. Terry McDermott, who never ate much more than a beef sandwich, had already finished eating, and Ray asked him to let them know when the others were going to leave for the pub. However, when they left the dining room, everyone except Roy Evans and Ronnie Moran had already gone. Ray and Jimmy went into the lounge, where they had one or two drinks and were joined by Phil Thompson and Mr Lloyd. Ray and Jimmy then moved to another pub, driven in the team coach, and arrived back at the hotel in the early hours. At two in the morning, when most of the team had already gone to bed, Ray and Jimmy were drinking at the bar with Mr Lloyd and his son. Terry McDermott suddenly appeared and Ray grabbed him by the throat in a fury, demanding to know why he had not told them when the others were leaving. At the same moment the phone rang and the landlord's son asked Ray whether his name was Alan. Ray, who was sensitive about being confused with his namesake, lost control and punched him. Mr Lloyd tried to protect his son and was also sent flying. The two players left the room, but returned a few minutes later; Ray hit

Terry McDermott and then launched into the landlord's son again. Jimmy shouted, 'We're all sticking together', picked up a chair and threw it at the landlord. The police then arrived, and Jimmy and Ray were taken into custody. Ray was put in a Ford Escort police car, but Jimmy was taken, screaming and shouting, to the station in the police dog van by a big ginger-haired policeman who elbowed and belittled him in front of a woman PC. Ray yelled for Joe Fagan and Ronnie Moran to help him and the two coaches accompanied Ray down to the station in the police car. Ronnie Moran stayed with Ray, who was sitting quietly in his cell. Meanwhile, Jimmy was hammering on the cell walls, shouting 'Let me out'. He was so incensed, his head seemed to be bouncing off the ceiling. Ronnie Moran berated them for their stupidity. Ray retaliated by claiming that Moran's stressful training sessions at Melwood were responsible. Someone in the police station then retorted, 'Well, you should know, Ray, you were at Arsenal!'. Joe Fagan, who was locked in with Jimmy, was desperately trying to calm him down. After about an hour, Moran and Fagan returned to the hotel.

The following morning the players were released but were not allowed to join the rest of the team. Instead they went into Wrexham and checked into a hotel. Jimmy, who was still half-drunk, shouted, 'Who's the good time girl in this hotel? Wake her up'. Later in the day Ray went for a walk and, when he got back, Jimmy asked him if he had located any good restaurants in Wrexham. When Ray said, 'No', Jimmy replied, 'Do you want me to build one then?'. The two of them then went off to play golf, but spotted a *Sun* journalist, so they turned round and started to walk up the hill backwards so they would not be recognized.

A month later, in front of press and television cameras, they pleaded guilty to causing an affray and were fined £150 each and costs. At the trial Jimmy was jumpy, but Ray appeared calm and collected. Other minor skirmishes were to occur when they were together in pubs and Chinese restaurants in Liverpool, but neither of them let the trouble off the pitch interfere with their Liverpool performances, and Liverpool finished the season losing only three of their last eighteen games, all narrow away defeats at Wolves, Spurs and Middlesbrough. Ray maintained his excellent disciplinary record on the pitch.

Avi Cohen, the Israeli international, who was never able to

establish a regular place in the Liverpool defence, made his home debut in the match against Aston Villa on 3 May 1980. After Johnson had scored a goal in the third minute, Cohen got off to an inauspicious start, scoring an own goal. Twenty minutes later, however, he raced up the pitch and drove home a low cross from Dalglish into the far corner of Villa's net to restore Liverpool's lead. Liverpool then asserted their authority, playing the highly skilled attacking football with which they had opened a substantial mid-season points gap, and Johnson scored again with a fierce shot in the seventy-second minute. Six minutes later, Kennedy brought the game to a rousing climax with a graceful header that Blake could only help into his own net. Meanwhile, Manchester United had lost 2–0 to Leeds United, thereby handing the League Championship to Liverpool. The Liverpool side now virtually selected itself again, with Johnson partnering Dalglish up front. Fairclough continued to make sporadic appearances, and towards the end of the season Sammy Lee, the diminutive local lad, broke into the side for a few games. Liverpool finished as the highest scoring side in the First Division with eighty-one goals, Johnson claiming twenty-one and Dalglish sixteen. The Liverpool midfield also chipped in with their now expected contribution: Kennedy scored nine goals, McDermott, ten, Case, three and Souness, one.

In the FA Cup, after beating Grimsby Town, Liverpool astonishingly came up against Nottingham Forest again and at last avenged their numerous Cup defeats, seeing off Forest 2–0 at their own City Ground. The Reds then beat Bury at home 2–0, and in the quarter-finals went to Spurs and won 1–0, with a volley from Terry McDermott seeing them into the last four. The semi-final against Arsenal was to be one of the most gruelling encounters ever to occur in the FA Cup. The first game at Hillsborough ended goalless, and two games at Villa Park, with extra time, both ended one-all. Finally, after seven and a half hours of football, watched by 168,000 fans, in which only five goals had been scored, Arsenal went through to the final with a 1–0 victory at Highfield Road, Coventry. Everton also went out after a replay with West Ham and so the final, which had been tipped to be an all-Merseyside affair, became an all-London derby, and Ray Kennedy was again denied the chance of fulfilling his dream of a double Double. The decade ended with Paisley having collected silverware in five of his six seasons as manager. On the advice of the Liverpool scout, Geoff Twentyman, Paisley also gambled on the £300,000 transfer of a young Welsh striker with only a handful of games for Chester under his belt. Over the next decade, Ian Rush would score goals to emulate any scored by former Kop heroes and become one of the greatest strikers ever to play for the club. Steve Heighway was gradually fading from the scene, after playing three hundred and thirty-one games and scoring more than fifty goals.

A certain type of woman is attracted to the glamorous high-profile life and athletic prowess of professional football players, and each player attracts his own following. Bob Wilson was said to attract a rather more mature, sophisticated group of admirers, whereas Best was kept sane on his own admission by romantic encounters with more than a thousand attractive and willing girls throughout the sixties and early seventies. Most football players have a classical double standard with respect to their attitudes to sex. On marrying, they endeavour to become loving husbands, caring deeply about their wives and children but, at the same time, avail themselves of the ample sexual opportunities that come their way. Group sessions are not uncommon and one that Ray was involved in during a trip to Amsterdam led to two of his recently decorated colleagues being reproved by another, 'If only The Queen could see you now'. Most women on meeting Ray were captivated by his good looks, his charm and his endearing shyness. Beatrice, the air hostess on the Aer Lingus charter who got to know Ray quite well, described him as:

> A big affable Geordie who was strong, muscular and sturdy. Underneath his broad, macho veneer there was a soft, gentle human being. We struck up a friendship from almost the first flight which lasted for seven years, but was never an affair. Any girl would have fallen for his swarthy Mediterranean good looks and his easy manner. He was quiet and shy which I found endearing, and it was always my impression that he was chased by women rather than that he was a womanizer. He always spoke fondly of his mother.

He also spoke fondly about Janet, who was now a teenage model. One particularly persistent lady from Germany would follow Ray round the world and even turned up on the beach when Ray was on holiday in the Mediterranean with his wife.

Controversy continues to rage as to whether sex before matches weakens a player. Particularly in Italy, players are kept in seclusion for several days before an important game, away from their wives or girlfriends. Shankly's view was: 'Of course a player can have sexual intercourse before a match and play a blinder. But if he did it for six months, he would be a decrepit old man. It takes the strength from the body'. Shankly would sometimes ring up the wives of his players the day before a big game and, after giving them all the same story about how wonderful their husbands were, beg them to deny conjugal rights for the sake of the club. Ray's view mirrors that of Charlie Nicholas, who said that if sex ruins your game then most married players would be out of a job.

Ray had reached the zenith of his career. He had maintained his trim physique, was much more confident and now felt that his mind was completely attuned with the movement of his body. He had become an essential part of the Liverpool team and his achievements were acknowledged by Jimmy Greaves, who acclaimed him the English player of the 1970s. Greaves explained his surprising choice:

> Kennedy collected votes as a midfield schemer and as a striker. He has proved himself world class in both positions. Liverpool never functions as smoothly without him patrolling the midfield and coming through as an auxiliary striker when the opposition least expect it. There is a famine of outstanding left-sided players in our game and I fail to understand why he has not won more England caps.

Professional football is permeated with fear and insecurity and everyone, from manager to scout, is constantly looking over their shoulder. To survive any length of time one must learn to be ruthless, calculating and self-centred. Although the best football clubs are run like an extended family, they are also microcosms of a capitalist society. Someone has to lose in life for the system to survive, and only the winners grow and thrive. Pursuit of dishonest advantage, in a business where decisions have to be made as rapidly as on the stock market, has become an accepted practice. The players, too, must become focused on self-survival or return to the anonymity whence they came. In this environment, although superficial working relationships and camaraderie are commonplace, true friendships are hard to foster. Getting on with one's colleagues is one thing, but forging deeper bonds based on shared interests is quite another. Successful players have powerful urges to dominate when they are on the field of play, and a team-mate one year may be an opponent the next. Although most players will conceal these drives with a veneer of modesty and self-effacement, they are never far from the surface. A player must see the team he represents as part of his own persona — victory for the team becomes a victory for him — and the stronger these feelings of interrelation and group identity, the more effective the team will be. Eamon Dunphy explains the mechanics:

> If you take two players who work together in midfield, they will know each other through football as intimately as two lovers. It is an unspoken relationship, but your movements speak, your game speaks. You don't necessarily become closer in the social sense, but you develop an unspoken understanding.

Ray Kennedy and Jimmy Case fitted this model closely, but in addition there was a binding friendship and empathy which linked their working lives for nearly seven years. Both men shared a northern working-class background, both had two brothers and a sister, and both had fathers who did not excel at football. Case's father was a boxer and rugby player who worked as a fitter's mate on the railways. Perhaps more significantly, both men had mothers who were highly ambitious for their children. Like Veronica, Jimmy's mother also spent the last penny of her bingo earnings on football boots. However, Jimmy Case had had an inner city upbringing and was a home-town boy who had supported Liverpool throughout his childhood. Even now, after more than ten years away from the club and a disinclination to return to Merseyside to live, Case is still drawn to Anfield, embraced by the mutual respect he and his contemporaries had for one another and sustained by his achievements. Case's father still drops off trout for the Liverpool boot room in gratitude for all they did to help his son.

When Ray arrived, Jimmy was still a part-time apprentice. He

was singularly impressed by the way Ray carried himself, by his
professionalism, his basic decency and his financial freedom
which had allowed him to buy a house in Ainsdale without the
club's help. The two players came over to others as shy, rather
retiring characters, and both preferred to sit back and size up a
situation before acting. In some ways they were short on self-
confidence, yet both possessed a latent aggression and anger
which emerged to great effect on the football pitch and occasionally with catastrophic results off it. Neither were born leaders in
the Tommy Smith mould and tended to shy away from taking
responsibility or meting out discipline to others. Jimmy Case was
very much the junior partner, and to this day Ray advises him on
professional decisions. The good habits instilled by Arsenal were
serving Ray well, although he rarely spoke to Jimmy about his
London period.

Case and Kennedy got to know each other particularly well on
the many away trips in Europe and always used to sit together
near the back of the plane on the left. Both got on well with
Barney and were frequently invited into the cockpit of the Aer
Lingus plane. On some of these trips the spare seats were filled
by Liverpool VIPs, and Barney would liven up the flight with
bogus announcements of engine failure, or that he was enjoying
his fifth whiskey.

When Ray arrived from Arsenal, the Liverpool squad all
assumed he was particularly well versed in European travel and
would follow him off the plane like sheep. Ray played on this
and on one occasion led the whole Liverpool contingent, including John Smith, a director, into a public lavatory.

Before going to sleep Ray would always read a book; he
particularly enjoyed the spy thrillers of Le Carré and Frederick
Forsyth. He and Jimmy shared a love for cloak and dagger
intrigues and were always on the lookout for some conspiracy or
mystery to solve, especially where the machinations of the
directors and coaches were involved. Muhammad Ali was their
hero and they would read books about him late into the night,
admiring 'The Greatest's' ability to promote himself and deal
with the media.

They were the tidiest and best organized of all the Liverpool
players, and were prepared for every contingency on the away
trips, with needle and thread, tin openers and pen knives. They

usually took their own supply of food in case the local menus were unpalatable. They cleaned each other's shoes, brushed and ironed each other's clothes and were ever alert to remove dust or scales from one another's jacket collars. On arrival at a European destination, one of them would explore the neighbourhood near the hotel to select the best restaurant for the evening meal and then they would both go on a shopping spree, always bringing back something original for their families. Ray had a particular fondness for buying good quality leather shoes. After sampling the local night-life, the two would frequently end up alone in the pre-selected restaurant drinking an expensive wine and savouring the best cuisine. They acquired a genuine taste for good food, and Ray particularly was interested in learning about new dishes. One day, on a holiday trip to Blackpool with the Liverpool team, all the players were dining in a restaurant when Joe Fagan came up to the table where the two friends were dining. He looked at Ray and said: 'We know Phil and Terry will be in a night club, Emlyn and his party are off to a restaurant, but where will you two be?' Ray and Jimmy had developed a reputation for eccentric and unpredictable behaviour.

Jimmy continued to live in South Liverpool and was constantly under pressure from fanatical supporters. Even if he took a trip to the end of the road to visit the shops, he would often end up in several heated discussions about the previous week's game. Like all players, Case and Kennedy had to learn to deal tactfully with the petty jealousies, the threats and the snide remarks they encountered every day. They learned to sign autographs graciously, handing the book or programme back in a particular way to avoid reprisals, or accusations of disinterestedness. Liverpool players were public property and Jimmy particularly bore the brunt of this, with Ray on safer soil in Southport.

Despite their closeness in the team, they did not mix at all socially; they rarely visited one another's homes and were unaware of one another's family life – neither had much clue what the other did once he got home. Malcolm Sale, one of Ray's old pals from the Arsenal days, who renewed his contact with Ray after a Spurs match at Anfield, told me that when he went up to Southport for an evening out with Ray and some of the London lads, Jimmy would never come out with them. Malcolm noticed subtle changes in Ray's behaviour, in that fame had made him a little more distanced from them, at least in the presence of the club. Malcolm was impressed by Ray's contacts in the city; frequently they were treated to free meals · in restaurants even when they were closed to the public.

In some respects a similarity existed between the Kennedy-Case partnership and that forged with Peter Taylor and Brian Clough during their playing days at Middlesbrough. Originally, Taylor, like Ray, was the father figure, but as the relationship developed, the roles became more intertwined and confused. Taylor describes the two men's partnership in Tony Francis's biography, *Clough*:

> We were like an incompatible couple, fatally attracted to one another by a single passion. Football was the love affair we shared, though we had nothing else in common . . . we could have been high on drugs – instead it was football. We became closer friends than anyone will understand.

Clough and Taylor, like many footballers, were intrinsically lonely. Taylor had no friends in Middlesbrough during his playing days and Clough, although surrounded by his family, felt distanced from the rest of the town:

> Young lads have nowhere to go in football. I had a nice home so it wasn't too bad for me, but you've still got to have some mates. The mates I had in Middlesbrough worked from 8 a.m. to 6 p.m. No mates were there at half past twelve when I finished work.

Ray Kennedy, aged twenty-nine, entered the 1980s by signing a new four-year contract with Liverpool, which would effectively tie him to the club until the end of his career. Don Howe, his old Arsenal coach, assessed Ray's career at that point:

> Ray has this superb control. He never seems to be going full out. You never see him have to sprint after the ball or chase back after a break. That's the mark of a top class midfielder. If there is anybody in the League I would bet to keep his cool and hit the mark when needed, it would be Ray. He is better than anyone at that including Dalglish.

Liverpool got off to a poor start again in their League

programme, winning only three out of their first seven games
and, in contrast to the previous year, failed to accelerate later on.
In fact, it was not to be Liverpool's year largely due to a dearth
of goals; Terry McDermott was the only player to get into
double figures. Although Liverpool lost only eight games, the
same as the 1980–1 League Champions, Aston Villa, they ended
the season with seventeen draws and finished a disappointing
fifth, their lowest position since Ray had joined the club. Paisley
blamed this on the high injury rate and the unsettled side. In
January, after eighty-five home games without defeat, they were
beaten by bottom of the League Leicester City, 2–1. In December,
against a powerful Ipswich Town side, Ian Rush made his League
debut. His overriding recollection of the game is of Souness,
breathing fire with his fists clenched at half-time, ably supported
by Joe Fagan and Ronnie Moran. After a Liverpool half-time pep
talk, the players often came out feeling superhuman. Another
man to make his debut in the 1980–1 year was Ronnie Whelan,
signed for a pittance from the Irish club, Home Farm.

In spite of their capricious form in the League, Liverpool got
off to a reasonable start in the European Cup. In the first round
they met the part-timers from Finland Oulun Palloseura in freezing weather in a small stadium surrounded by a running track.
Liverpool were only able to manage a one-all draw away, with a
goal from Terry McDermott; in the return leg, however, they hit
ten goals to their opponents' one, with Souness scoring a hat
trick and Ray chipping in with a sixty-sixth-minute goal. The
Finnish goalkeeper came in after the game looking as if his
mother had just died and thankful that the team did not have to
play Liverpool every week. In the next round Liverpool had
much stronger competition from Alex Ferguson's Aberdeen team,
which was loaded with experienced Scottish internationals. At
Pittodrie in the Granite City, Liverpool scored early through
McDermott and then closed up their defence to win 1–0. Back at
Anfield, Aberdeen were hit by Dalglish and Hansen, who both
scored in a 4–0 victory. In the third round, Liverpool faced the
Bulgarians, CSKA Sofia, who had looked a useful side in dispos-
ing of the European Champions, Notts Forest, in an earlier round.
In the first leg at Anfield, despite some good play by the
Bulgarians, Liverpool won 5–1, with Souness excelling with a hat
trick of searing shots. In the away leg Johnson gave Liverpool

victory again, with Ray Clemence saving a penalty. This brought
Liverpool to the semi-finals of the competition with three former
multiple winners of the European Cup, Bayern Munich, Inter-
Milan and Real Madrid.

Steady advancement was also occurring in the League Cup, a
trophy which in the twenty years of its existence had never
adorned the Anfield board room. For many years Liverpool had
regarded the Cup as an extra burden to their already crowded
season and considered it a bit of a Mickey Mouse trophy. In the
first round, first leg, against Bradford City from Division Four, it
looked as if Liverpool might go out early again when they
casually lost 1–0 away. They made no mistake in the return,
however, with a 4–0 victory, and they disposed comfortably of
Swindon Town and Portsmouth in the next two rounds. After
quarter-final success against Birmingham City, Liverpool met
Manchester City in the semi-finals. At Maine Road, Ray scored
the winning goal and Liverpool drew one-all at home, putting
them through to play West Ham United at Wembley. Between
the two Manchester City ties Liverpool had gone out of the FA
Cup 2–1 to Everton. West Ham, who had a longstanding
reputation of playing attractive football, fell behind in the final to
a controversial Alan Kennedy goal which he scored with Sammy
Lee lying on the floor in a clearly offside position. However, in
the last minutes of the game, West Ham were awarded a penalty;
Ray Stewart scored to earn them a replay. At Villa Park two
weeks later, the Hammers went ahead with a Paul Goddard goal,
Dalglish equalized and Hansen snatched the winner to give
Liverpool the League Cup for the first time in their history.

Ray Kennedy is probably remembered most in the boot room
at Liverpool for his away performance against Bayern Munich in
the Olympic Stadium in the second leg of the European Cup
semi-final. The two teams had met twice before in European
competition, once in the Fairs Cup and once in the European Cup
Winner's Cup, with honours being even. In the first game at
Anfield, Liverpool, without Souness and Johnson and with McDermott dislocating his finger in the first minute, were held to a
goalless draw. Ray Kennedy also had to have a pain-killing
injection into his right knee ligament injury. After the game, the
charismatic German international Paul Breitner claimed that Liverpool lacked subtlety in their play and relied on pressure to break

down defences. On arrival at the Olympic Stadium for the return, this newspaper cutting was pinned on the Liverpool dressing-room door by the coaching staff to motivate the team.

Ray was rooming as usual with Jimmy Case and now remembers how the night before the game the two of them could hear Paisley, Fagan and Moran downing the Scotch and arguing over the team selection in the room next door well into the early hours. Souness and Phil Thompson were both injured, so Ray was given the captaincy. Disaster struck when Dalglish limped off after a few minutes to be replaced by the inexperienced and unpredictable Howard Gayle. Although the teams went in even at half-time, Gayle had run the German defence ragged and sapped their confidence. However, as he became more and more niggly in the second half, he was substituted, with Jimmy Case coming on. Late in the game, with no score and the tie heading for extra time, David Johnson was struggling with a hamstring injury so Paisley signalled Ray to push forward. Johnson later learned that Paisley was so displeased with this turn of events that he turned to one of the armed guards and said, 'Lend us the gun and I'll shoot the bastard'. Despite his bumbling, benign exterior, Paisley was totally ruthless when it came to Liverpool Football Club. With nine minutes to go, Johnson on the right crossed the ball over the head of a marker to Ray, who coolly brought the ball down and then hit a shot past the keeper with his right foot. As Ronnie Moran was to say afterwards, not only was this a goal with his 'standing peg', but Ray also had the intelligence to bring the ball down and compose himself instead of just hitting it first time. Despite a last-minute equalizer from Rumenigge, the classy and dangerous German striker, Liverpool were through on the away-goal rule.

After the game Paisley singled out Sammy Lee for doing a wonderful man-to-man marking job on Breitner. Breitner retracted the remarks he had made after the earlier game, saying that Liverpool were not unintelligent in their play, it was just that they played simple, straightforward football. Later that night, Ray was toasted as 'The Kaiser' in every beer keller in Munich that he visited. After the game Paisley also paid a tribute to his captain:

Apart from that night in Rome four years earlier I don't think I have ever been so proud of the team. They did Merseyside and England proud and that bit of luck I'd wanted was there in Ray Kennedy, the man whose ability was appreciated far more here in Europe than back home.

Liverpool had now reached their third European Cup Final, which was to be against Real Madrid in Paris. Although much more vulnerable than in their glory days of Puskas and Di Stefano, the Spaniards were still a force to be reckoned with and had in their side Uli Steilike, the former Borussia Mönchengladbach player who had played in the Rome final. They also had former West Bromwich Albion black winger, Laurie Cunningham, a genius on his day, who tragically died ten years later in a road traffic accident in Spain. The Kennedys went to Europe to support Ray, and Trevor remembers the Parc des Princes seeming to move with the swell of the crowd.

In the dressing room before the game, Ray got changed in his usual way, putting on his shirt first, then his shorts followed by his left boot – for such a large man he has a very small seven and a half shoe. Jimmy Case described the dressing-room routine at Liverpool before a game:

> Very few of us showed nerves. We always felt so confident; we often used to work out how many goals we'd win by, not whether we'd win. Terry Mac would watch the racing on television until 2.30, loosen his tie at 2.40 and then go straight out onto the pitch without a warm-up. Alan Hansen would relax so much he'd nod off and be singing 'You don't go changing or re-arranging' just as he went out. Others would be doing press-ups. Ray would usually be quiet, reading a programme. In those days, even when things seemed to be going wrong, we always felt we could sort it out. Ray always liked to follow me out.

The first half of the European Cup Final was tedious and boring, with neither side creating many chances and Clemence having to make only one important save when he cut out a dangerous cross from Cunningham. Real Madrid defended in numbers and cynically when necessary. Alan Kennedy and Dalglish had shots saved, and Ray Kennedy and McDermott shot wide. In the second half, Liverpool were under pressure for long periods, but Thompson and Hansen held firm in the centre of the defence. The dangerous Spanish winger, Juanito, posed little threat as, apparently against his manager's instructions, he played too deep. McDermott was nearly through on one occasion, only to be floored by the inappropriately named Angel just outside the penalty box. As extra time approached, Ray Kennedy pushed aside Sammy Lee in order to take a long throw in. He hurled it towards the byline on the left for left back Alan Kennedy, nicknamed 'Barney Rubble' from the Flintstones, to run on to. Kennedy's namesake went past two despairing tackles, one of which nearly took his legs off, and blasted a superb strike into the far corner of the net when the keeper expected a cross. Apart from the goal it had been a poor final, over-cautious, with the fear factor being eminent. As the travelling Kop choir spilled out into the Paris evening singing 'Gay Paree, Gay Paree', the French press were bemoaning a fourth successive dreary final of what they described as 'chloroform football'. This third European Cup win made Liverpool incontrovertibly the most successful British side in post-war history and, with another medal heading home to Tillmouth Avenue, Ray Kennedy one of their most successful players.

Ray had finished the season with eight League goals; he had also scored what proved to be the winning goal in the semi-final of the League Cup at Maine Road. This was a vintage Kennedy goal with a perfectly timed run to the far side, creating oodles of space and allowing him to finish clinically with a left-foot drive. Ray had been made captain for a few games as a mark of his increasingly vital role in the side. Eddie Marks, an accountant from Ince Blundell, who has occupied the same seat at Anfield for forty years, recalled one hilarious episode when Ray came out leading the side and the rest of the players stayed in the tunnel, leaving him to appreciate the jeers and hoots of laughter alone. Ray was excited about the prospects of bringing the cup back to Liverpool. He joked that now the customary tankards awarded to the winners of the League Cup had been replaced by medals, it was finally worth winning. There had also been further happiness for Ray and Jenny with the birth of their son, Dale, in January.

Ray's remarks at the end of the season are illuminating:

At Liverpool in the last two seasons everything has come together. My brain has co-ordinated with my legs and I go

out on the pitch feeling I could do anything. I have gained an
inner feeling of confidence which I lacked at Arsenal. I see
myself as a steady player who has very few bad games even if
I don't achieve the heights of some of the others here. If I get
five out of ten in the papers on a Sunday I still worry for the
rest of the weekend, but fortunately this doesn't happen very
much these days. I don't set myself targets because you are
only putting more pressure on yourself and every game at
Liverpool is like a cup final anyway. I still get a big kick out of
hitting the back of the net with the ball and begin to worry if
I go a few games without scoring.

However, off the pitch, there had been a court case, and
whispers that Jimmy and Ray were becoming difficult to handle.
Ray had also become so disenchanted with the England international set-up that he had made the sensational decision never
to play for his country again. This was a particular tragedy for a
man who some years earlier had set his heart on a World Cup
winner's medal.

12 Al-bion, Al-bion, Al-bion

They come in at night, leave in the early morning.
I hear their footsteps, the ticking of bicycle chains,
Sudden blasts of motorcycles, whimpering of vans.
Somehow I am either in bed, or the curtains are drawn.

This masculine invisibility makes gods of them,
A pantheon of boots and overalls.
But when you see them, home early from work
Or at their Sunday leisure, they are too tired

And bored to look long at comfortably.
It hurts to see their faces, too sad or too jovial.
They quicken their step at the smell of cooking,
They hold up their children and sing to them.

(DOUGLAS DUNN)

R AY's late call-up by Don Revie for the game against Wales on
24 March 1976 marked one of the most astonishing turn-arounds
in a player's fortunes. Within the space of a few months Kennedy
had metamorphosed from a heavy, increasingly reluctant striker,
proving to be a financial embarrassment, to a sleek, industrious,
perceptive midfielder. Revie had telephoned Paisley at Anfield
and told him Kennedy was in the team and when his boss broke
the news to him at Melwood Ray couldn't believe it: 'I thought
it was a joke. The boss came over to me and asked if I'd like to
play football for England. I was sure he was taking the mickey so
I said "Sure, when do they want me?" It's amazing, I wonder
what's in Don Revie's mind now that I'm playing in a different
position'.

In the absence of both Gerry Francis and Roy McFarland,
Ray's team-mate, Kevin Keegan, who had been nurtured back
into the England fold a year earlier, had his rehabilitation confirmed by his appointment as captain. Clemence, Neal and Thompson made up the Liverpool quintet. Also in the England team
that day was the West Ham midfielder, Trevor Brooking, who
over the next five years was to become a major stumbling block

in Ray's attempt to establish himself on the left of midfield. Kennedy's first game for his country was a resounding success in which he contributed to the 2–1 victory with a debut goal: 'After a wicked shot from a Brooking cross which sizzled past the post, Kennedy broke the deadlock in the seventy-second minute, when Keegan challenged Ian Evans in the air for a powerful Brooking cross which fell to Kennedy who hit it home from the corner of the penalty box'. In his new, deeper midfield role he was able to express completely his exquisite ability to read the course and rhythm of a game apparently effortlessly. Ray's early self-effacement in front of the press, so evident at Arsenal, was now being replaced by a confidence and greater belief in his abilities. He announced: 'The goal I scored tonight is going to make people sit up and take notice. My form since I switched roles can't be a fluke, otherwise I wouldn't be playing for Liverpool, would I?'

Although this had been a depleted England side in some areas, there were no major midfield omissions apart from Gerry Francis. If Ray could keep his Liverpool form he was in with a real chance of securing a regular position in the national side. However, Ray played further games against Wales and Northern Ireland in the Home Internationals before having a poor performance against the Scots, following which he was dropped for the next seven games. He was recalled against Luxembourg in the World Cup qualifying rounds. England won comfortably enough, 5–0, with Ray being singled out by many observers for his composure and measured passes. Revie commented afterwards: 'I'd watched Ray playing for Liverpool in the away tie of the European Cup with St Etienne. He's got a lovely left foot, sees things well and gets goals'.

Ray went with the England squad on their three-match tour of Latin America in June 1977. This was to prove the first of many frustrations in that the many hours of air travel, the days spent cooped up in far-away hotels with nothing to do and the long hours of training with the England squad resulted in about twenty minutes of football for Ray as substitute late in the games against Brazil and Argentina. Most of Ray's memories of this tour relate to off-the-field incidents:

I remember us driving through Buenos Aires in the team coach. I looked back out of the window and saw a car full of armed police escorting us. Trevor Francis pulled back the flexible paper rack on the chair in front of him and let it go suddenly. I thought I'd been shot.

Ray had always had difficulties with Revie whom he regarded as a deep person, difficult to fathom or get close to. Revie gave Ray the impression that he was not at ease in his role as the England manager. After England had failed to qualify for the World Cup following defeat by Poland, and Don Revie had resigned to take up a highly criticized, lucrative managerial post in the Middle East, 'the Don' expressed the view to a newspaper that the Liverpool side would have trounced the national team.

In September 1977, together with half the Liverpool side Ray was picked by the likeable Ron Greenwood to play against Switzerland at Wembley. Greenwood's selection for the game based around the Liverpool club side was greeted with roars of criticism. Even Bob Paisley was unhappy, but for a different reason. Greenwood's omission of the crucial fourth man, Jimmy Case, in the midfield quartet completed by Callaghan, Kennedy and McDermott meant that the unit was fatally disrupted by the omission of the 'runner'. Paisley believed that if all four had played and England had failed to perform, then the critics might have been vindicated. As it was, Ray was pushed forward to stop the opposite full back attacking and was therefore denied the free role he enjoyed playing at Liverpool.

Two minutes from the end of the game, the FC Zurich player, Rene Botteron, was escorted to the touch-line with blood pouring from his nose and sporting a bruised eye and cheek-bone. The Swiss ace later accused Kennedy of deliberately elbowing him and putting him out of the game. Ray, who had played against Botteron in the European Cup semi-final the previous year, pleaded his innocence, blaming the incident on Botteron running across him, leading to an accidental collision. The match ended in a dreary, goalless draw.

After the return match with Luxembourg in 1977, Kennedy, although frequently in the squad, did not play again until 1979 against Bulgaria. Despite his disappointment at failing to secure a regular place, he was still positive and hopeful about his England career and had become increasingly ambitious in his quest for acclaim and more honours:

I am hoping that if things go right for me I will be in with a chance for the World Cup. I am twenty-eight now and I shall be just right at around thirty. So I have two years to aim to establish myself with England. It's nice to be in the squad for next week and I am hoping that will be the start. I have been so fortunate in the medals I have won and the World Cup is the one thing I haven't played in so far. I've been happy with a couple of my England performances, but to do well you have to be in a settled side, not one where everyone is fighting for places and playing only for themselves.

In fact, Greenwood was adopting a policy of trying to find and stick to his best team, building it round a core of Liverpool players, but the busy demands of the English League programme left insufficient time for harmonious blending. This affected Ray more than most as his *modus operandi* depended on everyone working selflessly for one another and having the time to plan moves down to the last detail in training. Thrown into a team of gifted individuals, but without a set pattern of play, Ray was bound to flounder. For most games Greenwood continued to prefer Brooking whom he had managed at West Ham and who was considered by many to be more creative. Ray, to a degree, accepted Greenwood's selection dilemma: 'I never felt Ron Greenwood could afford to play Trevor and me in the same team. However, even though I know a formation and blend is important, what puzzled me was when they played someone else not naturally a left-sided player in that position'. Ray was aware that he had as yet failed to reproduce the consistency in his England performances that was present, week in, week out, at Liverpool, but at twenty-eight he felt he had six years or even more left in the top flight.

On the night of the Bulgaria game Ray met up with Malcolm Sale and Terry Fenton and took them down the players' tunnel onto the pitch at Wembley. They then walked across the pitch together, with everyone wondering who Ray's friends were, and made their way towards the royal box where a meal had been laid on for the players because the game had been postponed. Ray sat his two friends opposite Ron Greenwood and Geoff Hurst, the assistant manager, and when the soup was brought said in a loud voice: 'I'm not eating that muck, let's go somewhere else'.

In 1980 Ray was selected for the match against Spain and was excited about his prospects: 'This is the first time in an England team I have been given the right job to do. I want to do it and keep it'. For this game many critics considered that the best available England side had been picked, with the exception of Kennedy in place of the disappointed Brooking. When quizzed by the press about this surprising decision Greenwood quipped: 'I am trying to make sure Trevor is fit to play the rest of the season for West Ham so that they can win promotion from the Second Division'. Perhaps more revealingly, however, in a quiet aside, he went on: 'You have to keep one or two cards up your sleeve'.

Ray gained further international honours that year against Argentina and Wales, and was selected for the European Nations Championship in Italy. In the first game, he came on as substitute against Belgium and, despite a groin injury, played the second game against Italy, where he nearly snatched the winner with a shot that hit the post. After this game he remembers Greenwood smiling at him as they got on the team coach. At that precise moment he sensed that his opportunities for further honours were negligible. Brooking returned for England's final game against Spain, which they won 2–1, a result which Ray greeted with mixed feelings. By this stage he was so disillusioned with the England squad system that he wanted to come home from Italy as soon as possible. This victory in the last game meant that there was a remote chance that England could qualify for a play-off; the possibility of having to stay on longer as a supernumerary squad member brought him out in a cold sweat. In fact the Italy v Belgium game ended goalless, which meant that England was eliminated. Ray, along with one or two other similar-minded players, breathed a sigh of relief as the team returned home to the customary deluge of abuse and criticism from the press.

One of the things which Ray had found extremely difficult to adapt to in the England set-up was the profusion of coaches. Sexton, Venables, Hurst, Robson, Howe and Taylor were all there to support Greenwood. There were so many, it was difficult to find jobs for them all to do. For example, one would be delegated to take the four-a-side, another heading practice, another defending, and so on, and there was so much information, much of which was conflicting, that Ray felt the players needed a psychiatrist, too, at the end of each training session to straighten out their minds. He also felt that there was a predominance of representation with a London-based interest, and wondered why Clough, McMenemy and Paisley were not also brought in as advisers. Some months before the European Championships, Greenwood had apparently come to a hotel where Liverpool were staying before a game against Middlesbrough and had said openly that he would like Fagan, Paisley and Moran to act as assistants to the national side, but this had never been followed up.

On his return from Italy, Ray became increasingly convinced that his England days were numbered. Greenwood clearly preferred Brooking and, perhaps equally significantly, Kevin Keegan also preferred Brooking. What Ray saw as 'an old pals' act', and the absence of direction and cohesiveness, steadily sapped his enthusiasm. One day, while at home in the close season, he bumped into Vince Wilson, sports writer for the *Sunday Mirror*, and, in the course of conversation, blurted out that he was beginning to feel as if he did not want to play for England. The reporter immediately got excited, seeing a scoop in the offing, and egged Ray on. Before agreeing to the story, Ray went to talk to his father, who advised him against any such statement, and then to Bob Paisley.

When Ray told his manager that he was considering an announcement Paisley replied: 'To be honest Ray, I think England have used you as a bit of a convenience over the last few years'. In his autobiography Paisley expressed the following view about the national side:

A player picked for his country is anxious to do well in order to win prestige and the chance of representing it again. That's where the trouble starts. Many international players are too interested in safeguarding their own positions — even at the expense of the side. And managers contribute to this. How many times have you read that manager X told his new cap to 'Just go out and play your normal game'. That's the classic case of a manager avoiding his responsibility. There are players in the game today who are more interested in representing their countries than their clubs ... some of these protect themselves in League matches if they know an international game is coming up ... It is not easy to adopt that attitude if you are a Liverpool player because our game is based on team work with everyone pulling their weight. Any shirker would stand out like a sore thumb.

The Liverpool manager also remarked:

Ray was totally misused by England. He had so much control and was such a good shielder of the ball that an opponent virtually had to knock him over to take possession. He has a great footballing brain and his striker's instinct never left him. We knew his strength at Liverpool and we played to his abilities which were recognized throughout Europe. For England he was played quite wrongly in a defensive role, being asked to pick people up. Ray closes people down by positional skill and does not need to chase around the pitch.

By 1980 Liverpool sides were built partly around his strength and vision. In Paisley's view Kennedy was played either too deep or too wide and was always asked to man-mark, which was never part of his natural – or Liverpool's – game.

After thirty squad selections and only seventeen caps, Ray publicly announced in the *Sunday Mirror* on 1 March 1981 that he did not want to be considered for England. For many of the squad call-ups Ray had not even been on the substitutes' bench, and was relegated to the stand. His torment had become so great that he would just stay in the Wembley Hilton with friends and head home to Ainsdale even before a game had finished. The *Sunday Mirror* article began: 'I feel more pride in the red jersey of Liverpool than the white shirt of England'. Ray described how the constant reporting to the England hotel, the regular training, followed by the predictable rejection, had eventually knocked the stuffing out of him:

It has reached the critical point where it has affected my performance with Liverpool and that cannot be good. It is time to stop. I have been moving in some club games as though I had lead in my boots. I am resigning here and now as Greenwood's bridesmaid. I refuse to be an England convenience again and want that worry off my back.

At the time of the article Ray still felt that he might be selected any time for England, particularly if a fall guy was needed after a disastrous result. He also began to feel that had he not been playing for Liverpool he would never have been selected in the first place. The article continued:

> I want to make it perfectly clear that I have not lost pride in my country. I am simply sick and tired of the treatment I have received. My Liverpool team-mate, Phil Neal, came back from an England game and said that Greenwood hadn't forgotten me – that was the message. What a way to be told. My white shirts which I have always refused to swop after matches will, however, remain treasured possessions. But I've had enough of England. I wouldn't be doing them or myself any good by pretending and going through the motions.

His concluding remarks illustrate his perception:

> Although I was always proud to represent my country and would become as emotional as anyone when the national anthem was played, I never felt I was playing in a team for England. There was no unit and I felt out on a limb. The whole set-up was not my scene. I found it hard to perform well in the role I was given and in any event never played at my best at Wembley. Internationals, like finals, were never my strongest point.

Many of Ray's friends felt that he might live to regret this decision, if only for financial reasons. For instance, he was depriving himself of potential earnings from promotions and advertising of up to £20,000 if he had been picked for the World Cup in Spain in 1982. The week after the *Sunday Mirror* article, Bob Wilson, his old Arsenal team-mate, wrote a letter in the *Sun* begging him to reconsider. While sympathizing with Ray's feelings and drawing an analogy with Jimmy Greaves, who had told Sir Alf Ramsey that he didn't want to play for England, Wilson's article concluded: 'I still say Ray has got it wrong. He didn't think before rushing in, something of which he is never guilty on the field. If he gives up now Ray may become the Liverpool midfield man who played the occasional game for England'. Ray received no direct feedback from the England camp but, following the Liverpool home game against Bayern Munich in the European Cup, Barry Davies, the BBC football commentator, came up to Ray and said, 'I hope you got paid well for that article'. Ray was incensed, but got his own back a few days later when, after scoring the decisive goal in the second leg against the Germans in Munich, Davies had to apologize in order to get the post-match interview.

There were also those who belonged to the school that considered Ray to be big, slow and lazy, and the Brooking supporters who felt Ray should never have got a cap in the first place. In his essay 'Upton and Other Parks' published in *Saturday's Boys: The Football Experience*, edited by Lansdown and Spellius, Sebastian Faulks, the novelist and a Hammers' fan, expressed this view forcibly:

> Throughout his England career Brooking was accorded his place only grudgingly. If the manager could find a plodder – a Trevor Cherry, Ray Kennedy, someone who was supposed to have a higher work rate – then he would be dumped. Kennedy finally declared in a huff that he had not been picked enough for England and didn't wish to be considered again. That he should have been capped at all is one of the more remarkable aspects of English football history.

In the opinion of Phil Parkes, Brooking's team-mate in the West Ham goal:

> Ray's not in Trevor's class and it's difficult to compare them except that both give the impression of being a bit lazy. Trevor is the kind of bloke that every mother wants her son to grow up like, he appeals to all age groups and is almost too good to be true. He doesn't smoke or drink and is a tremendous advert for professional football.

Ray himself is less enthusiastic about Trevor Brooking's abilities, pointing out that the West Ham player rarely dropped back to mark his man, rather he would float up the field, hoping that his marker would not score, and then look to capitalize on the break. He felt Brooking would never have been able to perform Ray's role for Liverpool. At the same time, however, he recognized Brooking's creativity and eye for the opening. Trevor Brooking, interviewed before Ray's testimonial match in 1991, was generous in his praise for his former rival:

> Both Ray and I started as strikers, but he was much more successful. He had one of those chests which soaks the ball up like a sponge. To be able to hold up a ball is a great ability.

He had a marvellous understanding with John Radford of
Arsenal. Both Ray and I lacked a bit of acceleration and the
midfield therefore gives you more time. Ray Kennedy was not
always recognized as the outstanding player he was, but if
you ask people at Arsenal or Liverpool they will tell you what
they think. He was never a star player, but his team-mates will
confirm that he was a crucial cog. If a shot which hit the
woodwork against Italy in the European Championships had
gone in, who knows how many caps Ray would have gone on
to get.

Ron Greenwood was equally magnanimous in his praise:

When I took over from Don Revie Ray was one of the
stalwarts of the side and he and the other Liverpool players
helped me to settle in. Ray was very physical, a great supporter
and a great passer. He had classic touches and was a gentleman
player – an important member of the England squad. Ray
never ran around much but he was always handy to score
goals and he was a player others looked up to. He is a man I
have always had a great respect for.

When I spoke to Lawrie McMenemy, Graham Taylor's deputy in
the present England management team, just before the game with
Turkey he told me:

The best tribute I could give Ray would be that if he was with
us now he would be an automatic choice for England. He was
a manager's dream, who started off as a classical old-fashioned
striker who went where the boots were flying and angels
feared to tread, and through his strength of character had a
second coming as an attacking midfield player. I always saw
him as a gentle giant type.

13 Walking Alone

A strange woman. Her ghost
still, after twenty years roams
the dark corridors of my mind
called up by the lilt of Tyneside vowels
                                    (JOHN WARD)

THE unexpected departure of Ray Clemence to Spurs meant that Liverpool opened their 1981–2 campaign with Bruce Grobbelaar, the Zimbabwean former soldier, thrown straight into the limelight. Poor understanding between the new keeper and the Liverpool defence led to early away defeats against Wolves and Ipswich, with home draws against Villa and Middlesbrough. Ray's assessment was to prove amusing with hindsight: 'I think we're just missing the understanding at the back because of the new goalkeeper. It's not down to him, it's a question of getting used to him'. After more than ten years, the Liverpool defence are still getting used to Brucie!

After twelve seasons in the Football League, Ray Kennedy was sent off for the first time for reacting to an incident with Alun Evans. He had gained the reputation of a tough, uncompromising professional who beat his opponents without breaking the rules. When flattened, he would normally just get up and get on with it, realizing that if he flared up he had lost the battle. The Liverpool boot room shrugged this episode off as an isolated incident but, in a League Cup fourth round match against Arsenal

at Highbury on 1 December, it happened again after a skirmish
with Arsenal's Peter Nicholas.

The sending-off incident between Ray and Nicholas provides
an insight into Graeme Souness's personality and loyalty to his
team-mates. In Mark Lawrenson's autobiography, the incident
and the subsequent events are described as follows:

> In the League Cup Tie at Highbury, Peter Nicholas kept
> catching Ray late with flying tackles. Ray finally snapped and
> took a swing at Nicholas under the ref's nose. In the second
> leg at Anfield with twenty-five minutes gone Nicholas over
> ran the ball just as Graeme Souness connected with a tackle.
> Nicholas was carried off, but didn't complain. Later in the
> Wales–Scotland match another violent clash took place be-
> tween them. Graeme had still not forgiven him for getting
> Ray sent off.

Prior to these two dismissals Ray had rarely been booked,
never mind sent off, yet here, within the space of a few weeks,
his disciplinary record had been blemished twice. Fellow professionals had always marvelled at his emotional control in big
games and had contrasted it with his edginess and short temper
which were often to the fore in training. Bob Paisley, who knew
Ray's strengths and weaknesses inside-out and had handled him
superbly over the last seven years by never shouting or directly
criticizing him, could tell something was wrong.

Liverpool had decided to get rid of Jimmy Case in order to
split the increasingly troublesome Kennedy-Case partnership.
After refusing an offer to join John Toshack's Swansea City, Case
was transferred to Brighton and Hove Albion. Meanwhile, Ray
seemed reluctant to take on the responsibility which his position
as one of the senior players of the side demanded. Without his
buddy, Jimmy Case, he was now rooming with the impressionable
youngster Sammy Lee. Ray felt adrift and uncommitted – the
same feelings he had experienced at Arsenal in 1973. He attributed his uncharacteristic behaviour on the pitch to this mounting
frustration and unhappiness brought on, in part, by Case's
transfer.

In October, Bill Shankly died of a coronary in Broad Green
Hospital. Since his retirement Shankly had become more and
more alienated from the club he had helped to build. His

relationship with the directors had never been easy and the club had been unclear about the role he wished to play. A director's post was undoubtedly there for the asking, but the club never formally offered him one. He complained that he was no longer invited to away games, and his seat in the directors' box was often empty. When the team returned from Rome with the European Cup, he told the press, 'If you think I'm a wee bit jealous then you're bloody well right'. He could still be seen from time to time at Melwood, and on one occasion he told the groundsman, Eli Wass, never to retire. It became obvious to all that he was regretting his decision to go, especially as even greater success had flowed to the club during Paisley's reign. As time went by, he was seen frequently as a guest of other clubs, including Tranmere and Manchester United, and suspicions were raised that he might be informally advising Liverpool's competitors.

At the memorial service held at the Anglican Cathedral on 21 November 1981, enthusiasm, integrity and inspiration were emphasized as three of his greatest gifts. Gerry Marsden sang 'You'll Never Walk Alone' in what proved to be a highly emotional service. Shankly's legend has lived on in Liverpool, not just through the Shankly Gates at the entrance of the club, but in the tales of generations of fans, many of whom were too young ever to have experienced his charismatic personality. The death of Shankly, the man who had signed Ray, proved to be an omen for his own departure from Liverpool.

By December Liverpool had lost four games and drawn six. Ray made his last League appearance for the club against Nottingham Forest on 5 December, when his first goal of the season helped Liverpool to a 2–0 away victory. Liverpool, who were still involved in four domestic trophies, then left for Tokyo on 13 December to play against Flamenco, the Brazilian side. Ray, increasingly tired and beginning to feel his days at Anfield were numbered, was more concerned with a post-match visit to a geisha house than the game itself. The Brazilians finished off a jet-lagged, match-weary Liverpool with three goals in the first twenty minutes. This was the last game Ray would ever play in the number five shirt.

Liverpool's season was again to end with distinction but without Ray Kennedy. The side had won through to the final of the League Cup again, where they faced Spurs and Ray Clemence. For most of the game Spurs held the lead, but Ronnie Whelan, now established in Ray's number five shirt, scored a late equalizer. Paisley, sensing that the Spurs players were out on their feet, tactically insisted that before extra time started all the Liverpool players remained standing. This master stroke gave them the psychological edge, and Rush and the new South African-born winger, Craig Johnston, who had played his early football in Australia, saw Liverpool through to their second successive League Cup winners' medal.

In the European Cup they had again been drawn against the Finnish side Oulun Palloseura in the first round; they won 1–0 away and then slaughtered the opposition at Anfield, this time 7–0, with Ray Kennedy scoring a forty-sixth-minute goal. In the second leg, Liverpool negotiated a difficult tie against the Dutch side AZ67 Alkmaar, and, remarkably, met CSKA Sofia in a rerun of the previous year's quarter-finals. However, the potential threat the Bulgarian side had presented the previous year proved on this occasion to be Liverpool's undoing, with the Reds going out 3–1 on aggregate.

The FA Cup campaign was equally disappointing, with Liverpool losing in the fifth round 2–0 to Second Division Chelsea at Stamford Bridge after convincing wins in the earlier rounds against Swansea and Sunderland. After a shaky first half of the League season, Liverpool came back with a late surge to wrest the championship from Ipswich Town by four points. On 6 March Liverpool lost at home to Brighton, with Jimmy Case plaguing his old team-mates. After that, however, they won eleven games on the trot and made it to the end of the season without further defeat. Kennedy's fifteen League appearances in the first half of the season entitled him to yet another League Championship medal.

Ray had always dreamed of finishing his playing career in the North-East. Once it became clear that his future was now away from Liverpool, he set his heart on a move back to the club he had supported as a child. Negotiations began at Roker on 23 January 1982, when Liverpool played Sunderland in the Cup; Sunderland wanted to take him on loan for a month, but Liverpool refused. Discussions with Alan Durban, the Sunderland manager, and the club chairman took place, but Ray was unable to agree personal terms. At thirty he was anxious to secure his future and was not prepared to take both a drop in salary and a short-term contract, particularly as he was leaving Liverpool with two years of his existing contract still to run. The Liverpool board were also not prepared to let him go for a song as they felt that he had a fair amount of football still left in him. In the end Ray got the distinct impression that Sunderland did not want him badly enough and that they were more interested in securing the services of Jimmy Nicol, the full back from Manchester United, who was already there on loan. When negotiations seemed to be slowing down, Stoke City, who had just sold Adrian Heath, also made enquiries, but Ray was still at that point keen to move to Sunderland. Then, out of the blue, John Toshack rang him up and asked whether he had already signed for Sunderland. Ray was impressed by his old team-mate's genuine desire to have him at the Vetch Field, a lightning deal was sealed and Ray was on the way to South Wales for £160,000.

Toshack had converted Swansea City into a mini-Liverpool and it was a standing joke at Anfield that when the phone rang in Bob Paisley's office it was likely to be John Toshack at the other end. Leaning on all the experience he had gained at Liverpool, Toshack had brought Swansea from the depths of the Fourth Division to the First Division in five seasons, and his signings had included Tommy Smith, who had continued to train at Anfield and negotiate a weekly contract, Ian Callaghan, Phil Boersma, Max Thompson and Colin Irwin. Other Merseyside signings included Bob Latchford and Gary Stanley from Everton. The big Welshman was excited by Kennedy's signing and hoped his former playing partner would give balance and motivation to his side who were, astonishingly, challenging for the First Division title.

Paisley had become convinced it was now time for Ray to move on. He described Ray's departure from Liverpool in his autobiography:

We had a heart to heart talk after the suspensions and Ray admitted something was bothering him but couldn't put his finger on it. Something seemed to be nagging away at him and he was increasingly frustrated. The outcome of our talk was a mutual agreement that it would be better for Ray

personally as well as for the club if he tried to re-kindle his
career elsewhere. The fact that we understood each other so
well made his departure far less painful than it might otherwise
have been. Having to tell great players they are past their
best, or that it is time to move on is the most unpleasant job
in football management.

Paisley was to devote five pages of his autobiography to
Kennedy's ups and downs at the club, including this tribute:

> Ray's contribution to Liverpool's achievements was enormous
> and his consistency remarkable. So much so, in fact, that on
> the rare occasions he missed a match his absence was felt
> deeply simply because he was a midfield power house with
> tremendous vision and knowledge of the game. His experience
> as a forward helped him enormously in tight attacking situa-
> tions. He had the ability to open up a game and give you the
> width of the park. When intercepting a loose ball he would
> invariably hit a telling pass – and running on to one himself
> he was as good as anyone I've seen. In my view he was one
> of Liverpool's greatest players and probably the most
> underrated.

Graeme Souness, in his autobiography *No Half Measures*, put a
slightly different slant on Ray's move: 'Everyone knows that
Jimmy Case, Ray Kennedy and Terry Mac all left the club earlier
than their ability warranted because they occasionally overdid
the leisure time'. Liverpool Football Club continues to take an
extremely hard-bitten, unforgiving attitude to players who
damage the club's reputation. If indiscipline or misdirected aggression cannot be sorted out promptly behind the locked doors of
Anfield, then a player is transfer-listed. In any event, the pressure
for places is so great that by the time a player reaches his early
thirties he is hard-pushed to maintain the fitness and motivation
needed to hold down a regular first team place.

Ray had made three hundred and eighty-one appearances for
Liverpool, with a further three as substitute, and he had scored
seventy-two goals, mainly from a midfield role. His vast collection
of medals now included three European Cup winners' medals,
five League Championship medals – one with Arsenal – two FA

Cup winners' medals, one of which was with Arsenal, and three other European Championship medals. On moving to Swansea, Ray acknowledged:

> It was entirely my decision. I felt completely stale mentally and needed a change. Sometimes I think back and can't believe that an ordinary boy from Seaton Delaval could have won three European Cup medals. Recently my consistency, which has been the secret of my success here, has been slipping a bit and I knew something was not right. Unlike other clubs, Liverpool finds you out straightaway if something is wrong.

He also had this to say about his ex-boss at Anfield:

> No man has had a bigger influence on my career than Bob Paisley. His knowledge of the game is fantastic and we could always talk to one another. I don't know how he thought up that new role for me, but he realized for sure I'd lost my appetite up front. Despite my size I was never a battering ram centre forward. Yet Liverpool wanted me to be the man who won the aerial battles and challenges, to create space for Kevin Keegan. It did not work and I ended up in the reserves. That was when Bob came up with his master stroke. I spoke to him before the game against Notts County to say goodbye. It really got to me. He knows the game so well that he has beaten teams with his tactics before the players step out onto the pitch. That's his secret, the way he lines his teams up and the formations he plays. Bob made me into a better player and he will go on doing that for other lads at Liverpool. He always keeps his feet on the ground and his dry humour was never far from the surface. Before one international several players were caught on a late night binge and their names were plastered all over the papers. I remember Bob saying he'd better ring Greenwood up and ask him to send Terry McDermott home because he must be ill as his name was not among the culprits.

Despite seven triumphant years, he continued to underestimate his influence: 'I wasn't the kind of player who was looked on as a star at Liverpool, but I worked hard for the team. I have always been in good sides, but I've never been carried by the other lads'.

After he had gone, the Liverpool boot room were as enthusiastic as Paisley. The Scouser Ronnie Moran, who is still with the club after forty years' service as player and coach, described Ray's qualities as 'great skill and strength and [he] could pass, head and shoot. He was a good hard trainer with natural ability and will be remembered here as a battler. He would fit my definition of a players' man'.

Joe Fagan, another Liverpudlian, who had played football at Manchester City before joining the Liverpool boot room and finally succeeding Bob Paisley as manager, remembers Ray as one of his favourite players who could be relied on to give a steady, unostentatious performance. Bootle-born Roy Evans made only nine League appearances for Liverpool after being a promising England schoolboy international and hung up his boots prematurely at twenty-five. In 1974 he joined the back room staff and, for many seasons, did a superb job in grooming young reserves for their first team initiation. Evans had this to say about Ray:

> Ray listened carefully and picked up everything. He paid close attention to instructions generally and not just those given specifically to him. When Bob moved him to midfield he thought at first he had to run up and down the left-hand side like an outside left, but he soon learned that that was not necessary. He was a very compact player, a quiet man off the pitch but not to the point of being boring. He was meticulous, very organized and picky about his food, and Ray and Jimmy Case were a great partnership here. I will remember him as a true professional.

Ken Addison, the commercial manager at Liverpool, remembers Ray as a man's man, always approachable and dependable when asked to help out at charitable functions and social events. He recalls spending a marvellous night with Ray at an amateur boxing tournament at which Ray gave the prizes. He also made special mention of Ray's sense of humour, and remembered the two of them killing themselves laughing at the unexpected match-winning goal by Alan Kennedy in the European Cup Final against Real Madrid.

Ray's team-mates were equally flattering:

RAY CLEMENCE:
Ray was a tremendous player for Liverpool Football Club. He was strong, powerful, would move from box to box and

would score important goals, usually coming in late at the far post. He helped out defensively, had a big heart, big lungs and the club always got a good ninety minutes. Before a big game I remember Ray always being quiet, concentrating on the business ahead, perhaps a little keyed up. He enjoyed life to the full and mixed well. Like most professionals at the time he worked hard and played hard.

PHIL THOMPSON:

I'll always remember the goal Ray scored at Bayern Munich when he took a pass from David Johnson, brought it down calmly with his chest and rifled it in with his right foot. Every team needs midfielders who score and Ray had a habit of coming in late and hitting screamers. He had a fantastic temperament on the pitch, always taking things calmly, and nothing ever seemed too much for him. He was always one of the lads and there was a great camaraderie between us. He had the strength of an ox and superb timing. When he arrived at Liverpool he gave the impression that he was already a good player and didn't need to work at it, but he soon realized this was not on and he was able to adapt. Ray was a bit of a schizo and sometimes, on the training ground, he would get a look in his eye that was very threatening. He was sensitive and would hit out if anyone said something against him.

Women were always chasing him, but I often heard him say his wife and family were the most important things in life. The Kop never really took to Ray because they expected him to be running to the corner like Steve Heighway. The Kop prefers triers like Joey Jones and Alan Kennedy who couldn't get near Ray in ability. Off the pitch he needed to be handled quite gently, and everything had to be organized just right otherwise there would be trouble.

STEVE HEIGHWAY:

Ray was a very strong player who could run and run all day. He understood his role clearly at Liverpool and had great positional sense. Off the pitch he was a quiet man with only two or three close friends, but always mucked in when we were out together. He was involved in making and finishing goals. He was a strong-willed professional who defined a role for himself at the club and fitted it perfectly.

IAN RUSH:

Ray was a senior player when I arrived at Liverpool. I remember him as always being polite, and prepared to give time to the youngsters. He made people welcome and it helped to give me confidence and bring the best out in me. He was one of the most knowledgeable players I have ever played with and very intelligent on the pitch.

KENNY DALGLISH:

Ray was a marvellous player who had already settled in when I got to Liverpool. In my first game he laid a goal on for me to score at Newcastle. He was a great finisher and nine times out of ten he'd hit the target with his head. Off the pitch he kept himself to himself.

JIMMY CASE:

At Liverpool if you looked as if you were giving a hundred per cent the crowd would never get at you. The Kop like triers, people who get stuck in. At first they couldn't work Ray out playing at inside left and there were murmurs he was a waste of money. Even though the people at Liverpool know a lot about football they didn't understand Ray's way of playing. The players, on the other hand, recognized his superb vision, his maturity on the pitch and his courage in holding up the ball. I was in my early thirties before I began to pick up some of those skills. At Anfield I would usually come in white with my work effort and rely on pressurizing oppositions to command the midfield.

14 The Vetch

Dead men and miners go underground
Deeper than vegetables or the rock
Than the Cro-Magnon arrowhead or sounding
Whale, deeper and darker than a black
Burial, they both go down into dirt.
But the dead stay down. We forget them
The sometimes smiling miner of Glynneath
He comes up as murky as his shirt
Out of the belly of South Wales. Let them
Elated this Saturday be happy beneath
An unfalling bright sky. Their work is done
Rigging a drift, riding a spake,
Hacking the seam. A week's work's done
And – fine and unlikely as a birthday cake –
These men enter the Saturday of the sun

(GEORGE BARKER)

SWANSEA City under the managership of John Toshack were challenging for the League Championship, and Ray was hopeful the move would lead to even more medals. In a game in which dog eats dog, greed and selfishness are encouraged, and players are taught to behave like mercenaries, it was every man for himself. Ray had learned these lessons painfully under the tutelage of McLintock and Smith, along with how to look after himself in an era before agents. He had been able to negotiate a salary compatible with that he had been receiving at Liverpool, and a four-year contract had been agreed by the Welsh club. Ray moved to a luxury home three miles from the Vetch Field.

Emotionally the choice of Swansea over Sunderland was a strange one. Ray knew no one in South Wales and didn't trust the Welsh. At Liverpool he had had one or two dust-ups with Joey Jones, and Peter Nicholas, now the most capped Welsh player of all time, probably precipitated Ray's Anfield departure after the sending-off incident. Ray had also dampened the Welsh Football Association's Centenary celebrations five years earlier with his first England goal. Then there had been the fighting at Llangollen and the court case. Furthermore, although Toshack and Ray had been team-mates, Ray had been bought originally by Shankly to replace the tall Welshman up front, a role Toshack had made his own and one which he had not been prepared to relinquish without a fight. At Liverpool Toshack had been closest to Emlyn Hughes and had little in common with Ray. It was also no secret that Toshack's dream was to make the Swansea side a haven for talented Welsh players, who could then develop an understanding which would pay dividends in the Welsh national side. However, Ray justified his decision to leave the most successful club in England to me, saying:

> I just needed a change to get myself moving again. I had won everything and was determined not to outstay my welcome. In some ways it would have been easier for me to have carried on with the set routine and picked up my money, but that was never my style. I hoped I could go forward with a new challenge at Swansea. They offered me the best opportunity and as a club they were on the move. They were sixth in the Football League, four points off the top and Sunderland were near the bottom. I had known John Toshack for a while and that influenced my decision, and I was impressed by the way he came in quickly and sorted things out. They either want you or they don't.

After an eight-week lay-off, Ray made his League debut for the Swans against Manchester United, and helped his new club to victory, rekindling hope of what had in recent weeks become a faltering championship challenge. The *South Wales Evening Post* reported his initiation: 'By Kennedy's standards it was a gentle introduction. The know how and experience were always apparent and if the absence of first team practice was missing the confidence was clearly evident'. Swansea had decided to play just two men up front and concentrate on preventing Manchester United exploiting the midfield skills of Butch Wilkins and Bryan Robson. The United attack missed several clear early chances and, following the introduction of the wayward genius, Leighton James, Swansea scored twice just after half-time in delightful moves involving James and another capricious talent, Alan Curtis. After the game Ray said: 'How can anyone rule us out? We must still be in with a chance of the championship'.

After a mid-season break on the Costa del Sol, Swansea gained their fourth away win of the season with a twelfth-minute Robbie James penalty against Notts County. Dai Davis, the veteran Welsh goalkeeper, who had been barracked for much of the season by the Swansea crowd because of a cluster of early season errors, had a sparkling performance. Before Christmas, a Swansea fan had run onto the pitch with two wooden sticks with gloves on the end and a placard reading 'You need hands' to goad the goalkeeper. It was also rumoured in the town that he had taken to using Velcro gloves to improve his performance. Ray put in another calm, authoritative midfield performance, particularly evident as County began to come back into the game through their talented Scots striker Iain McCullough.

In his third game for the club, at Ayresome Park in front of Middlesbrough's lowest gate of the season, Ray scored his first goal, swooping onto a Leighton James free kick to put Swansea ahead after thirty-seven minutes. He was also later bundled over in what Swansea felt was a clear penalty. Middlesbrough equalized from the penalty spot and the game fizzled out.

Liverpool were Swansea's next victims as the team moved into second place in the League. At Roker Park on 20 February Ray had another splendid game, watched by a paltry 13,163 long-suffering fans. The game was settled by a spectacular thirty-yard drive from the irrepressible Leighton James. Swansea then went to Arsenal, who were also in the bunch of eight teams challenging for the championship. Despite an understrength side, Swansea defeated the Gunners 2–0, with the Yugoslavian, Ante Rajkovic, and the young defender, Chris Marustik, having particularly good games for Swansea. The first goal came in the first quarter when Ray's old adversary, Peter Nicholas, made an error in the Arsenal defence, which gave Ray the chance to score. Kennedy then combined well with Curtis, who went close before another poor Nicholas pass allowed him to run into the heart of the Arsenal defence and win a disputed penalty to complete the double over Arsenal. Ray was providing a solid framework in midfield on which the wayward talents of Leighton James and Alan Curtis could thrive. Although Swansea's success had been largely attributed to organization and discipline, there was no shortage of flair and skill.

As the season began to approach its climax, Ray's impact on the side, while still valuable, dwindled a little. He was by now aware of increasing tension down his right side and difficulty stretching for balls on the right. At times during games his mind would wander to what he would be doing after the game. On occasions his distribution was uncharacteristically erratic and the odd scoring chance went begging.

In the defeat at Everton Ray limped off the pitch, but he was back with a workman-like performance in the Welsh Cup Final against a competitive Cardiff City side; the 2–1 victory earned him a tankard to add to his trophies and guaranteed Swansea a place in European football the following season. This, their first highly successful season in the First Division, fell short of the championship, which went to Liverpool.

Although to the Swansea support Ray was justifying his high transfer fee, he knew by now that the move was a disastrous mistake. He felt alone, Jenny was unhappy, and he felt there was no cohesion in the team. He was unsettled by what seemed to be a split between the Welsh-born players and the rest of the side. He felt that some of the Welsh boys were closing ranks and passing the ball to one another at the expense of the team's performance. The divisions between the two factions in the team led to friendly banter on the coach with the 'foreigners' cheering every time they left Wales and making sniping comments such as 'Seen any good-looking sheep recently?' on returning to the Principality.

His relationship with Toshack was becoming increasingly uneasy. At times, he would seek solace in drink to forget his mounting tension and unhappiness. Ray felt that, although Toshack had a good footballing brain and was a shrewed tactician, his capacity to draw the best out of players was limited. Toshack, in turn, respected Ray's footballing opinions and when he arrived promised to build a young side round his former team-mate.

Despite Swansea's recent success, trouble was round the corner, as the club's infrastructure was shambolic and their financial affairs were in disarray. Swansea had still not completely paid off the transfer fees of Colin Irwin and Ray to Liverpool nor that of

Gary Stanley to Everton, and the League banned them from purchasing other players until these debts were cleared.

By coincidence Ray and John Toshack were both on holiday during the summer break on the Algarve and bumped into one another. Ray expressed his doubts and concerns for the future season. He highlighted the lack of team spirit and the problem of the Welsh faction. Toshack was dismayed on hearing this and replied, 'Oh, don't say that, Ray'. Despite these worrying remarks – a clear indication of Ray's disenchantment – Toshack elected him captain for the 1982–3 campaign.

The return to fitness of the exciting young Welsh defender, Jeremy Charles, bolstered the squad, but the season got off to a poor start with a 2–1 defeat against Watford, with John Barnes and Luther Blissett spearheading their opponents' attack. Ray put in a steady if uninspired performance after coming back from an ankle injury. Toshack commented after the game: 'One or two individuals slipped into old habits, but overall I was quite pleased'. Swansea's season ticket sales were dropping despite the past year's successful season and, in their next game, the team went down 4–1 at Stoke with some of Toshack's tactical switches going hopelessly wrong. Ray remembers feeling heavy and extremely slow on a muddy pitch.

Swansea were then hammered 3–0 at home by a rampant Liverpool side, with the Welsh team manager, Mike England, seeing little to excite him in the seven Swansea Welshmen. He was, however, greatly impressed by the incisiveness of Ian Rush, liberally supplied by provider Dalglish, now playing in a deeper role. After the game, Ray summed up his side's performance: 'There was not much we could do about it. Liverpool completely outplayed us'.

Despite the woeful start to the League season, Swansea had advanced to the last sixteen of the European Cup Winners' Cup, following wins against Portuguese and Maltese opposition. In one of the one-sided victories against the Maltese side, John Toshack had made a rare playing appearance as substitute.

After conceding eleven goals in four League matches, Toshack decided to push Ray back into central defence to mark Steve Archibald, the Spurs striker. This move had been considered as a possibility on the flight home from Malta, but it was not until the Saturday morning that Toshack rang Ray up at home and confirmed that he would be playing in defence. This switch seemed to work, with a much more determined and organized performance coming from the Swansea defence, which provided the framework for a desperately needed 2–0 victory. After the spate of injuries which had hampered Toshack's early season selection, his side now seemed to be picking up, and on 9 October they got a one-all draw away from home against fellow strugglers Brighton. The *South Wales Daily Post* reported: 'It was a fitting reward for a recovery orchestrated by skipper Ray Kennedy, back in the familiar midfield role and a growing stability in defence where Kennedy himself had operated successfully in the two previous matches'.

The game was watched by a six-man delegation from Paris Saint Germain, Swansea's next opponents in the Cup Winners' Cup and one of the European clubs which had previously expressed interest in signing Ray when he was at Liverpool. Paisley had rejected the offer without a second thought. There is little doubt that Ray would have been a success in French football, although he may have found life more difficult in the Italian League. His speed of thought and ability to read a game, combined with his capacity to extract players from the play, appealed particularly to continental managers.

Not long after this, Ray was again injured and, as the season wore on towards Christmas, his performances became increasingly pedestrian. In November, with his side going 3–0 down away at West Brom, Alan Curtis still out of form and Leighton James on the verge of leaving for Rotherham United, Ray was injured and taken off. Immediately Swansea seemed to switch up a gear, with the unsettled James pulling out one of his most arrogant and exciting performances to get a point for Swansea. After an encouraging win against Liverpool 2–0 at the beginning of December, Swansea went down 2–1 to Nottingham Forest in what would have been a complete massacre if it had not been for a great performance by Dai Davis in the Swansea goal. The local press were by now on Kennedy's back: 'It was in midfield that Swansea's main problem lay. That fighting spirit which has for so long been a hallmark of their game was notably absent. Ray Kennedy in particular seemed unwilling to work and his usual composure on the ball was lacking'. By Christmas, Swansea were joint bottom of the League with Sunderland and Birmingham City.

Toshack was becoming increasingly desperate to revive his flagging team and would go round to the younger players' homes in the evenings to cajole them and advise them on how he wanted them to play on the following Saturday. Ray refused to allow Toshack to visit him in the evenings and was by now openly disputing some of his manager's decisions.

Swansea was about to blow up when I arrived, but I wasn't to know that. The club was rotten to the core, in debt with underhand payments going on as well as wage top-ups. The Vetch Field is opposite Swansea gaol and I used to say we should go across the road to get our pay. Some of the Welsh boys like Alan Curtis, Jeremy Charles and Robbie James were OK, but there was no real knitting together of the team as had occurred at Liverpool and no forward planning.

Ray had sustained a niggling hamstring injury which had kept him out of the last five games and meant that he had only played in eleven of the first twenty-three League games of the season. Toshack and the coaching staff began to suspect that his injuries were not the whole explanation for his unavailability. Ray complained to the doctor and Phil Boersma, his old team-mate who was the physiotherapist at Swansea, that he had difficulty stretching for balls on his right side and that his leg felt stiff. Boersma remembers Ray's right thigh muscles being continually stiff and in spasm. He also recalls Ray always playing in long-sleeved shirts and gripping the cuffs with his fingers. Both Ray and the training staff at that time were aware that he had had some problems putting his right foot on the ground when he started to run, which would disappear once he had been moving for a few minutes, but it was laughed off on the basis that Ray was a notorious slow starter.

Ray's form had been poor; his most effective games were the two or three he had played out of position in defence. Things came to a head in the new year when he reported unfit just before a reserve team game against Crystal Palace. Toshack accused him of not playing well because he was not trying and not keeping fit. A few days later, playing against Newport Reserves, he was pulled off with a recurring injury after seven minutes and, as he went off, he observed Toshack talking to the Swansea chairman. 'After the game Les Chapple, the reserve team trainer, told me I had been suspended from the club for two weeks'. Although Ray bumped into Toshack immediately on leaving the ground, the manager refused to give him any explanation for the decision. Ray was ordered to stay away from the Vetch Field and was also stripped of the captaincy. Swansea were in a perilous position, for which Toshack blamed himself. His decision to suspend Kennedy was explained to the press as follows:

> I have done this in the best interests of the club. It is always sad when you have to take this action whether it be Ray Kennedy or anybody else. You have to do what you think is right. You can be patient and let it go for as long as you can, but there comes a time when something has to be done and enough's enough. Robbie James will take over the club captaincy. His heart is in the club.

Gordon Taylor, the Professional Footballers Association supremo, was asked by Toshack to get involved. Taylor concluded: 'I've spoken to Ray and John Toshack and it has been decided to treat the two weeks' suspension as a cooling-off period, especially as the player will not suffer financially'. During the period of suspension speculation mounted that Ray might be transfer-listed for a bargain £30,000, with Newcastle United's manager, Arthur Cox, expressing an interest. Leighton James, whom Toshack considered another bad influence on the young players, was given a free transfer. The view in the Liverpool boot room at the time was that Tosh should never have signed Kennedy on his own, but tried to negotiate a Case and Kennedy package deal. Ray was not transfer-listed, but Doug Livermore, the coach, made him change alone in the reserve team dressing room and do long lonely training laps. In Toshack's opinion Ray was now far from being a mature leader and motivator but was an increasingly bad influence on the younger players. It was not long before Ray was joined in the 'sin bin' by Bob Latchford and other senior players.

By February, the team were three off the bottom, averaging only a point a game. On 6 February Ray returned in midfield and, although Swansea lost 3–1 at home to Watford, Ray seemed to have regained some of his composure and enthusiasm. He followed this with a fair display in the next game against

Hereford in the Welsh Cup. The side then lost 1–0 at Spurs, with Ray coping fairly well in a defensive role. He told the press:

> You can bank on me to battle all the way and help John Toshack get Swansea out of trouble. I've had my own problems, but if it's left to me I'll see out the last two years of my contract here. Since Tosh arrived at Swansea it has been success all the way until this season and how he copes with the first setback of his managerial career will be crucial for both the club and himself. We are involved in a battle for First Division survival and I'm not afraid of that even though it's a completely new experience. It has been a Liverpool-style run here at Swansea for the last six years and for a small club that is incredible. But Swansea are not Liverpool or Arsenal. You can't expect to compete with the big boys year in, year out, unless you have solid foundations. My impression at the start of the season was that anything less than a Wembley appearance would be considered a failure here. Now we must be realistic and I want to play my part in the relegation fight. I've never cheated in thirteen years of First Division football. I've played with injuries and I am prepared to do so again provided I know I won't be a passenger. However, if I reckon I'm not fit to play I expect my word to be taken. I should not have to prove myself on that score. Despite our problems and what has happened to me I have no regrets about coming to South Wales. Even though I'm a Geordie I'll fight tooth and nail to stop Swansea being relegated.

Despite these reassuring words, Ray's form dipped again and he was back in the reserves by the end of February. Rumours were afoot that Tampa Bay Rowdies, the top North American side, had made inquiries about him. Ray told the press: 'I haven't had an official approach, but I think I have still too much to offer to go there yet'.

John Toshack kept on at Ray, saying that his attitude was all wrong, that he was lazy and overweight, and accused him of hating the Welsh. Ray felt that he was being made the scapegoat for a struggling side by a club on the verge of disintegration. Robbie James, who had replaced Ray as captain, supposedly because of his loyalty to the club, was cynically transferred to Stoke City. Ray's banishment to the reserve team's dressing room, either alone or with one or two other exiled senior players, continued. Under the supervision of Doug Livermore, now in charge of the first team at Spurs, Ray was asked to run himself to the ground with extra training after the others had gone home.

Towards the end of February, Swansea played away at Southampton and, on the coach journey down to the south coast, Toshack had a long heart-to-heart talk with Ray and then went back to his seat at the front of the coach in a euphoric state, excitedly turning to Phil Boersma and saying, 'I finally got Ray going, he now really wants to play'. Once the match started, however, it was apparent that nothing had changed and Ray was so slow and awkward that Toshack was obliged to substitute him before half-time. The manager was finally convinced that he had made a gross error of judgement in buying Kennedy. At the beginning of March, Ray was put on the transfer list, with Toshack commenting, 'Ray has had difficulty settling here in Wales and we feel the time is right to release him'.

No one expressed an interest in buying Ray, and Swansea slumped to joint bottom of the League, along with Jimmy Case's Brighton team who had, however, reached the Cup Final. Ray, who had kept in contact with his friend, rang Jimmy before the Wembley game to wish him success. At a time when his own career was in tatters, Ray generously observed:

> Jimmy Case can change a game with one rocket shot. It's the hardest in the game. He was underrated at Liverpool but did a superb job, always protecting his full back with his tremendous defensive skill. He was a great competitor who was always on the go, working and putting himself about a bit.

On 23 April, Ray played in an important relegation battle at Luton Town which Swansea lost 3–1, virtually sealing their fate. The local paper reported that Kennedy's composure had helped Swansea, but for much of the game they had been on the rack and had now gone almost a year without an away win. Swansea gained a courageous one-all draw with Ipswich Town, but this extended their run without a win to six games. Ray maintained his place in midfield, with Toshack, in desperation, giving more and more of his promising youngsters their chance to establish regular first team places. Swansea then won 2–1 against Aston Villa, with Ray playing with renewed confidence. However, the battle to stave off relegation was finally lost at Old Trafford in the last game of the season. Meanwhile, Bob Paisley, who had announced his intention to resign, on Graeme Souness's instigation had gone up to collect the Milk Cup at Wembley, and Liverpool finished League champions, eleven points ahead of their nearest rivals, Watford.

With Ray still on the transfer list at the beginning of the 1983–4 season, the atmosphere at the Vetch had soured even further, with several directors jockeying for supremacy and the players being asked to take a drop in salaries and bonuses. The club were about £1.5 million in the red. The players met with the directors for a frank discussion. It was put to the players that if they were prepared to take a drop in wages then the besieged Toshack would stand a better chance of staying at the helm. Bob Latchford, the former Everton and England international and the team's PFA representative, then asked each player if they would agree to a drop in salary. Ray refused to answer.

In the preliminary round of the European Cup Winners' Cup, Swansea were drawn against FC Magdeburg, a rugged East German outfit. In the first leg, with Swansea heading for a useful one-goal cushion, Chris Marustik, the young defender, inexplicably hit a forty-five-yard suicidal back pass to the new Swansea keeper, Jimmy Rimmer, who was left stranded in limbo with the East German striker, Streich, almost unable to believe his good fortune in being able to pounce on the ball and score. Marustik was inconsolable after the game despite Toshack's cold comfort, 'Don't worry, Chris, it can happen to anyone. We all make mistakes'. According to Ray, however, after the game Toshack kept mentioning the error over and over again and wouldn't let it go. In the return leg, Swansea went down 1–0 to miss out on a lucrative first round tie against Barcelona.

The power struggle in the board room finally led to the resignation of Malcolm Struel who, with Toshack, had brought the club back into the top flight from Fourth Division football. Auditors were called in and the club secretary, Gordon Daniels, was relieved of his duties. Disappointed and temporarily disillusioned with management, Toshack was forced to leave the club in September; he asked for no compensation and donated £1,000 to help the junior side. Ray was then called in to see the directors and remembers thinking that after Toshack's resignation he might be offered the manager's post. The club, however, just agreed to terminate his contract and allow him a free transfer.

The differences in managerial approach between 'hard man', John Toshack, and his old boss and father figure, Bob Paisley, were outlined in an article Ray wrote in the newspapers. Throughout his playing career, he had tried to stick to a rule never to drink excessively in the forty-eight hours before a match. On one occasion, on a Thursday at Liverpool, a friend had returned distressed from a funeral and asked Ray to join him for a drink. Ray was offered Drambuie and gin for the first time, which he enjoyed, so he decided to have a few more. The following day he paid the consequences: on getting up to go to training at Melwood he felt half-dead. He managed to get through the training session although he got a few strange looks from the back room staff and Bob Paisley. The game that week was at Manchester City and Ray was determined that there would be no comeback on his midweek indiscretions. Early on in the game he put in a good hard tackle on Paul Power who then had to go off the pitch. After the game, Paisley came up to Ray and said, 'That was a good tackle, but I don't think it was the injury that made him go off'. When Ray asked his mentor what it was, Paisley, with a twinkle in his eye, said that Power must have smelt Ray's breath. Ray used this example as an indication of how discipline was kept at Liverpool without the need for ranting or raving or vicious fines.

After only forty-two League games spread over three seasons in which he had scored just two goals, Ray Kennedy finally left Swansea; he was now thirty-two, unemployed and hoping for offers. After more than a month of inactivity he was approached by Tommy Docherty's son, the former Sunderland player, Michael, who was managing Hartlepool United, then the bottom club in the Football League. After Liverpool, Hartlepool was like dropping off the edge of the world. Although Ray had expected better offers, he was grateful for employment and signed terms on a match-to-match basis. Although Hartlepool were not exactly the dream ticket he had been looking for, at least he was back in his beloved North-East: 'I was a little surprised nobody else came in, but I'm impressed with Mick Docherty and now it is up to me to show I can still do a job. It's been so long since I played, I'm dying for a game'.

15 The Crying Game

The terrace is said to be haunted.
By whom or what nobody knows; someone
Put away under the vines behind dusty glass
And rusty hinges staining the white-framed door
Like a nosebleed, locked; or a death in the pond
In three feet of water, a courageous breath?
It's haunted anyway, so nobody mends it
And the paving lies loose for the ants to crawl through
Weaving and clutching like animated thorns.
We walk on to it,
Like the bold lovers we are, ten years of marriage,
Tempting the ghosts out with our high spirits,
Footsteps doubled by the silence . . .

(PETER REDGROVE)

RAY was about to experience a standard of football he had almost forgotten existed. He enjoyed having money in his pocket and had acquired a taste for the good life: his standard of living as well as his football was about to suffer. The Kennedys first took a flat in Blyth, and the furniture removers bringing their belongings from South Wales commented on the step down in property. Ray and Jenny, however, were happy to be back home.

Like Seaton Delaval, West Hartlepool came into being in the heyday of the Industrial Revolution. Coal, steel and shipbuilding were the major industries and people came from all over the British Isles to seek employment in the docks, shipyards and pits, and on the railways. In the North-East the town has always had a reputation for idiosyncrasy. Tradition has it that a French ship was grounded during the Napoleonic wars and a monkey, dressed as a French sailor, escaped ashore. As the monkey spoke gibberish superior to the Hartlepudlian population's, it was hanged as a French spy. Repetition of this story within the town of Hartlepool is done at one's peril.

Hartlepool United Football Club is more than eighty years old and had entered the Football League in 1921. In a town where Rugby Union has always had a strong following and where unemployment has been severe in recent years, the club's greatest achievement to date has been survival. Since its inception, Hartlepool United has languished in the nether regions of the Football League, never getting beyond the old Third Division (now Second Division) or beyond the fourth round of the FA Cup. It has been sustained by the dreams and courage of a few local businessmen, determined to keep a football team alive against all odds. However, the club has spawned a number of successful players and at present is enjoying a period of relative good fortune. Brian Clough and Peter Taylor began their formidable management partnership at Hartlepool in 1965 before moving to Derby County. At this time the club was in such a desperate financial situation that Brian Clough took lessons in driving a coach in case of emergencies. In the year before Ray signed up, Hartlepool United had finished in twenty-second position in League Division Four and had been forced to apply for re-election to the League for a record thirteenth time.

Jokes about the football club abound:

Halifax Town fan: Where's the Victoria Ground?
Hartlepudlian: Just follow the crowd and you'll find it.

The Halifax fan then attempted to do so and ended up in the local Woolworths. Another commonly repeated gag is:

Fan: What time is kick-off?
Club Secretary: What time can you get here?

Ray, unlike his mate Jimmy Case, did not adapt easily to playing in what he regarded as grossly inferior circumstances. The Victoria Ground had originally been constructed for West Hartlepool Rugby Club in the mid-1880s on a piece of land bought from the railway. It formed part of a large limestone quarry and was little more than a maze of dilapidated allotments. In 1948, 17,045 fans converged on the Victoria Ground to watch Hartlepool United play Hull City, but the ground still consists of a single matchwood main stand plus some poorly constructed sheds and open terracing. The visitors' dressing room was branded a slum by a visiting Torquay United side and is affectionately known as the 'Black Hole of Calcutta'. The roof of the club offices lets in water and, in Clough's time, one sheltered part of the terraces was littered with bantam feathers, as a former manager had kept chickens there.

Despite the hand-to-mouth existence of the club, Ray had managed to negotiate a personal contract with Vince Barker, the club's chairman, for £250 a week, £125 of which was to be paid in wages, with the rest in hand. Despite the illegality of this, Barker insisted that, in order that everyone knew where they stood, Ray should have the details put down formally in writing.

John Duncan, the manager, was a former Spurs player who, in fact, lasted only nine weeks at Hartlepool, as he was offered a better deal at Chesterfield. At the time of his departure he claimed to have put the club on an even keel by outlining what was required, and said that he had done all he could with the limited resources. He justified his move to Chesterfield by saying that the Midlands club had much greater potential.

Vince Barker, who ruled with an iron fist, had already almost destroyed and then saved the club single-handedly in his few years in office. He appointed Michael Docherty as Duncan's successor, and then dismissed John Bird, the club captain, on the grounds of the player's mounting business interests. The latter decision was overruled by the Football League in an appeal by Bird. Barker, extolling Docherty's virtues on his arrival, stated that one day he would be as famous as his father, Tommy, and that he gave Hartlepool hope for the future.

Docherty had pinned a note on the door of his office on arriving at Hartlepool which read: 'It's not the size of the dog in the fight, it's the size of the fight in the dog'. He immediately tried to sign a big name, and negotiated with the ex-Burnley and England international winger, Dave Thomas. The Hartlepool supporters managed to raise the £3,000 asking price by Portsmouth, but Thomas was unable to agree personal terms. Hartlepool began the 1983 season where they had left off the year before, winning only one of their first seventeen League games and going out early in both cup competitions. Barker, while in public still affirming his full support for Michael Docherty, was already beginning to criticize his team selection and accused him of being too trustworthy. He reminded his young manager, somewhat tactlessly, that football managers were employed to be con men. On 15 December, two days after Docherty had moved into a house in Hartlepool, Barker fired him. Ray still had to prove his fitness, but there were rumours that he might be made player-coach. As a consequence, when Michael Docherty, hell-bent on vengeance, came to ask Ray for the letter Barker had given him outlining the illegal salary payments, Ray refused. In the end Billy Horner, the assistant manager, was reinstated for a second term of office.

On 17 December 1984, Ray made his debut at Reading and scored a goal, but the Pool lost 5–1. On Boxing Day the club got their second win of the season, 2–1, against fellow strugglers Darlington Town. In the new year it was announced that the club owed £25,000 to the police, £7,000 ground rent, and a residual £29,000 of an initial demand of £51,000 to the Inland Revenue. Two new directors joined the board and injected badly needed cash. One of these, John Smart, a director of a public works company, had ambitions to take over the running of the club and organized the first official sponsorship for Hartlepool United through his company, New County. The other new director was Peter Mulcaster, a Smart supporter and owner of a Middlesbrough roof company.

Under Horner, some improvement in performance occurred so that Hartlepool were able to take twenty-six out of the last fifty-four points. A 5–0 defeat at Hereford in April, however, led Horner to call his team 'tanner ball players, all frills and after you Claude'. Ray played in a home defeat against Stockport County on 5 May in front of only 790 people, the lowest gate ever recorded at the Victoria Ground. The club finished twenty-second in the Fourth Division, which led to yet another ignominious application for re-election. However, the season had finished on a high note, with Hartlepool beating promoted Doncaster Rovers. Andy Linighan was transferred to Second Division Leeds United for £60,000, providing a much-needed injection of capital. Because of recurring injuries, Ray played in only seventeen games for Hartlepool United, in which he managed three goals.

On moving home to the North-East, largely at Jenny's instigation, the couple had gone into the licensing trade, taking over a run-down pub, the Melton Constable at Seaton Sluice. Ray had initially hoped they would be offered the tenancy of the Hastings Arms in Seaton Delaval. This didn't work out, but the brewery promised him a more prestigious pub on the coast. After he finished training at Hartlepool, Ray would go to learn the rudiments of licensing in a seedy pub in Blyth, where he would pull pints. One day the landlord's rottweiler attacked him and bit his shirt sleeves. The thought of spending the rest of his life as a publican was already filling Ray with horror, but he could see that his footballing career was nearing its end and he was predicting that he would be in non-League football before too long.

The prospect of Hartlepool United surviving in the Football League looked remote, particularly as Maidstone United, the forward-looking Kent club who shared their ground with a Rugby League club, had produced a smart glossy brochure to gain votes. Smart asked Ray if he would come down to London with the Hartlepool management team to help canvass votes from his First Division friends. Smart and Ray got on the train at Newcastle-upon-Tyne and, before Barker joined them in Darlington, Smart had promised Ray money and a player-coach deal if he would support him against Barker. When Barker got on, Ray flatly refused to agree to help until he got his outstanding wages, which were reluctantly handed over. The Hartlepool delegation stayed at a poky little hotel and then made their way to the all-important League dinner. On arrival, Ray saw the Arsenal and Liverpool delegations on large tables at the front, while Darlington and Hartlepool were squashed into a little space at the back of the dining hall. Ken Friar and Peter Robinson, the Arsenal and Liverpool chief executives, came up to speak to Ray and both reassured him that he could rely on their votes; Smart was suitably impressed. Hartlepool managed to get thirty-two votes, ten more than Maidstone United, with Halifax Town and Chester getting fifty-two votes and Rochdale fifty. Maidstone later claimed that they had been robbed by a change in the agenda which had proposed that there would be automatic relegation of the bottom club of the Fourth Division to the Alliance League and promotion of the Alliance League champions. To celebrate, the Hartlepool contingent decided to go to Stringfellows, the trendy night club in the West End, but Horner was worried that they wouldn't be able to get in. On arrival, one of the doormen immediately recognized Ray and asked them all in, again impressing Smart. Before the day was out, Smart had ousted Barker as chairman and, on the way home to Newcastle, offered Ray the player-coach job.

In the summer of 1984 Ray took the family to Cyprus to stay in a popular resort in the Protaras-Ayia Napa area on the west coast of the island which borders the Thecelia base, one of the two permanent British military bases maintained on the island since its independence in 1960. A few miles east of the base lies Larnaca, one of the island's main towns situated on its southern coast and home of the island's only international airport.

The pride of Larnaca is Pezopolikos Football Club, founded in 1927. The club was initially established for walking enthusiasts before switching to football in 1937. It has been in the First Division of the Cyprus Football League since 1950 and has won the League Championship and Cup on a number of occasions. Managers of the top Cypriot clubs are now usually from overseas and professional, whereas the majority of the players are amateurs, although, since 1980, the Cypriot Football Association has allowed each First Division team to have two non-Cypriot professional players.

In the 1983–4 season Pezopolikos reached the final of the island's Football Cup and morale was high. The board had decided to employ a distinguished Greek coach from the mainland and had authorized its chairman, Mr Andreas Haholiades, to go to Greece to negotiate and finalize the deal. While he was away, however, a waiter in the hotel where Ray was staying approached the former Liverpool player and asked whether he would be interested in playing and managing the club. Ray expressed an interest and then returned home, having heard nothing further. When Haholiades arrived back in Cyprus having completed the deal, he found the rest of the board of directors waiting for him on the tarmac at the airport. When the directors asked him whether he had signed the Greek and he replied in the affirmative, he was bewildered to see the look of despair on their faces. The reason soon became apparent when one of them told him: 'Ray Kennedy is willing to sign for us as player-manager.' The chairman was speechless. Ray Kennedy was a legend to Cypriot football supporters and the idea of signing a player of his calibre was irresistible. Pezopolikos were briefly in a dilemma, but the Greek manager who had signed terms could not come at the last moment because of a family tragedy, which gave the club the opportunity to sign Kennedy.

As Ray was negotiating next season's deal with Hartlepool,

Jenny called him from the pub to say that the Larnaca club were on the phone offering him a player-coach deal. In view of the continuing problems at the Victoria Ground in agreeing terms, Ray opted to give Cyprus a go, initially on his own while Jen stayed behind to run the pub. In August 1984 Ray arrived in Larnaca to begin his new challenge. The ex-chairman now recalls how impressed he was on first meeting him at the airport; he remembers a giant of a man, extremely athletic and handsome, and even more impressive in the flesh than the man he had seen playing for Liverpool and England on Cypriot television. Ray professionally laid down his terms, which were immediately accepted by the club. Chairman Haholiades now remembers: 'There was real euphoria in the air. In the first friendly games we had larger crowds coming from all over Cyprus to watch Ray and the team than at any previous League game and a strong police force had to come to maintain order'. However, it was not long before initial excitement began to fade. The early perform-ance of the team was disappointing and Ray Kennedy was a shadow of the player they had all seen at Liverpool. To the players, including the captain of the team, Lakis Lambrou, Kennedy appeared heavy and slow, which they all attributed to lack of fitness and the age factor. In retrospect, Lambrou, the team doctor, Dr Andreas Antoniades, and the physiotherapist, Christakis Toumazis, all remember how Ray kept one of his arms fixed to his side as he was running round. 'Nobody thought anything of it at the time and believed that it was his style of playing', Toumazis recalls. Scrutinizing his records from 1984 he also noted:

> He was definitely overweight and I was impressed by the number of muscular strains and cramps he developed. He was always in the gym getting physiotherapy even during pre-season training. I've never seen so many frequent muscular strains in any Cypriot football player, never mind a profes-sional player, and I've been the Pezopolikos physio for the last twenty years. I was also struck by Ray's proclivity to sweat continuously. During one training session he drank about six cans of soft drink and then lifted the bath-sized bowl that we kept the drinks cold in ice and drank the cool water of the melted ice. He also used to avoid training as much as he could.

I wondered if it was because he thought that the more he trained the more he'd get injured.

By this time Ray was also aware of stiffness in his leg, and had noticed some quivering of the fingers of his right hand. He was finding it extremely difficult to run properly in training and, alone, without Jen's moral support, began to drink more than he should; even small quantities of alcohol caused his speech to slur. Ray soon learned that the Cypriots expected everything they demanded to be delivered immediately, whereas his own requests and demands would be put on the back burner unless he made an almighty fuss.

The club's poor early results began to worry the chairman, who asked for a meeting with his manager. Haholiades relates:

> Kennedy was totally elusive. He would find all kinds of excuses to avoid me, but eventually agreed to meet at a place called To Kastro along the Larnaca beach where he used to love sunbathing and swimming. We arrived there and found him in the sea. We had to put on our swimming costumes and join him. I remember he was very vague in his replies, but was certain that things would look up by the beginning of the League season.

However, things got no better, and Ray frequently substituted himself or at times did not even pick himself for games. The chairman was now convinced that they had made a big mistake in signing Kennedy. Following a local derby game, which Pezopolikos lost, Ray was summoned before the board to give an account of himself. The day after the report, Ray found himself sitting next to the chairman at another game and was ignored. The following Tuesday at the next board meeting, Ray stormed in and in front of an astonished row of faces confronted Haholiades, who apparently owned half the island, shouting, 'Nobody does that to me', and, according to the chairman, used foul and abusive language. As Ray continued to let off steam, he remembers watching the chairman sink lower and lower in his chair, and after Ray had left the chairman asked the board to choose between him and Kennedy. This gave the board the opportunity they had been waiting for and they unanimously voted in favour of Ray, and chairman Haholiades resigned. Ray was secretly congratulated afterwards for his performance in the board room and Mr Loukis Loukiades took over as chairman. The board frequently wished to know Ray's team selection well in advance and it became common knowledge, following an article in the newspaper by Tommy Cassidy, that rigging of games and bribery was rife in Cypriot football.

Lambrou remembers Ray affectionately: 'All the players loved him but unfortunately for us the results were disappointing.' Most of the team worked in restaurants, in hotels, or as hospital porters. Ray nicknamed one of the more excitable players 'Stropadopolous'. Although Ray loved Cyprus and working with the players, he was finding it harder to cope mentally and physically. The new chairman, Loukiades, who got on extremely well with Ray and found him to be a kind, gentle man, was baffled by the poor performance of the team. Ray continued to substitute himself or not pick himself for League games and Pezopolikos dropped from third to bottom in the League. The season that had begun with high hopes and dreams for the championship was turning sour. One of Ray's closest friends on the island was Andreas Antoniou:

> Ray loved sunbathing on the beach near the castle area and we would meet daily. He really enjoyed Cypriot cuisine especially Mezedes and his favourite restaurant was Militzis which specialized in barbecued meat dishes. He was one of the nicest people I ever got to know and I became close to both him and his family. I also noticed that he kept one of his arms tucked to his side while walking and that his shirt was constantly soaking wet with sweat. I was sad to see him recently as he was a completely different man to the one I had known in 1984.

Ray also voiced his disappointment to Antoniou that he had not spent some of his time playing for the European sides that had expressed interest in him, as they would have made him a millionaire.

Towards the end of December 1984, Ray requested leave to go back to England, but the chairman and the board were reluctant to let him go, with the team showing few signs of improvement. They threatened to dismiss him if he went ahead, but Ray went all the same. He returned briefly in early January

1985 and handed in his resignation. Loukiades remembers: 'He was the only manager or player whose contract was terminated who did not ask for a penny of compensation. We were all very sad to hear of his medical problems later on'. Pezopolikos under a new manager went on to finish sixth in the League and won the championship three years later. Ray, however, has never forgotten the beautiful beaches, sunny climate and Cypriot cuisine. His friend, Antoniou, recalled with a smile: 'He comes every year for his holidays and we all look forward to seeing him again and again'.

Ray returned to the Melton Constable, increasingly certain that his footballing days were over, and resigned to giving pub management a trial.

16 Old Footballers Should Be Shot

We sit in front of the wireless
waiting for the latest news
on the state of our affair
You knitting socks for our footballers overseas
me wishing i was there
The bulletins are more frequent now
they are broadcasting by the hour
The headline in the *Echo* reads
'Love turned Sour'

(ROGER MCGOUGH)

THE Melton Constable was a necrotic dump when Ray and Jenny took over. One of its more distinctive features was the number of snug rooms always in great demand for illicit liaisons and shady business deals. Ray revelled in the intrigue of these encounters, and found amateur espionage much more to his taste than trying to be polite to irritating customers. The denizens of Seaton Sluice had a reputation locally of being 'wild eyed jumping jacks', and Ray was apprehensive they might prove difficult to control. It was not long before a group of his old acquaintances began to congregate in the main bar around the large coal fire and the piano. Some had already been banned from most of the other local taverns, and it was to their credit that they never betrayed the Kennedys' trust by causing trouble in the Melton Constable. Although Ray had been drawn back to the North-East by his strong roots, he was beginning to realize that, in many respects, he felt more at home in London or in the north-west, where he had more contacts and the people reacted more warmly to him. About this time he visited a clairvoyant who told him that he would die far from home.

By the time Ray returned from Larnaca, the brewery had

fulfilled their promise of totally refurbishing the Melton Constable, which was now one of the most attractive hostelries on that stretch of the coast. Thanks largely to Jenny's communication skills and her enthusiasm, the pub started to flourish and began to attract visitors from further and further afield. It was not long before it had become so popular that the council agreed to remove the yellow lines from the roadside in order to allow cars to park outside. Ray hated pub life and was frequently discourteous, abrupt or irritable when serving. He often turned his back on customers and would try, whenever possible, to avoid any sort of conversation. Fortunately, as he became more and more aware of his difficulties in handling coins or pulling pints fluently, he was not behind the bar enough for much trouble to break out. Instead he would spend long hours upstairs doing the orders or accounts and worrying obsessively that the pub was not attracting enough customers. At lunchtime on Sundays, he would sit looking out of the window, lugubriously counting the number of cars parked outside and pronouncing prophecies of financial doom. Every night Jenny worked downstairs and would crawl upstairs in the early hours, exhausted and wanting to go straight to sleep, but Ray, who had been mooching about upstairs on his own, would be clamouring to talk to her. The relationship was reaching breaking point with Jenny branding her husband lazy.

Veronica Kennedy was aware that trouble was brewing with her son's marriage, and would come to help her exhausted daughter-in-law by doing some of the domestic chores around the pub. One day Cara, then aged nine, confronted her grandmother in the pub to ask her which of her three sons she loved the most. Although Veronica replied that she loved each of her children for who they were, Cara would not let the issue go and replied, 'I know you love my Dad best, Nan'. Veronica then knew that Ray had put his daughter up to it and burst into laughter. Certainly there was a close and special affection between her and her eldest son and both possess a strong stubborn streak to their character.

On leaving Swansea, Ray had felt that although he was only thirty-one, his days in football were pretty much over. However, like so many old pros, he was unsure precisely which direction his life should take, and continued to hanker after 'just one more season'. In January 1985, after returning from Cyprus, he offered his services to Newcastle United: 'I have kept my weight down and reckon I am capable of at least one more season. Money is the last thing on my mind. All I want is a further chance.' Newcastle were not interested, but in January Ray joined his former England team-mate Colin Todd at Ashington, who were in the Second Division of the Northern League. The Ashington chairman was prepared to pay Ray £100 a week in his desperate desire to resurrect local interest in this historic cradle of soccer. However, after six games, Ray was finished, such had been his physical decline. The Ashington physiotherapist was alarmed by the stiffness of Ray's right leg on the massage table and was amazed he could run at all.

On several occasions, he turned out for the Melton Constable team in the Sunday League, although he could barely lumber up and down the pitch. He was playing five-a-side games with more success during the week and his friends observed that, although he was slow to get going, once he was in his swing he was able to perform reasonably competently. They also noted that he had great difficulty in fastening up his laces. Ray would also go out and play snooker with his friends and it was during some of these games that he began to notice that a scotch would help to soothe his troublesome stomach discomfort. Moving round a snooker table was at times inexplicably difficult.

In the summer he was offered a job coaching children at Pontin's and Ladbroke's holiday camps, which at least allowed him to escape from pub duties. The schedule was gruelling, with long hours of driving in which he covered up to 1,500 miles a week striving to meet ludicrous deadlines between camps. He came to dread one particular journey which involved a break-neck race down a long winding road: 'I found it impossible to get my right arm comfortable resting on the car door with the window open. The arm felt heavy, restless and aching. Sometimes the car would seem to be drifting, with a mind of its own, towards the middle of the road.'

At the holiday camp in Minehead with Colin Bell, the former England and Manchester City player, and Danny Hagan, Ray complained of tiredness, sickness and headaches. In the hotel lounge he found it difficult to cross his left leg over his right, and his friends commented that he was 'slumped like an old man' in the chair. Signing autographs for the children had become a

dreaded ordeal, for his previously neat script had dilapidated into
an illegible scribble. At the camps he would often be asked to
join in football games involving the boys' parents, many of
whom would make a beeline for him in order to show off in
front of their mates. Although Ray's physical prowess had
deteriorated alarmingly, he had not lost his common sense, and
he elected to lay off the ball to someone else before anyone
could get near him. This was in stark contrast to his predecessor,
Peter Osgood, who would see the games as a bit of a challenge
and complained at the end of summer camp season that he had
had more holes kicked out of his legs in those weeks than in a
season of League football.

Desperation was setting in. Ray knew there was something
wrong but did not know where to turn. Everyone blamed his
irritability and lethargy on situational depression, stemming from
problems in coming to terms with life now that the final whistle
had blown. It was growing-up time and he couldn't handle it.
Being on a football field in front of 50,000 delirious fans every
week is a sensation that is difficult to match. Even sex doesn't
last forty-five minutes each way and have a brass band playing
half-way through. The abrupt withdrawal of this weekly 'fix' can
leave a desolate void. Some throw themselves desperately into
football coaching or management in a vain attempt to remain in
contact with the peaks and troughs of the people's game. Others
seemingly hell-bent on self-destruction, womanize, prop up bars
or gamble — fatal labyrinths which inevitably culminate in divorce,
debasement and debt. Coping with everyday life off the pitch was
certainly a problem for Ray, but it did not explain the changes
that were happening to him.

On 4 November 1984, he was finally told he had Parkinson's
disease.

17 The Physician's Tale

What drug can make a withered palsy cease to shake?
(TENNYSON)

FRAGMENTARY descriptions of the Shaking Palsy can be found in the Sanskrit incunabula, hidden within the hieroglyphics of the Pyramids and recorded in the gospel according to St Luke. The first comprehensive medical account, however, was provided in 1817 by a Shoreditch apothecary, James Parkinson. His *Essay on the Shaking Palsy* begins with an arresting account of the illness:

> Involuntary tremulous motion, with lessened muscular power, in parts not in action and even when supported; with a propensity to bend the trunk forwards and to pass from a walking to a running pace, the senses and intellect being uninjured.

Parkinson had the opportunity to study six patients. The first was a gardener, aged fifty-five, who had developed a shaking motion of his left hand. He complained that the movement of the hand was slow and that he walked with a shuffle. The second patient was a former attendant at the magistrates' court, who had been reduced by his illness to an impecunious existence in the work-house. The illness had been present for ten years when Parkinson first saw him, and he presented a bent, bowed appearance and relied on a stick to potter and slouch about. His limbs were in constant agitation, and his speech was slurred and quiet. This patient was of the firm conviction that his disorder was incurable and had been caused by drinking alcohol to excess. When Parkinson encountered the next case, an elderly sailor begging in the street, he noted in his book that the wretched man was forced 'to go on a continued run and to employ his stick every five or six steps to force him into a more upright posture by projecting the point of it with great force against the pavement'. This man told Parkinson that sleeping on a damp, cold, Spanish prison floor was responsible for his ailment. The next patient consulted Parkinson for a rib abscess, but casually mentioned that he had also been aware of a severe shaking of one hand for more than five years. The patient after that, again encountered in the street, had been obliged to employ an attendant to help him walk. The attendant would steady him by placing a hand on each shoulder and then advance twenty paces and prepare to prevent his employer from falling forward as he broke into an ever accelerating propulsive trot. The final patient was seventy-two and had impaired use of the left arm followed by tremulousness which later spread to the right side; he slurred his speech, and dribbled saliva. This patient's wife commented that he would find stepping over a pin difficult because of his inability to raise his feet.

James Parkinson was interested in the possibility that injuries to the upper part of the spinal cord, or rheumatism, might be important causes, that disturbances of the bowels might trigger the first symptoms and that many of the main symptoms closely resembled the natural ravages of ageing:

> Seldom occurring before the age of fifty and frequently causing but little inconvenience for several months, it is generally considered as the irremediable diminution of the nervous influences, naturally resulting from declining life and remedies are therefore seldom sought for.

Although Parkinson warned his readers against premature irrational therapies, he resorted to the application of ointments causing blistering of the skin and to blood-letting in the hope of helping his desperate patients. Parkinson's admonishments went unheeded, and ignorance of the cause of the illness which now bears his name did not prevent even the most eminent of nineteenth-century physicians from administering a wide range of potions and nostrums, including gland extracts, opium, strychnine, calabar beans and hemlock. Cures taken in low, wooded southern regions, using electrical stimulation, were also encouraged.

Many of Ray Kennedy's playing colleagues have been eager to put forward possible explanations for the development of his illness, some of which bear an uncanny similarity to those propounded by their nineteenth-century predecessors. Jimmy Case told me that he felt Ray's illness may have been unmasked by difficulties in coming to terms with the end of his football career. John Toshack raised the possibility of cumulative injury from repetitive ball-heading, a theory Ray refuted, pointing out that Toshack himself had probably headed the ball much more and had not developed the illness. Kenny Dalglish pointed a finger at Ray's highly strung personality and wondered about hereditary factors. Ray's father has, in fact, got a slight tremble of his head. Tommy Smith, at a dinner held for Ray at Anfield, jokingly said: 'I have been thinking about you and me, Ray, and wondering why you have got this Parkinson's disease and I haven't and the only thing I have come up with is that it must be caused by too much sex!' Ray himself had begun to wonder whether the Anfield boot room had laced his pre-match tea with drugs which had poisoned him in a delayed fashion.

Although Parkinson's disease starts most often in the elderly, and the risks of acquiring the illness increase steadily with age, it can occasionally develop in young adult life. It is intriguing to speculate whether the years of arduous physical training which Ray had undertaken might have unmasked the illness prematurely. In this regard the observations of Dr Brian Curtin, the Spurs doctor quoted in *The Glory Game* by Hunter Davies, are of interest:

Pat Jennings had his hands behind his back in the best Prince Philip style. I could see them visibly shaking. I pointed them out to Dr Curtin. 'I've noticed it for some time,' he said, 'it means nothing, but footballers who are going to get diseases in later life can perhaps get the signs earlier than other people.'

Pat Jennings' tremor was almost certainly an exaggeration of the normal tremulousness we all get when anxious or after exertion, but it is well recognized that episodes of profound emotional trauma or stress may bring the first signs of Parkinson's disease to the surface. It is equally feasible, however, that while a football player is keeping physically and mentally fit he is able to stave off illnesses which would otherwise have emerged and that once his level of fitness slips on retirement, symptoms emerge. Ray is drawn more to this possibility.

Most professional football players are highly competitive, aggressively self-centred, stable extroverts, and it is hard to find a successful one who leads an abstemious, celibate existence. Although clubs encourage their players to settle down, after marriage it is quite common for the men to observe a temporary loss of form, with weight gain and sluggishness. The adulation of the fans, the constant curiosity of the media and the erratic life style not surprisingly may lead to psychological difficulties. Binge eating, alcohol-related problems including violence or reckless driving, gambling and marital disharmony all probably occur more commonly than in the general population. To my knowledge, Parkinson's disease is no more common in footballers, although it does occur.

One of Ray's contemporaries and adversaries, Chris Garland, who gained England Under-23 honours, had periods at Chelsea and Leicester City, and played for his home-town team Bristol City in all four Divisions of the League, also developed Parkinson's disease in his thirties. Like Ray, Garland was accused of alcoholism: 'My hands and legs started shaking uncontrollably and my speech became indistinct.'

Jock Wallace, Malayan jungle fighter and former Scottish international, who managed Rangers and Leicester City, has also contracted the disorder. One of Wallace's memorable quotes while managing Lineker's Leicester City referred to his days in the jungle: 'We were ambushing and being ambushed: it sharpens your instinct and teaches you survival. I never stood cowards and lazy bastards and I still don't'. Like Ray, Wallace adopted a positive attitude towards Parkinson's:

I'm fighting against my illness and I'm winning. But I'm pretty convinced it was the pressures of managing Rangers during my second spell at the club which brought it on. Running a football club can be a great life, but as Kenny Dalglish [nervous breakdown] and Graeme Souness [heart disease] have found, there is a price to pay. The pressures show in different ways. Look at Alex Ferguson. He's developed a nervous cough and Jim McLean of Dundee United has forgotten how to smile.

Two other post-war professional footballers have also contacted me with details about their Parkinson's disease.

Of the theories put forward by Ray's colleagues to explain the illness, the possibility that heading the ball might have been responsible deserves the most serious attention. The modern football has a weight of 400–450 g and this may increase by ten to twenty per cent on a wet, muddy day. The ball not uncommonly travels at speeds above fifty miles an hour and may hit the head with an estimated impact of 200 k pascals. Throughout his professional career, Ray Kennedy probably received around 5,000 head blows either from heading the ball or – less commonly – by direct contact from other players. During the act of heading, either from a standing or running jump, power is generated from a back to front movement from the hips and involves backward movement of the trunk. In order to absorb the force of impact of the ball, the head and neck must be held as rigidly as possible and the ball should be met squarely in the middle of the forehead. Timing is also crucial if the ball is to be propelled effectively. It has been demonstrated that rotational acceleration is the main cause of brain injury and, by bracing strengthened neck muscles, a player decreases this rotation and minimizes the extent of any damage. If bad or awkward contact occurs, however, difficulties may arise; as Ray told me: 'If you catch the ball wrongly it makes your eyes water and your head ache'. Heading practice quite frequently can provoke headaches, neck pain and dizziness. Footballers' migraine is an unusual condition in which, three or four times a season, within a few minutes of heading the ball, a player develops tunnel vision or flashing lights in front of his eyes, followed within half an hour by a severe throbbing headache which may last for several hours. Head injuries involving concussion are not infrequent in footballers, although Ray, despite a bad facial injury with a broken nose, was never affected in this way. Occasionally, more severe trauma, brain haemorrhage or even death can occur.

In his monograph, *Heading For Goal*, Paul Baynes describes how, while playing for VS Rugby second eleven, he was accidentally elbowed in the head when jumping up for a ball in the box. Although shaken, he carried on after a dose of the magic sponge, but then shortly afterwards he started to spin round and round on the half-way line and it was decided he needed hospital attention. On the journey he lapsed into coma and required emergency brain surgery for a blood clot on the brain. His outlook for recovery was considered bleak, but within nine months he had fought his way back to a virtually normal life. Tragically, in his mid-thirties a Parkinson's syndrome presented with him becoming unable to stop his feet running away from themselves while he was jogging. Baynes's Parkinson's syndrome may represent one of the very rare instances when a severe head injury has been primarily responsible for the development of the illness.

Of the sixty or so English Football League players who have died while playing football, about thirty had sustained head injuries and in eight this had occurred as a direct result of heading the ball. The effect of minor repeated head injuries is unknown, but concern has been expressed that footballers might be at risk of injury from the 'punch-drunk syndrome' or *dementia pugilistica* of boxers. Some years ago a survey was done asking British neurologists whether they had encountered the punch-drunk syndrome in other sportsmen; professional footballers were mentioned five times. One of these was a centre half, much given to heading the ball, who was able to return it with interest, even when the ball was blasted at him from close range. Another player, Rodney Marsh, the charismatic QPR striker and a contemporary of Ray Kennedy, was judged to have damaged his hearing as a result of heading the ball and received some compensation from the Football League.

The punch-drunk syndrome occurring in boxers is believed to be due to cumulative brain damage and presents with changes in the boxer's personality, dementia, drunken-like unsteadiness and slurred speech. Sometimes it presents with a clinical picture closely resembling Parkinson's disease, as in Muhammad Ali's case.

Ali's medical history is described in detail in Thomas Hauser's biography, *Muhammad Ali: His Life and Times*. I have also had the opportunity to discuss his case with one of the neurologists he consulted, Professor Stanley Fahn of New York. Ali had a slight slurring of his speech as far back as 1978. Before his fight with Holmes in 1980, he was given thyroid hormone and amphetamines and, within a round of that bout, he was sweating, profoundly fatigued and short of breath. After that he was admitted to hospital at University College, Los Angeles on two occasions; it was noted that he was slow, he also drooled, slurred his speech and shuffled when he walked. Brain scans revealed some mild damage to his brain comparable with head trauma. In 1983 he was started on L-dopa tablets and he improved. When Stanley Fahn examined him, he found abnormalities which convinced him that Ali's illness had been caused by cumulative trauma. Ali considered that most of the damage had occurred during the third Frazier fight in Manila. The beatings Ali sustained in his last fights were probably the result of slowed reactions due to Parkinson's syndrome. Ali's belief in his own omnipotence has led him at times to deny the presence of his malady; getting him to take his tablets regularly has proved a continuous battle. He has been particularly attracted to a form of treatment advocated by a Yugoslavian quack who informed him that his condition was caused by a poison in his blood which can be removed by regular blood exchanges, calling to mind the blood-letting originally advocated by James Parkinson.

While it seems probable that Ali's Parkinsonism is part of a punch-drunk syndrome, there is no convincing evidence to implicate head trauma as the cause in Ray Kennedy's case. Furthermore, Ray does not show the additional physical signs which Professor Fahn found in Ali and which are considered incompatible with Parkinson's disease. Nevertheless, one could make a case for professional footballers having routine neurological examinations, together with a brain scan, at regular intervals during their career. The possibility that repeated minor head trauma might be an important occupational hazard leading to brain damage years later needs to be carefully examined as well. Although the cause of Ray's Parkinson's disease remains obscure, diminished movement, muscular stiffness and trembling are the direct result of loss of a small cluster of pigmented nerve cells in the grey matter of the brain. These nerve cells secrete a hormone called dopamine which is vital in programming our movements and in modulating our emotions.

About ten years ago in the Bay Area of San Francisco, a minor epidemic of Parkinson's syndrome occurred in junkies, all of whom had bought a designer street narcotic from a kitchen chemist. Unfortunately, one particular batch had been prepared sloppily and contained a by-product called MPTP which was subsequently shown to cause Parkinson's syndrome when injected into monkeys. This catastrophe has raised the possibility that Parkinson's disease might be caused by a group of as yet unidentified toxins in the environment. Although it is inconceivable that all the patients in the world could have been exposed to MPTP, this compound is very similar to the weed-killer paraquat and a group of ubiquitous compounds called pyridines. Another interesting clue is that individuals who have never smoked tobacco are twice as likely to get Parkinson's disease. Parkinson's disease occurs all over the world and has even been reported in Indians from the Amazon rainforest, suggesting that either we should be looking for many different poisonous substances; alternatively, the causative agent may be naturally occurring and widespread. Many doctors are also attracted to the possibility that excessive quantities of toxic substances may be produced within the patient's own nerve cells which cannot be scavenged successfully. In years to come, these fashionable theories may seem as ludicrous and implausible as those put forward by Ray's team-mates.

Although the cause of Parkinson's disease remains elusive, there have been major advances in alleviating the symptoms of the illness. The first breakthrough occurred almost by chance one hundred years ago. In Parisian salons during La Belle Époque it was fashionable for ladies to administer tincture of belladonna to dilate their pupils, thereby enhancing their allure. Unfortunately, this also stifled repartee by causing a dry mouth. The father of neurology, Jean-Martin Charcot, who practised at the large city asylum in Paris called La Salpêtrière, reasoned that belladonna might be useful in controlling the profuse drooling complained of by many of his patients with Parkinson's disease. Up until that point he had treated his patients either by suspending them from the roof of his therapy chamber, stretching their spines, or by sitting them in a specially devised 'shaking chair' in which they were vibrated violently for one hour. To Charcot's delight, not only did belladonna help the dribbling, but it also improved the shakiness, and muscular aches and pains of his patients. Tinctures of related plants of the potato family, including henbane and the thorn apple, were shown to produce comparable benefit. Bulgarian belladonna therapy, introduced by the plant collector Ivan Raeff, gained the unwarranted reputation of being particularly beneficial, although it contained no more than a white wine extract of belladonna with pills containing charcoal, bread dough, sawdust, calamus root and nutmeg. Eventually these elaborate concoctions were superseded by pure alkaloids given as tinctures or smoked as cigarettes. Drugs with the same actions as these early exotic potions are still used to help trembling and stiffness, but are now manufactured in laboratories and carry ungainly names like benzhexol (Artane), procyclidine (Kemadrin) and orphenadrine (Disipal).

The most effective treatment for Parkinson's disease is L-dopa, which first became available twenty years ago. It has revolutionized the life of most patients and its introduction into medical practice was greeted by sensational press coverage, with headlines such as 'Sick old man chases nurses' and 'Cripple throws away his wheelchair after cure by miracle drug'. Although this amino acid is produced synthetically, it is found in large amounts in the pods of many beans and pulses. In certain parts of the world, where the cost of synthetically produced L-dopa is prohibitive, leguminous plants are used as a viable, cheap, naturally occurring alternative. In the foothills of the Himalayas a plant called the snake root grows. The roots of this plant contain a substance which is useful in the treatment of high blood pressure and have long been revered in India for their sedative properties. However, when introduced into Western medicine, it was found to induce symptoms of Parkinson's syndrome and depression in a few people. It is now known that extracts from the plant deplete the levels in the brain of the hormone dopamine. Growing close by the snake root is another plant called the cowhage, whose beans have been sold for centuries in the market-places of India as treatment for many different ailments. These beans contain large quantities of L-dopa, adding credence to the witches' adage that the antidote can be found close to every naturally occurring poison.

L-dopa is not a cure, but it is a remarkable treatment which has helped doctors control the physically disabling symptoms of Parkinson's disease. It is taken several times a day, in tablet or capsule form, and is converted within the brain to the chemical messenger, dopamine. It can be considered as a replacement therapy in the same way as insulin injections are used to treat sugar diabetes.

Thanks to L-dopa, doctors are no longer afraid to tell patients they have Parkinson's disease. It is probable that new drugs will be found soon which will be even more effective in replacing the chemical deficiencies within the brain that occur with Parkinson's disease. There is also a reasonable hope that treatments which could prevent further nerve cell death and spare-part surgery to replace the wounded and dead cells may become realistic therapeutic options by the twenty-first century. If protective treatments become a reality, early diagnosis of Parkinson's disease will become essential, and Ray's and other patients' 'remembered symptoms' will assume a greater relevance in assisting doctors to refine their diagnostic skills in picking up early disturbances of movement.

18 From Player To Patient But Still Not Human

> How nerves sometimes operate by themselves without any command from other functioning parts of the soul. This is clearly apparent for you will see paralytics and those who are shivering and benumbed by permission of the soul, which soul with all its forces cannot prevent these parts from trembling.
>
> (LEONARDO DA VINCI)

WHISPERS had been circulating for some time that Ray was a sick man and Alec Smales, a long-time acquaintance and a scout in the North-East for Liverpool, had got wind that something was amiss. Tommy Smith had also rung Ray to say that he had heard rumours that he was ill. Ray realized that some form of public statement now had to be made to head off misinformed gossip, and he contacted Mike Ellis, a trusted journalist friend. On 11 January, 1987 the news broke in the national press:

TRAGEDY OF ENGLAND HERO — RAY

The article stimulated a flood of letters from well-wishers, and correspondence from people with Parkinson's disease, which contained words of encouragement or cries for help. Old acquaintances who had lost contact also sent their sympathies. The Professional Footballers' Association readily agreed to cover his medical expenses. In the Melton Constable, people would stare and whisper to one another. Some were sympathetic, a few appeared embarrassed and others just didn't understand.

For the first few days after starting treatment, Ray felt sick and developed headaches, but within a month or two the replacement therapy was starting to work, the side effects were getting less pronounced and the improvement in his physical well-being obliged him reluctantly to concede that the specialist's opinion had been correct. All that remained was a slightly stiff, awkward right hand which would occasionally quiver when he was tired or under stress, a poker face and a right foot which scuffed against the floor towards the end of the day, wearing out the sole of his shoe in record time. Ray also began to find it difficult to strike his heel down first when stepping forwards.

In Ellis's newspaper article, Ray had developed a theme which was contrary to currently accepted medical dogma, but which had been touched on in several Parkinson 'patient biographies' and which struck a chord with many of the patients who wrote to Ray following its publication: 'Slowly it had dawned on me that I had not just got Parkinson's disease but that it had been creeping up for years while everyone thought I was normal.' Although vague symptoms such as aches and pains, feelings of tiredness and depression are recognized by the medical profession as early symptoms of Parkinson's disease, the concept that subtle abnormalities of body language, temperature control and behaviour might be evident ten to twenty years before the shakes appear is controversial. Could Ray's high level of fitness have kept the illness at bay until his playing career had finished, whereupon the stress of readjustment unmasked the symptoms? Many individuals with Parkinson's disease are able to date the onset of their illness to a particular trauma or upset, but a stressful life event may simply be the straw which breaks the camel's back and unmasks pointers which can no longer be ignored. Could it be that a highly observant, introspective, professional sportsman might be able to pick up harbingers which would be ignored or pass unnoticed by the young man in the street, or rationalized by the elderly as signs of ageing?

Ray has produced a detailed chronological record of his 'remembered symptoms' before diagnosis was made:

The premonitory period (1966–1986)

1966 Slow, cumbersome and clumsy as an adolescent.
1968 Vacant, inattentive expression, profound mental and

physical fatigue, lack of self-confidence, inexplicable drenching sweats and defective body thermostat.

1969 Single episode of difficulty doing buttons up with right hand after intense physical exertion, stiff 'John Cleese' upper body posture.

1970 Lack of emotion when playing football, rarely jumping in the air after scoring, short backlift when kicking ball.

1973 Depression and binge eating.

1975 Right hip pushing forward uncontrollably when walking, mildly impaired balance, difficulty with star jump co-ordination in training.

1980 Right leg scuffing on the ground occasionally [confirmed by me on family cinefilm taken when Ray was on holiday by the Mediterranean], feelings of tiredness and tension down the right side, mounting paranoia and suspiciousness, tetchiness, irritability.

1981 Increasing physical discomfort when training, stiff right arm and poor arm swing with abnormal wrist posture [confirmed on video footage from television clips].

1982 Rigid right leg, difficulty stretching for balls played to the right side, profound exhaustion, going to bed twice a day, shoulder pains, transient brief tremble of right index finger on two occasions immediately counteracted by changing hand posture.

1983 Stiff, slow, difficulty starting to move, loss of stamina, running like a cart horse.

1984 Chest discomfort with choking, abdominal distension and discomfort, nausea, changes in bowel habit, return of quiver in fingers of right hand, small quantities of alcohol causing speech to slur, reluctance to run, unprovoked drenching sweats.

1985 Right arm tense and uncomfortable when driving, constant need to change posture of right arm and leg, stooped posture, drooling on pillow at night, writing difficulties, difficulty moving freely in confined spaces, difficulty rubbing shampoo in with right hand, walking slower, clumsy eating.

Symptoms and signs at diagnosis in November, 1986

Anxious immobile facial expression, stiff awkward right finger movements, heavy right leg, loss of arm swing on the right

when walking, coarse slow tremble of fingers of right hand at
rest, speech low pitched and slightly slurred.

Many of Ray's recollected symptoms could be dismissed as
anecdotal or inconclusive or are open to alternative interpretation.
For example, some could be ascribed to a recurrent agitated
depression, whereas others bear similarities to the chronic fatigue
syndrome or 'yuppie flu'. In a recent medical article on Parkinson's
disease it is stated: 'One must always listen to the patient's
account of his symptoms with healthy scepticism.'

However, there can be little doubt, based on my own scrutiny
of Ray's memorabilia, cinefilm collection and hours of television
footage, that abnormalities of posture and movement were
present down his right side at least five years before the clinical
diagnosis was made, and at a time when he was fighting to
preserve his reputation at Swansea. Support for the view that
there may be a long incubation period for Parkinson's disease can
also be mustered from other patients' accounts. For example, one
of my patients, a marathon runner, began to experience the
clawing up of one foot after running about fifteen miles; the
tension would relax after a period of rest, only to recur after
prolonged exercise. It was several years after this that the tell-
tale signs of Parkinson's disease appeared. Another patient noticed
a tremor in the fingers of the left hand, only when yawning, five
years before the diagnosis was made. A keen tennis player
suddenly noticed difficulties in throwing the ball up accurately to
serve; an elderly man began to roll to one side when swimming;
and a third man had been aware of difficulty in cutting up his
food at stressful dinners for ten years.

Ivan Vaughan, a childhood pal of John Lennon and Paul
McCartney, developed Parkinson's disease in his thirties. In his
book, *Ivan*, he relates how two years before the diagnosis was
made his trouser belt kept shifting to the left, leaving the buckle
off-centre. About this time he started to experience excessive
fatigue and perspiration after physical exertion, and after one late
night he noticed that the following day all his movements were
broken into jerky, slow component fragments. Dr A. W. Thompson, a general practitioner with Parkinson's disease, reported
inappropriate mawkishness and a tendency to over-react emotionally to the extent of producing social embarrassment, which was

an early sign followed by a crippling loss of self-confidence. Dr Cecil Todes, in his autobiography *A Shadow Over My Brain* presented with the complaint that his automatic self-winding watch kept stopping due to an unrecognized reduced movement of the left hand. Another doctor diagnosed himself by recognizing the tell-tale expressionless face in photographs of himself at his daughter's wedding. A slight catch in one leg going upstairs followed by a momentary quiver of one finger were the early signs in Margaret Bourke-White, the *Life* photographer.

Sidney Dorros, in his book *Inside Parkinson's: A Patient's View* is convinced that his illness began in childhood. His parents chided him for the sad, vacant look he always conveyed on childhood snapshots. When he looked back at these pictures after the diagnosis had been made, it seemed to Dorros that his expression already foreshadowed the Parkinsonian mask. At school, as an adolescent, the doctor commented on his phlegmatic demeanour and, on taking up a teaching post after graduation, a sixth-grade pupil told him to smile more. Dorros became a 'workaholic', toiling through the night with punishing schedules, a commonly reported behaviour pattern in patients who develop Parkinson's disease. 'My compulsion to work as if time were running out may not only have been a cause of the rapid onset of Parkinsonism, but also an effect of the condition; for Parkinsonism includes tendencies to hurry as well as to go slow.'

Despite the caution and scepticism of Ray's medical advisers, his meetings with patients over the next few years were to convince him further that the illness had started to affect him during many years of otherwise normal existence. 'When I met other patients and listened to their experiences more and more little niggles which I had put to one side but couldn't explain fitted into place. Some of the things that had happened to me had happened to these people too in their lives before Parkinson's'.

Jock Wallace, the former Rangers and Leicester City manager, describes the onset of his Parkinson's disease as follows:

The physiotherapist at Colchester diagnosed me. He took me aside and said 'Big man, I think you have Parkinson's disease'. I'd been eating sloppily, my hands were shaking and my calves ached. I'd recognised what I now know to be the early stages of the illness during my second spell at Ibrox, one of the reasons I'm convinced stress is behind it. The pressures of managing Rangers the second time round brought my Parkinson's out.

The symptom which cannot be ignored by patient or doctor alike is a tremble of the fingers or foot. The tremor may be misconstrued as a drink problem or as chronic anxiety, a suspicion which may be reinforced by the appearance of genuine panic attacks, occurring as a subconscious reaction to often unacknowledged failing motor skills. I have heard of stage fright in a seasoned performer as the first sign. A consultant ophthalmologist in a pamphlet of autobiographical accounts by doctors with Parkinson's disease relates the onset of his condition:

Then one day at the height of my career, it happened, a sudden brief tremor in my hand lasting a few seconds. In that one moment I lost my status as a good eye surgeon. I was devastated. I completed my operations for the day and couldn't bring myself to go back to the operating theatre again after that, ever again. I made feeble excuses to my patients and sent them to other doctors for their operations. Little did I know that I'd started on the downward path of Parkinson's disease. It was not diagnosed for another two years during which time my confidence for doing even minor office procedures went down and down.

Ray found it difficult to discuss the disorder with his general practitioner and the visits to hospital were short and infrequent. In desperation he began to carry out his own investigations, spending long hours in Newcastle bookshops, pouring over medical tomes in his desperate quest for information. What he read would often reduce him to tears. Although the pills were helping, at home he was frequently cantankerous and short-tempered. To the general public, however, he maintained a brave face: 'Do not feel sorry for me, that's the last thing I need. I have to take pills for the rest of my life but I have a feeling that one day I'll be cured. Parkinson's disease doesn't kill you. If I take my time and I'm sensible everything will be OK.'

A deputation from the Parkinson's Disease Society came to visit him at the Melton Constable and, without much hesitation, Ray agreed to allow his name to be used to increase public awareness. Within a few months his face was seen next to those of fellow sufferers Terry Thomas, Kenneth More, Mao Tse Tung, General MacArthur and Dame Anna Neagle on posters on the escalator walls of the London Underground. The stark message read: 'Parkinson's disease can be Anybody's disease. You can help it be Nobody's disease'.

Beatrice, the hostess from Aer Lingus, who had lost contact with Ray towards the end of his run as a 'six-year money-man', was rising to the surface in the Tottenham Court Road shaft when her eyes lit on Ray's face. She read the stark caption on the hoarding and was overcome with waves of nausea. As she continued up towards the light, tears came to her eyes. How could a young man so full of life and vigour be reduced within five short years to a cripple locked inside his frozen body?

A month after Ray had gone public, and the possibility of a testimonial had been raised by Arsenal and Liverpool, Ray and Jenny bumped into the Sunderland manager, Lawrie McMenemy, in a hotel forecourt. McMenemy was impressed with Ray's physical appearance. 'You're not looking bad, Ray, for a man with Parkinson's disease', he said. McMenemy then invited Ray to take up a coaching job with the club, who were struggling in the depths of the Second Division. This was in part to relieve the pressure on his son, Chris, who was looking after both the youth squad and the Sunderland reserves. McMenemy could see that Ray was in two minds, but Jenny was enthusiastic, and he finally accepted, even though there was no payment initially. In fact, Ray would have to wait several weeks before he even received travel expenses. On his first day at Roker Park, the club he had supported since childhood, he was introduced by the coaching staff to the squad one by one. Ray remembers to this day the expression of fear and the empty, lost looks on the players' faces. He had never come across a more gloomy, negative atmosphere at a football club. Nevertheless, Ray was grateful for his chance and was now feeling so well that he really believed that he had got the illness licked. 'For a while I thought I was cured and was going round to everyone saying "Give us a pint".' Three days after arriving at Roker he watched an atrocious display by the first team against Derby County. After the game, McMenemy asked Ray his opinion; he replied tactlessly, but with that endearing directness which characterizes football people:

'You haven't got a team, Lawrie, there's nothing out there, no pattern, no nothing'. McMenemy blew out his cheeks, said nothing, walked out of the treatment room and never asked Ray's opinion again.

Ray believes that McMenemy was trying to create a similar set-up to that he had enjoyed at Southampton with some talented senior players like Keegan, Channon and George bringing the youngsters on. These were players with such ability you could just give them the ball and they'd get on with it. Unfortunately, at Sunderland, there were no senior players of that ilk. Furthermore, the squad lacked respect for McMenemy's number two, Lew Chatterley. By the time Ray arrived at the club Chatterley seemed unable to communicate with the players; he walked round the club as if he had the world on his shoulders. He would never say more than a word or two to Ray when their paths crossed and was woefully short on charisma. Resentment was building as the team lurched from one crisis to the next and, more than once, Ray felt like knocking on Lawrie McMenemy's door and asking for Chatterley's job. Ray told Jenny that he was convinced Sunderland would be relegated to the Third Division and he warned Chris McMenemy that, if his father didn't get rid of Chatterley quick, the club was doomed. Under mounting stress, Chatterley cut Ray dead on one occasion and appeared increasingly like a man on the verge of a nervous breakdown.

After several weeks in the job, Ray began to sense that McMenemy was beginning to see him as a potential threat to Chris's progress. When any positive publicity came Ray's way, McMenemy was always at pains to point out that his son, Chris, was in charge, and not Ray. On one occasion when praise of Ray's efforts with the youth team filtered through, McMenemy was reputed to have said, 'Don't you know Ray Kennedy is a sick man?'. Despite the bad atmosphere, Ray was grateful for the opportunity to coach, and enjoyed and coped well with the youth training and the travel to away games. There seemed to be no rapport between the management and the players, and the training was haphazard. However, McMenemy remained optimistic and kept talking about the play-offs for a First Division place.

While he was at Sunderland, Ray renewed his acquaintance with Lennie Hepple, an ex-Geordie miner and former British rock and roll champion, who was now the proclaimed guru of movement and rhythm. Hepple had worked under three different England managers and advised thirty-eight First and Second Division football clubs, as well as having consultancies with professional golfers and tennis players. By correcting uneconomical body postures and encouraging movement fluency, Hepple had had considerable success in correcting awkward and eccentric body movements in sportsmen. Peter Shilton and Bobby Moore both considered Hepple to be the single most influential adviser in their careers. He had also transformed his own daughter from a gauche teenager into the British Ladies' Table Tennis Champion. She married another footballer who had benefited from Hepple's treatment, Bryan 'Pop' Robson. Hepple was advising Sunderland when Ray arrived. After Ray told him that he had come down with Parkinson's disease, Hepple reminded Ray of the sessions they had had together in the Greenwood England squad. At that time Ray had the reputation in some circles of being slow and awkward. Hepple had observed that Ray moved like a person much older than his years, and there was an unusual premature economy of movement. One day the squad was on the team bus going to a game with Wales when Hepple noticed that, whereas Colin Todd's head and trunk seemed to be in constant motion, reacting to the bumps of the journey, Ray's upper body was stiff and stationary, especially around his shoulders. Hepple therefore recommended that Ray try to copy Colin Todd's body movement for the rest of the journey. After twenty minutes Ray was obliged to stop because he had become so tired with the effort of imitation. Hepple's intuitive skills in evaluating body language may have enabled him to detect subtle abnormalities in movement, indicative of the earliest stages of Parkinson's disease.

Towards the end of the 1987 season, Chatterley finally conceded defeat and resigned. Within hours his whole personality changed and he became pleasant and relaxed, conversing freely with Ray and reflecting on the pressures which football coaching can bring. A day later McMenemy walked out on the club too. As he was leaving, he bumped into Ray and his last words implied that if Ray stuck around there might be a permanent job beckoning. Despite the club's setbacks, Ray's confidence was increasing: 'I've got Parkinson's disease, but I've seen people in football with more shakes than me. I've got the illness under control and I'm winning the battle. I'm equipped to be a manager or coach'.

Bob Stokoe, who had managed the famous giant-killing Sunderland FA Cup-winning side, was recalled by the chairman, Bob Murray, to take over as caretaker manager, with Chris McMenemy as first team coach. Ray was promoted to be in charge of the youth team and reserves, and was offered a contract of £200 a week until the end of May. However, continuous interference in team selection from Stokoe soon made Ray's position impossible. Stokoe disregarded his opinion altogether and overruled him continually. In contrast to Lawrie McMenemy, whom Ray still regards as a friend, Stokoe failed to gain his respect.

At the end of the season Sunderland were involved in the relegation play-offs. Ray had already booked a family holiday in Cyprus but, on Stokoe's advice, cancelled it in the hope that he might be given a definitive contract for the next season. Unfortunately, Sunderland were relegated, Stokoe was dismissed, and Murray called Ray into his office. Ray relieved the tension of the meeting by saying to Murray, 'Have you got your axe sharpened?', and then went on to ask for the manager's job. Murray, however, told him that he lacked experience, and recommended that he go away for a few weeks and see who was appointed as the new manager. Realizing that he had little chance of further employment, Ray told Murray to stick Sunderland and walked out of the chairman's office and away from the club he had supported for so many years. In fact, the new manager, Dennis Smith, had already been lined up, and Ray need not have cancelled his holiday, as it transpired that the board had already made up their minds not to reappoint him.

On 5 October 1987, less than a year after the diagnosis of Parkinson's disease had been made, a cataclysm struck: Ray's wife walked out. He had returned to the Melton Constable after a late night out with friends and a little the worse for wear. Immediately a row broke out between the couple which culminated in Ray hitting his wife in the face in a blind fury and kicking her down the stairs. Jenny fled for refuge to a neighbour's in her dressing gown and a tee-shirt, and the police were called. Charges were not pressed, and the episode was dismissed as a minor domestic disturbance. To Ray, however, it was to prove much more than that. At a time when he was slowly coming to terms with an incurable disease, after society had callously turned its back on him, he was now to lose his wife and livelihood. After fifteen stormy years of marriage, Jennifer wanted a divorce. Her father told the newspapers, after the domestic incident had made local news, that he considered Ray Kennedy to be 'a Jekyll and Hyde character'. It transpired later that Jenny had been trying to break free for eight years. She had never forgiven Ray for an incident, when she was pregnant with Dale, when another woman had turned up on their Ainsdale doorstep and tried to take Ray away from her. She described living with her husband as 'like being on the edge of a volcano'.

After three years at the Melton Constable, the licence was withdrawn by the brewers and Ray went to live with his brother Michael, taking Dale and Cara with him.

Ray's initial optimism after starting treatment was now ebbing away fast. At the end of 1987 he was re-examined at the Royal Victoria Infirmary by Dr Bates, who was relieved to find that despite the recent domestic turmoil Ray's condition was still reasonably well controlled. The tablets had brought a marked improvement in the leg dragging and, apart from a ratchet-like stiffness of the right wrist and an occasional trembling of the fingers of his right hand, there was little for the neurologist to record. Ray, however, now feared the worst:

I knew I couldn't cope with the pub after my marriage broke up. As things stand I know I can only get worse rather than better and I have to face that. The pub was the last thing I needed. People in there thought I'd been drinking the profits away because the illness makes you slur your speech and gives you the shakes. To a stranger I probably looked and acted like a drunk, but it was not the booze that affected me. At times I couldn't bear to face going behind the bar because I was sure people were jumping to the wrong conclusions. When your marriage breaks up that's something to do with you, but when your health goes you're helpless. My chances of finding a job now are slim and someone told me I could be in a wheelchair in five years.

Jenny had started divorce proceedings and it became increasingly obvious that Ray's financial affairs were in even greater disarray than had originally been anticipated. The Inland Revenue

were making demands for around £150,000 in taxes going back
ten years. All Ray's assets were frozen while the divorce settlement was negotiated. Ray was to spend much of the next two
years in accountants' and solicitors' offices providing endless
repetitive statements. At the request of his wife's solicitors, he
was required to have an independent neurological examination
so that the nature of his disorder could be confirmed and
opinions sought regarding his likely future handicap. His resilience
and determination were severely tested over this period, which
he now considers to be the worst time in his life. Dr Bates's
report to the magistrates' court assessed Ray's prognosis as
follows:

> Parkinson's disease is a progressive disorder and he is likely
> to show deterioration over the next few years. When the
> disease begins as early as in Mr Kennedy's case then there
> is a significant risk of a deterioration over the next ten
> years ... he has had a gradually increasing requirement for
> therapy over the past fifteen months and although his symp-
> toms presently remain well controlled, I think it likely that
> he may develop complications of treatment in the form of
> involuntary movements or lessening effectiveness of medica-
> tion during the next five years. It is therefore likely that
> between his fortieth and forty-fifth year he will not be able
> to sustain gainful employment and he may well need to
> employ help in terms of his day-to-day care at some time
> during the fifth decade of life.

Ray, who was still coming to terms with the diagnosis was
now compelled to digest these unpalatable truths as reports of his
condition were scrutinized in the courts. His mood oscillated
wildly between profound desperation and unshakeable courage
and optimism:

> In a sense the setbacks I have suffered have made me more
> determined to sort out my life and I am not prepared to throw
> in the towel. Sometimes I think I got this illness to test my
> strength. On other occasions I wonder what I have done to
> deserve it. Sometimes I wish I had a broken arm so that
> people could see there was something wrong because there
> are days when I look as right as rain and people come up and

say 'You're looking well'. What keeps me going is a feeling deep down that I'll definitely be cured.

During this time, when Ray's world was falling apart, he continued to receive sound advice and moral support from Mike Ellis, who continued to push for a testimonial, Ken Friar, the Arsenal chief executive, and Tommy Smith. After a few weeks of living with Michael, the two brothers fell out irretrievably over a petty dispute. Ray left, and Michael cut himself off from his parents, who had taken Ray's side in the argument. Ray then moved to a small flat in Leazes Square, close to Gallowgate and St James's Park. Loneliness and boredom brought escalating unhappiness. Ray withdrew into himself and became more and more isolated, cutting himself off for long periods from his brothers and sister and his football contacts.

Cara and Dale, however, coped heroically with his frustration. Ray still recalls with pain an episode in which he was walking home with the children down a road where men were painting a new yellow line. He was desperate to get home as he could feel his pills wearing off, but Dale repeatedly disobeyed him by treading on the freshly painted line. Ray shouted angrily at his son and saw tears welling up in the little boy's eyes as he bent down to fasten his shoe-laces. After that, Ray vowed to himself never to upset his children again and to make sure that, whatever happened to him, provisions would be made for their long-term well-being. Cara and Dale never grumbled when their father's physical limitations precluded him from carrying out paternal responsibilities, and both of them have always been there when he has needed them most.

In desperation, Ray looked round for female company and for someone who could bring some stability and control into his life again. Ray remained attractive to women and he embarked on a pattern, which was to continue for the next few years, of having two girlfriends on the go at once: one who would assume a maternalistic caring role and the other who would play the role of playmate and mistress. However, his ability to dictate and dominate relationships with the opposite sex, particularly at the times when his illness was to the fore, had been compromised. Unless his life was planned precisely, he would be anxious and jumpy, and at times his ability to think clearly was impaired. It was not only Ray's concubines who were to change frequently, but also his accommodation.

In the summer of 1988, he was offered another opportunity to coach at holiday camps, this time at Pontin's Lancashire resorts. Kennedy's left foot had gone Pontinental: on Tuesdays and Wednesdays he was to be found in Blackpool, Thursdays and Fridays at Southport, and Sundays and Mondays at Morecambe. Ray replaced Trevor Hockey, the former Welsh international who tragically died of a coronary thrombosis at the age of forty-three. He coped well with the work and enjoyed the basic coaching and five-a-side games. He would entertain the children with football quizzes, show them videos of Liverpool Football Club and sometimes bring his collection of medals for them to admire. By and large, he found the kids were a joy, but some of the parents were a nightmare, always pushing their offspring forward or complaining about the least little thing. Ray was able to renew old acquaintances, especially that of Ian Kidd, a restaurant owner, who allowed Ray to stay in a flat owned by his parents in Southport at the end of the week. Ray's social life became so frenetic that Ian's parents complained that since he had moved in the front step had begun to wear out. As Ray toiled valiantly at the camps, not far away in his Southport home, Kenny Dalglish was basking in the success of another League Championship as manager of Liverpool.

By the end of the summer, Ray was back in the North-East and again at the New Hartley Club, presenting awards for John Maley, his old coach. As the financial turmoil of his divorce settlement and tax arrears rumbled on, Ray lived on the football pension which Arsenal had so shrewdly advised him to take out. The endless visits to tax offices and his accountant continued. Ray was by now drifting in an unnavigated sea of despair, a lonely forgotten invalid, with only Cara and Dale, Trevor, Janet and his elderly parents to support him.

He still found it hard to recognize himself in the Parkinson's disease he saw in others, and he was haunted by the helpless plaintive appearance of Terry Thomas: 'When I see those pictures of Terry it crosses my mind, could I end up like that?' Thomas's Parkinson's disease was picked up at a routine medical check-up by an Australian doctor who noted a tremor in his left hand. This had not been noticed by Thomas or his family. After the diagnosis had been confirmed in London, Terry Thomas's reactions were remarkably similar to Ray's, and are recorded in his autobiography *Terry-Thomas Tells Tales*:

> I feared it would affect my job prospects so at first I tried to hide it. But when rumours of my drunken behaviour on film sets began to flourish I admitted the real reason. As it was a condition that would get worse I knew it would be hopeless to hide it.

The difference between Thomas and Ray, however, was about thirty years. Terry Thomas was already in his sixties and entering that period of life when a graceful retreat from many physical activities is inevitable; Ray was at the peak of his physical fitness, still actively engaged in many sporting pastimes, virile and with most of his life still in front of him. Interestingly, Thomas's personality, in common with that of Ray and many other patients, conformed to the postulated Parkinsonian personality of nervy, perfectionistic introspection:

> I often think perhaps erroneously that being an incurable perfectionist in everything from carving to cuddling makes having Parkinson's even more of a burden to bear than for people who do not set themselves such gruelling criteria. When your whole life has been a challenge to do all that you do perfectly, it comes hard to have to accept that from now on there are going to be no impeccable performances.

Thomas elaborates further:

> There is no set pattern about the effect of Parkinson's disease. It affects different people in different ways. When a doctor asked me how it affected me I said, 'I get depressions'. And this doctor said, 'You can't blame Parkinson's disease for that. You've always had depression for obvious reasons. You have had all sorts of worries and it's natural they should depress you. You'd be depressed whether you had Parkinson's or not.' He was probably right.

On bad, lonely days, sitting talking to his mother, concerned more and more about Dale and Cara's future, Ray started to consider seriously the possibility of auctioning his twenty-one medals.

19 Good Spell United, Bad Phase Rangers

Doctor 'Can you walk?'

Patient 'Work? Aa canna even waalk!'
        (IN A GEORDIE ACCENT)

RAY's honeymoon period, during which he felt cured, did not last long. He was now divorced, his debts to the Inland Revenue and alimony settlements had finally been resolved, and Cara and Dale were living with their mother in a new home in South Wellfield near Whitley Bay. The children were regular visitors to their father's Gosforth flat, which he had bought in partnership with one of his girlfriends, Audrey Smith.

Ray's health was deteriorating and he had lost the conviction that he had beaten the disease. Despite consuming an increasingly varied salad of pills, a satisfactory balance could not be achieved. An admission to the Royal Victoria Infirmary did nothing to improve his morale, and he came out feeling worse than when he had gone in. In desperation, he finally contacted me, and I arranged with Dr Kerr and Dr Bates for him to be admitted to the Middlesex Hospital. It was clear that he had begun to experience a disturbance known as the 'on-off', or 'yo-yo', effect, in which the previously reliable response from each dose of L-dopa medication becomes increasingly unpredictable and brittle. On some days, and at some times, his tablets worked as well as they had ever done but, in contrast to the first two years of treatment, they were no longer dependable. Ray began to worry about dud batches, or that he was becoming allergic or resistant to treatment.

Everyday activities, which we all take for granted, were now a major challenge. His walking periodically degenerated to an embarrassing 'fairy step' shuffle, his facial expression froze in mid-sentence, conveying an impression of unfeeling idiocy, and his speech dwindled to a tuneless mumble. These impediments brought with them fear and a retreat into himself. At social engagements, like Cinderella, he would suddenly, without explanation, hurry to the door. At home he would sit apathetically, feeling ill, finding even a visit to the toilet or the kitchen a terrifying ordeal. Although the stiffness, slowness and shakiness were still restricted mainly to his right side, a much more dreadful and painful sign of the illness had now appeared in his dependable left foot. In the middle of the night, he woke with agonizing cramping contortions of the toes and calf and, when he got up in the morning, his left foot would be twisted, clawed and deformed. The only way he could get about was to crawl around on all fours, often relying on his children to provide partial relief by massage. Ray joked to Cara and Dale that he was in a 'Bad phase Rangers' and had to wait for a 'Good spell United' to return. This was his way of describing the 'on-off' effect of his drugs.

He was now acutely aware of the time course of each dose of L-dopa, which took about half an hour to start to work and had good effects for just under two hours. Even the 'switch-ons' were less satisfying than they had been and were now often associated with restless, jerky fidgets, racing, uncontrollable thoughts and a lurching stride. These 'on' periods came as a blissful release to Ray, but were frequently more distressing than his slow 'offs' to those around him. The contrast between Ray's personality on and off the field of play, which had earned him the reputation as a bit of a Walter Mitty, was now compressed into violent drug-related swings occurring every few hours.

Each day presented its own conundrums and ever-changing cycles of movement. During a visit to Ray's home, I was able to 'map' a typical day in his life.

4 a.m.

Ray struggles to get out of bed and finds it extremely difficult even to turn over. He then totters slowly to the kitchen to eat some chocolate or clean the cooker. Gripped by a fretful motor restlessness, he then walks around before going back to bed for two or three more hours' drugged sleep.

8 a.m.

Ray wakes up to face a new day completely locked within a straitjacket, uncomfortable and at 'disease with himself'. His left foot starts to twist painfully, bringing him to his knees and forcing him to grovel along the floor on hands and knees. He then sits on his feet to try to relieve the discomfort and waits, drenched in sweat, for the first tablets of the day to kick-start him into action. He feels as if he is looking out from within an iron mask, unable to think. His stomach is distended and swollen, and he doses himself with laxatives to keep his torpid bowels moving throughout the day.

9.30 a.m.

The L-dopa suddenly starts to work, bringing, with its benefits, paddling, jerking movements of his right leg. His head starts to jerk from side to side – 'good for Wimbledon' – and his speech accelerates. He then embarks on the uncertain adventure of breakfast, trying desperately to avoid spilling food or drink over his clothes. His mind and body are now two or three jerks ahead and he feels anxious and out of control. He sways to the garage disguising his jerky right arm by holding it 'Prince Charles fashion' behind his back. He then drives the twenty-minute journey to Seaton Delaval to visit his mother. For the next two hours he talks endlessly about his difficulties and worries to his parents. Finally he calms down.

Midday

He arrives at the gymnasium at Whitley Bay and immediately freezes to the floor, unable to move for ten minutes. After twenty minutes on the exercise bike he seizes up again and has to be lifted off by one of the gym assistants. Deep feelings of hopelessness and depression descend and he is trapped in a doorway for a few seconds as if an invisible force is blocking his way.

1.30 p.m.

The mere thought of lunch switches him off, with tightness in his chest and hints of the left foot cramp returning. However, just when it seems impossible for him to cut his food, the next dose of pills cuts in, throwing him into a bundle of restless, atavistic squirmings, but at least it allows him to get his food to his mouth to chew and swallow.

2.30 p.m.

Ray sleeps for about forty minutes, but wakes rigid, shaking and nauseous. He feels so ill that he would agree to anything in order to be left alone, totally dominated and controlled by his physical limitations. He has great difficulty in starting a movement, and more problems in sustaining it for more than a few seconds. In a strange way, however, he feels an inner contentment and a pleasant remoteness. The next dose of pills starts to work, enabling him to drive into Newcastle to chat with acquaintances in the shops and meet a girlfriend in Fenwick's for coffee. He hurries to buy two compact discs before the pills run out and then drives home furiously, slumping exhausted on the sofa, too drained to put on his new discs.

Evening

He stays in alone, brooding over the possibility of becoming a lonely old man at forty, staring at the walls. He tries to get something out of his trouser pocket, but the pocket seems too small and it takes him several minutes to complete even this simple task. Dinner leads to a volley of disjointed twitching of his limbs. Before he has finished his pudding, the battery has gone flat again, and he is lifeless, tired and transfixed like a wax model in Madame Tussaud's. Finally he struggles to bed to prepare for the challenge of tomorrow.

I described this state of mind and body in my letter to Ray's general practitioner:

He has in recent months developed a progressive fragility of response to an increasingly complicated regime of medication, aggravated by mounting emotional stress. He is now experiencing periods of severe immobility lasting up to four hours during which he is hardly able to drag the soles of his feet across the ground, his speech becomes ponderous and distorted, and his finger movements are laboured and reduced. Occasionally his right hand trembles when he is walking or sitting. During these periods he has abdominal bloating and cramps, with feelings of sickness. He is also indecisive and drenched in sweat from top to toe. Each Sinemet (L-dopa) takes between a quarter of an hour and an hour to work, following which he is able to move and get about his daily life for around two hours. However, his concentration is perturbed and he feels distraught and slightly out of control. In these periods he is able to play a round of golf or tennis, although his appearance indicates mild inco-ordination.

For periods of up to two weeks he was literally confined to the house, often crawling around the floor for much of the day, and heavily dependent on his children, mother and girlfriends. Even on good days, when he was able to get out and looked virtually normal to all the world, he would suddenly be attacked by unsettling, demoralizing motor blocks when his brain temporarily lost control of his body movements as suddenly as if someone had switched the light off. One day, when shopping in a local supermarket, 'Bad phase Rangers' descended and he was turned into a statue. After a wait of many minutes it became clear that he was not going to thaw, and Ray jokingly turned to one of the staff who had come to help and asked him to turn the key in his back ten times to wind him up again. In the end, he was carted out of the supermarket in a food trolley and dumped embarrassingly by his car. In a garden centre, a wheelbarrow was used to carry him out after he had been forced to the ground by his left foot going into severe cramp. Further humiliation occurred one day in a restaurant in Southport when, half-way through the meal, his 'bionic battery ran down', leaving him stranded and alienated, incapable of following the speed of the conversation, looking blank and gormless and unable to respond with emotional gestures. He recalls this frightening feeling of the conversation going on in his presence, but being ignored, looking in at his friends from the outside. He had entered the restaurant animated and happy, but within thirty minutes he had been reduced to an indecisive wreck, stripped of his dignity and pride. More and more of these degrading episodes were to follow and only his humour rescued him and kept him going.

Those around him could not be expected to understand and often reacted inappropriately. Some would shout at him as if he were deaf, others would try to pull him along when his feet were

Two old Gunners with new loyalties: Liverpool's Kennedy and Queens
Park Rangers' McLintock (*circa* 1976). (Colorsport)
Kennedy and Case in Europe.

OPPOSITE PAGE]

Right: Razor – midfield visionary, 1978. (Colorsport)

Centre: European Cup triumph in Rome, 25 May 1977. (Harry Ormesher)

Below: Liverpool team-mates training for England, *left to right:* Phil Neal, Phil Thompson and Ray Kennedy, with manager Don Revie. (Harry Ormesher)

Ray celebrates his European Cup semi-final success with his daughter Cara, April 1978.

Another Liverpool triumph: Ray with his guru, Bob Paisley, and Ray Clemence in 1979. (Express Newspapers).

Ray training with his Pezopolikos squad in 1984. Masking of the face and rigidity of the right arm suggest early symptoms of Parkinson's disease. (Char. Savvides)

The Melton Constable, Seaton Sluice, 1989. (Mrs J. Pulin-Lees)

Samples of Ray's handwriting in 1990.
Left: Before his first dose of L-dopa, his script is small and cramped. *Right:* Forty minutes after taking his pills, the fluency and boldness of his writing returns.

A visit to the Parkinson's Disease Society Brain Tissue Bank at the Institute of Neurology, 1991. Dr Susan Daniel shows a brain section to Gary Lineker, Dr Andrew Lees and Ray Kennedy. (*News of the World*)

SIR JOHN BETJEMAN
MUHAMMAD ALI
SIR MICHAEL REDGRAVE
TERRY THOMAS
KENNETH MORE
RAY KENNEDY
A.J.P. TAYLOR
DAME ANNA NEAGLE

PARKINSON'S DISEASE CAN BE ANYBODY'S DISEASE.

You needn't be famous. Men and women all over the
world suffer from Parkinson's Disease.
There are over 100,000 sufferers in this country alone.
There is no known cure. We need *your* help.

HELP MAKE IT NOBODY'S DISEASE

Please support
Parkinson's Disease Society
22 Upper Woburn Place, London WC1H 0RA. Tel: 071-383 3513
Patron: HRH The Princess of Wales

The poster used by the Parkinson's Disease Society on the
London Underground to promote awareness and raise money
for research. (courtesy of the Parkinson's Disease Society)

A meeting with the Princess of Wales, patron of the Parkinson's
Disease Society, in 1992. (pic Photos)

Ray with Muhammad Ali at Waterstone's Bookshop, Leadenhall
Market, 1992.

Ray acknowledges the teams at his testimonial on 27 April 1991. (Colorsport)

After his testimonial Ray shares a joke with Ray Clemence as David Speedie looks on. (Ian Sager)

stuck to the ground, causing him to stumble and fall over. Most commonly and damagingly, they would look away in embarrassment. As Ray began to face up to his disabilities, he started to use them to help him overcome everyday difficulties, often informing people of his handicap as soon as he met them. Some of the embarrassing situations he got into as a result of the illness now appear humorous to him.

A sudden freeze-up in Newcastle airport almost made him miss his holiday plane, but fortunately the ground staff came to his rescue and drove him to the departure gate in one of the buggies usually reserved for arthritic senior citizens. On arriving at the gangway of the plane, however, a dopamine surge, possibly triggered by adrenaline, resurrected him and, to the astonishment of the stewardesses and fellow passengers, he was able to jump from the wheelchair and run up the stairs of the plane to his seat. Once he had arrived at his hotel in Cyprus he was able to wind down, the on-off swings became less severe and he found that when a bad patch did occur he could disguise it perfectly by lying flat by the pool and remaining motionless like all the other sun worshippers. Towards the end of the holiday he ran out of medication and was obliged to take a taxi to the village doctor to get further supplies urgently. During the journey his last two pills stopped working, and the taxi driver had to lift him out of the taxi and escort him into the surgery. Fortunately, the doctor had some supplies of L-dopa and within thirty minutes of taking two tablets, Ray was able to stride out of the surgery as if there were nothing wrong with him and get back into the taxi. The taxi driver's eyes nearly popped out of his head at the apparent miracle. For some time after this visit, once word had got around the island, the doctor was swamped with desperate patients all expecting him to work miracles for them too.

Panics in crowds, accompanied by drenching floods of sweat and attacks of blind fear, were now everyday experiences for Ray. He became more and more dependent on members of the public to rescue him, many of whom misinterpreted his behaviour as that of a drunk or a drug addict. On Euston Station he was recognized and rescued by a porter who was a Gunners' supporter and who unlocked a toilet specially for him to use to sit down and rest. A London cabbie also came to his aid, bringing him back to the Middlesex Hospital without demanding payment.

As the months went by his ability to predict the exact time when his pills would run down became less and less reliable, and any food seemed to block the action of his drugs. The fear of constipation was becoming an increasing obsession as his stomach and bowels tied themselves in knots. However, in the periods of petrification when he was barely able to move about, the tremble which had been present before he started treatment remained absent. Driving his car presented no major problems even when a switch-off occurred, but on one occasion, on a return trip from Edinburgh when he stopped at a garage to fill up with petrol, he was incapable of getting out of the car and had to sit out an off period on the forecourt. Patients with Parkinson's disease are allowed to drive, provided the DVLC are satisfied after enquiry from the patients' doctors that the disabilities do not interfere with co-ordination and speed of reaction behind the wheel. On rare occasions Ray had become confused over the control of brake and accelerator and, on non-automatic cars, it was difficult for him to regulate the pressure on the clutch. The illness was slowly becoming more difficult for him to live with:

> It's hard enough to accept you can't play football any more, but not to be able to walk, talk or use your hands is soul-destroying. I'm feeling more and more resentful as time passes. It's when you stop that it really hits you and you feel like doing yourself in. It's embarrassing being stuck in public places for up to four hours. When first diagnosed I could always walk but now I can't even put one foot in front of the other. My brain knows what it wants to do, but the messages don't seem to get through. When I see all my Liverpool mates in successful management jobs it hurts because I know I could have been there too. Now I live from hour to hour, clock-watching to make sure I don't miss my pills.

The gradual realization that the medical profession did not have all the answers led Ray to explore other avenues of help. I asked Ray always to let me know about these other treatments in case they might be harmful or interfere markedly with his dopamine replacement therapy. I was also concerned that they would raise his hopes unrealistically and put him to considerable expense. He first visited an elderly doctor's wife who used aromatherapy and reflexology to treat all manner of ailments. Sir

John Betjeman claimed that his Parkinson's disease had been helped by a former Geordie miner, Joseph Corvo, who had massaged particular regions of the soles of his feet and alleviated body stiffness through zone therapy. Ray's therapist went to work enthusiastically, massaging him with a selection of aromatic musks and applying powerful magnets to his feet.

He next visited a famous faith-healer called Noel who had treated Susan Hampshire successfully and who had the reputation of being the second most powerful healer in the country after Matthew Manning. Before becoming a faith-healer, Noel had worked in a factory where his spiritual powers had reputedly stopped the machinery on more than one occasion. On the day of the appointment, Ray took Cara and Dale with him so that he would not be considered a crank. The healer told Ray that he had a brain disease and could be helped. He settled him down in a chair and then put his hands above Ray's head and applied an amethyst to his chest. At this first session Ray felt a frightening electrical power pulsing through his body and was aware of a clicking in his head. At a subsequent session the healer told Ray that his foot was earthed to the floor and, on attempting to move it, Ray found that it was completely paralysed for several minutes; on yet another occasion the healer correctly predicted a stomach upset. Ray's mother was so impressed by what her son told her that she, too, 'went for a blast' and the force was apparently so strong her hair stood on end. However, there were no lasting benefits to Ray's Parkinson's disease.

Ray became hooked on clairvoyants and visited several in and around Newcastle. He tried to visit the celebrated Gypsy Rose Lee, who worked from a caravan in Spanish City, the fun-fair referred to in the Dire Straits song, but the queues were always too long for him to be seen. He told one of the clairvoyants that during his footballing days he had often felt that there was a spirit behind him driving him forward and making him feel different from other people and that this spirit had now left him. The clairvoyant replied, 'No, you left the spirit', and went on to say that she had a four hundred-year-old Chinaman guiding her and providing her life force. Ray then visited a masseuse and yoga specialist in Jesmond, who relaxed him so much he fell asleep, and a naturopath in Seahouses who dispensed all manner of nostrums and concoctions.

Life for a Parkinsonian patient experiencing 'manic-depressive' swings of movement can be exhausting and demoralizing. Some patients, like Ivan Vaughan, prefer to forgo their medication for much of the day and try to battle with the challenge of life without a starter motor. Other patients overdose, preferring to gyrate vertiginously through the day, feeling jubilant but unreal. Like Ray, most patients end up somewhere in-between. A journalist with disabilities very similar to Ray's provided this illuminating account of the vicissitudes of Parkinson's disease under L-dopa:

One can adopt stratagems to save oneself from various kinds of embarrassment; I have a radio taxi account or if one goes off badly in the street one holds on to a lamp post until a taxi comes past. People are extraordinarily sympathetic and helpful. I find that an aluminium walking stick is useful. It is a sign that something's wrong and holding on to a lamp post is not necessarily because one is drunk. These 'offs' are accompanied by a curiously deep and malevolent depression. It isn't suicidal; I actually feel as if I am dying.

Almost as bad is the boredom and the frustration of not being able to work. My sleep is severely disrupted, I have about one hour's slumber when I would prefer six. I go to sleep at midnight; if I'm 'on' I sleep in my bed with my wife; if I'm 'off' I sleep on the floor. I find a bed totally unacceptable when 'off', because such slight control as one has over one's limbs is totally soaked up by the mattress, even ours which is a hard orthopaedic one. Equally the covers, even a light duvet, feel too heavy and restrictive. Only on the floor can I retain some control over my limbs. I haven't slept for longer than two hours at a stretch for about two years. Each time I wake I have a severe backache. To make my way downstairs sometimes is easy, on other occasions it takes up to an hour. I'm more absent minded now than I used to be and my memory is worse. Two odd observations: the summer before last a friend took me sailing in the Channel for two days – something I tremendously enjoyed. I was so busy and so relaxed in the moderate sea that I forgot my pills and had lasted half a day before I remembered them. I then started taking them, not because of any discomfort but for fear that any lack of agility on deck might have prejudiced the chance of my being asked again. And last spring I had an emergency operation for appendicitis which was done at four o'clock in the morning. I felt absolutely no need for any pills until ten p.m. the following day.

A further account runs as follows:

When I am mobile I feel optimistic and almost forget that I am going to be incapacitated again. The mobility is not as good as it used to be, I lurch a lot and my balance is not good. I still have twitchy involuntary movements. The problem is that I feel sleepy, because I can only sleep properly when I am relaxed, so a lot of the best time when I am capable of doing things I find myself asleep. When I awake I am usually stiff and feel a very strong tremor affecting my right side and my toes go into cramp. During the switched off state I feel weak all over and now my legs give way so that I can't walk unless I am held up. My feeling when this happens is one of deep depression and helplessness and I become extremely frightened about the future as more and more parts of my body become involved. For example, my face muscles are stiff and my mouth will not open wide enough for me to speak clearly. L-dopa does not work as well as it used to. When it works it does so slowly.

Cecil Todes, a consultant psychiatrist who developed Parkinson's disease at an early age, in an autobiographical essay published in the *Lancet* in 1983 writes:

It is interesting to compare the 'on-off' of nine years ago with my present experience, when the whole body is affected: in those days, 'off' revealed a chink in my defensive armour; today, 'on' has come to represent a gift gladly accepted from the Fates. The quality over twenty-four hours has also changed: in the early days, 'on' would last up to eight hours, but today I am happy with four hours and must often be content with just two. During the day, I experience small scale mood swings. Most striking is the depression and hopelessness just prior to coming 'on' with the first dose of the morning. Being 'on' is tinged with excitement and/or fixed orientation. I experience genuine, spontaneous flexibility only during my morning 'on' and after a mid-afternoon nap ... recent and medium term memory is now affected, although paradoxically, early childhood memories have become more accessible. When

'off', I am pre-occupied with my body and its limitations ...
twelve years of the illness have not diminished my fascination
with it — when on. There can be no other condition in which
the body can be so rapidly and completely transformed as if
the gods were breathing fire into it. The contrast when 'off',
and the feebleness of mind and body, is a perpetual reminder
of one's decline. In experiencing a two part existence in one
lifetime, I feel like Lear, who in his dotage could say: 'We are
not ourselves when nature, being oppressed, commands the
mind to suffer with the body'.

20 Chewing Water Lilies

I do not smile because I am happy.
Because I gurgle I am not content.
I feel in colours, mottled, mainly black.
And the only sound I hear is the sea
Pounding against the white cliffs of my skull.

(ROGER MCGOUGH)

APOMORPHINE was first synthesized by nineteenth-century German chemists from the narcotic morphine, and was used to treat behavioural vices in farmyard animals. The sacred and magical properties of the water lily used in religious ceremonies by the ancient Egyptians and Maya civilization of Mexico are probably due in part to the presence of apomorphine and related alkaloids in its tubers. However, apomorphine has had a chequered history in medical therapeutics. It was first employed to make people vomit after they had deliberately or accidentally swallowed poisons or sleeping pills, and then it enjoyed a vogue as a sedative. More recently it has been used to treat nicotine and alcohol dependence. The junky William Burroughs, author of *The Naked Lunch*, visited a South Kensington physician in the sixties for an apomorphine cure. The drug has also been recommended for its aphrodisiac effects. When administered to laboratory rodents, it induces stereotyped head-weaving and gnawing behaviour, effects which can be explained by its ability to stimulate dopamine systems within the brain. Unlike morphine, apomorphine is not addictive and, forty years ago in Boston, injections under the skin were shown to produce benefits in patients with Parkinson's disease. Unfortunately, the effects were short-lived and a constellation of disagreeable side-effects, including vomiting, fainting and sleepiness, precluded its introduction into clinical practice. Ten years later the highly effective L-dopa tablet treatment became available and apomorphine was forgotten.

However, by 1985, the shortcomings of L-dopa therapy were only too apparent and I therefore decided to re-examine the possibility of using apomorphine to treat the hundreds of desperate patients who were beginning to lose ground. My interest was fuelled by the introduction of the delightfully named medicine domperidone ('I didn't know you could get champagne on the Health Service, Doc'), which prevented many of the unpleasant side-effects without interfering with its effects on the region of the brain damaged in Parkinson's disease. With some trepidation, my colleagues and I proposed to inject apomorphine into a young woman in her thirties who had developed Parkinson's disease at the age of twenty-six and was experiencing the most profound yo-yo effects:

> After the birth of my child I was unable to move a muscle for hours on end I was so rigid. I couldn't speak although the words were going round and round in my head. As I felt my body stiffening I would take a pill. Half an hour later, as the paralysis increased, I would take another tablet. Then cramp would set in followed by a sudden burst of violent energy. It was so bad I had to be pinned down to a chair by my family. Without this restraint, I would be running from room to room, crashing into anything in my path with my arms flapping uncontrollably. I was becoming exhausted, burning up so much energy and my weight dropped to six and a half stone and as the intake of food reduced the effectiveness of L-dopa, I stopped eating. It was a vicious circle.

The rigid catatonic posture of this young woman as she lay flat on her back, unable to move or speak, in Campbell Thompson Ward at the Middlesex Hospital, still lingers in my mind. One milligram of apomorphine was injected under the skin of her abdominal wall. After four minutes, she yawned repetitively and, within another minute, the first signs of melting began with one or two stereotyped finger flexes of the left hand. Two minutes later she had leapt off her bed and begun stretching her legs in the hospital corridor, speaking clearly and cogently; only fidgety jerks of her hands and a weaving of her head marred the dramatic awakening which persisted for an hour and a quarter before she lapsed back into her Rip Van Winkle-like state. The apomorphine effect on a physical state formerly considered to be due to an irreversible nerve cell degeneration is one of the most dramatic phenomena I have witnessed in my medical career. Significantly, this young woman also did not experience any of the distressing and unwanted effects which had occurred in the Boston experiments forty years earlier.

From here, a whole programme of treatment began in which more than two hundred patients have been treated successfully, either by serial injections under the skin or by means of a continuous delivery of apomorphine through a compact, portable mini-pump which pushes the drug steadily from a syringe through a plastic tube into a needle inserted and secured under the skin of the abdomen. For many patients, especially the young, apomorphine has been like a second coming, returning them to the quality of life they experienced in the early days of starting L-dopa therapy, and even permitting some to return to work. By restoring mobility, others have been rescued from wheelchairs and, temporarily, from life in the slow lane where they were pitied for their apparent unfeeling imbecility.

Four years on and still receiving apomorphine through a battery-operated pump carried in her dress pocket or in a shoulder purse, the young woman who received the first injection continues to extol its virtues:

> I no longer lurch from one piece of furniture to the next, or need to hold myself on to a chair in order to remain seated. I have resumed a near normal life style and gained a stone in weight. Cramp is a thing of the past. I still switch off and I still go over the top, but on a completely different plane. My offs are not nearly so off and when I am on I am a lot more stable and I have periods of being really calm. Of course I have good days and bad days, but don't we all, and the difference that apomorphine has made to the family is incalculable.

I can still picture the look of relief on Ray's face when, on first meeting him in his room at the Middlesex Hospital, I told him that there were still medical ways of helping his Parkinson's disease. I was also struck by the preservation of his upright, athletic build which had so characterized his playing days and which contrasted with that of so many patients with Parkinson's disease who gradually shrink into themselves. Ray's first task in hospital was to plot out for me the pattern of his movement and mood swings during the day so that a programme of treatment with apomorphine could be planned.

To attempt to understand the peaks and troughs in everyday performance experienced by a patient with Parkinson's disease, simply on the grounds of rising and falling blood-levels of L-dopa would be a gross and erroneous simplification. Ray's body movements were now dependent on all sorts of other unquantifiable factors, including food intake, transitory emotional stresses, the quality of the previous night's sleep and the amount of daily physical exercise. All these variables interreacted with his drug treatment, leading to a pattern of ons and offs which varied substantially from day to day, even when his complex schedule of pill-taking was kept uniform. In hospital his fluctuations were less severe and more predictable than when he was at home, where every six weeks or so control seemed to go totally haywire for several days.

Nerve cells in the human brain convey information from one to the next by chemical and electrical potentials which produce 'all or none' signals. In other words, the nervous message is either completely transmitted or it totally fails to get through, with no intermediate response. However, the drug L-dopa leads to a flowering in many dimensions, with abrupt stereotyped effects on patterns of movement, mood and behaviour which defy reduction simply to the dose level of the drug. Patients with Parkinson's disease on L-dopa are forced discontinuously and uncontrollably through an increasingly narrow hour-glass of unstable space between their secure orbits of 'on' and 'off'. Adequate control of the malady is, therefore, likely to depend ultimately on far more than just a steady level of L-dopa entering the brain. Even before the L-dopa treatment is started, some patients experience remarkable, if ephemeral, liberations from their Parkinsonian state. For example, one of my patients with Parkinson's disease so severe that she was unable to move or speak could deftly and accurately whisk off a bluebottle which landed on the tip of her nose.

The neurological literature is also enriched by a series of remarkable anecdotes in which severely handicapped patients with Parkinson's disease, when confronted with life-threatening situations, such as a shipwreck, house fire or volcano, miraculously regain their powers of locomotion to enable them to escape danger. One of my favourite accounts of so-called *kinesia paradoxica* is of an elderly, chairbound man who was taken to the nurses' ball on New Year's Eve in the institution where he had resided for many years. When approached by an attractive young nurse who asked him to dance, he was able to rise from his chair and competently waltz the young lady off her feet before slumping back to his flexed, rigid, expressionless posture. These incredible reports and the acknowledged volatility of Parkinsonian symptoms help to explain why the ailment was for many years wrongly considered to be a psychological disorder akin to depression. What, in fact, these fascinating accounts indicate is that if the key which life-threatening situations seem to replicate could be turned consistently by artificial means, then the Parkinsonian corset might be permanently unlocked.

The first apomorphine injection Ray received had no effect at all, apart from bringing him out in an unpleasant cold sweat. The second injection, approximately an hour later, confirmed the drug's potential as an aphrodisiac, much to Ray's embarrassment and the amusement of the nursing staff. In an off period Ray's handwriting was now laboured, cramped and greatly reduced in size. Within twelve minutes of the third apomorphine injection, however, it had doubled in size and closely resembled the script he had had so much pride in as a player when signing autographs. Simultaneously, a spasm in his left foot cleared up and he was able to stride rapidly down the hospital corridor. Ray now had to learn the technique of injecting himself so that he could administer a rescue jab in times of emergency. The nursing staff provided the regulation orange and an insulin syringe. When I came to see him the following day he told me: 'I am still struggling, doctor, but the orange got better and went home!' Over the next few days Ray was taught to anticipate his switch-offs and inject before he started to spiral downwards. The deeper he sank before he administered the injection, the longer it would take him to come back up. Within five days Ray had become extremely proficient in the use of apomorphine injections, and his diaries revealed that he was now virtually able to eradicate the black immobile patches which had blotted out chunks of his days.

As I got to know Ray better I had given him ample opportunity to call me by my Christian name, but he always insisted on a formal address. One day, Dale, who had immediately started to call me by my Christian name, picked this up and asked his father why he always called me 'doctor'. Ray replied, 'Because I want to show him I respect him and his profession'.

Mastery of the new treatment was achieved despite frequent hospital visits from Frank McLintock, Sammy Nelson, Pat Rice, Charlie George and Peter Simpson from the Double team, and Jimmy Case who came up on the train from Southampton to see his old friend. Ray was also visited by Paul Gascoigne, Doug Livermore and Ray Clemence. Gazza found it hard to believe that there was anything much wrong with Ray at the time of his visit, but was fascinated by the injections and drew an analogy with Spurs captain Gary Mabbutt's insulin injections. Gazza told a representative of the press: 'I will do anything I can for Ray. What has happened is tragic. When I was dreaming of becoming a footballer he was one of the players I admired'. Ray was equally enthusiastic about Gazza, although he told me, after the Spurs man had left, that he wasn't sure the lad was all there. Gazza seemed to Ray to be restless, suspicious and, at times, his reactions were emotionally inappropriate. Apparently Gazza had asked some of the nurses on the ward, 'Do you know who I am?' Ray said, 'When I first met Gazza at Newcastle I told him he'd be captain of England and nothing that has happened since has changed my mind about that. He's come twice to cheer me up and I won't forget that in a long time'.

Ray described his disabilities to me during the second week in hospital:

When I go off I'm drained of energy. My body feels stiff, my face goes blank and my speech gets slow, quiet and slurred. I find it hard to think quickly and clearly, and can't remember things. My legs get stuck to the ground and I can't move my fingers freely. My whole body feels drained and I'm covered in sweat. Sometimes I slip further down and my left foot, and, rarely, my left arm, cramps up. Ten minutes after a jab I suddenly feel free again, my face comes back to life and my legs start to paddle about. My voice then seems to get louder and louder. Within another minute or two I'm rushing about, a bit fidgety mind, but keen to be on the move to make up for lost time. Apomorphine has restored my freedom and my confidence. It's taken the edge off my distress and now I know I'll never be helplessly paralysed for two or three hours on a stretch again.

Ray was convinced that the downhill course of the last two years had finally been halted and, by the time he left the Middlesex Hospital, he had regained his hope:

As a young kid I felt different, that feeling left me for a long time, but it's back now. It's got nothing to do with getting rich, but it is a deep satisfaction which is difficult to explain. I've got my inner strength back and feel I'm becoming a better person. I'm convinced that in my lifetime I will be cured.

Back in Seaton Delaval, Ray's parents couldn't believe the improvement in his mood and fluidity of movement. Veronica told me that she felt that her son was almost back to his old self. Ray was a little more cautious and attributed his improvement to chewing water lilies:

I can still be two different people within half an hour, but the two personalities are closer together. I have more control over my decision-making, and find it easier to make choices. I'd got into a situation with my pills where I didn't know where I was. I kept chopping and changing the dose every day and, in the end, I didn't know whether I was coming or going. Now I'm much steadier and, with the new regular fixed regime of pills and the injections as boosters, I have got my confidence back to get out and about. There are now times when I feel quite comfortable within my body and completely relaxed.

Ray's reaction to other patients with Parkinson's disease whom he met while on the ward was interesting. He was incapable of seeing himself in any way through their disabilities, and told me later that he found their presence disconcerting:

Why do they walk around like that with their slurred speech and emotionless faces? Are they trying to get sympathy? Why don't they take my regime of pills and injections so that they can feel normal again? I think God gave me this disease because he knows I'm strong enough to cope.

Ray returned to the North–East determined to rebuild his life and pick up the pieces of what had become a mounting catalogue of emotional disasters and crises. Rented flats, profligacy in the face of impending disaster, and a claustrophobic, highly dependent emotional relationship had brought him to the brink of collapse and now had to be put behind him.

21 Coming Out

Warra boora stotti fommi ganni?
Wirra birra bacci fommi da
Curra hevva tab, orra happni claggi slab
Mi murras possin clays shill nivva na
Gorra ganna skyul aminna hurri
orral gerra skelp aroon me gob
Iffya tark leik cloggi betti
tivva cuddi inna netti
Yikin parliamo geordie justa job.

(BOB HEDLEY)

THE 1988–9 season ended with Arsenal locked in a head-to-head confrontation with Liverpool for the League Championship. In the final game of the season at Anfield, Arsenal needed to win 2–0. Against all the odds, Michael Thomas scored a sensational winner for the Gunners in injury time. For many lifelong Arsenal supporters this was the most exhilarating moment in their lives. Four of these, Richard Artus, Mark Brown, Anthony Green and Anthony Spencer, decided to savour this exquisite thrill once more by organizing a supporters' lunch at a Hampstead restaurant in the summer. During the meal, the match was shown on television and a mini-auction took place in which a number of items donated by the Arsenal Vice-Chairman, David Dein, were sold off to raise several hundred pounds for charity. Encouraged by the event's success, the four men offered to stage a much larger event along similar lines in the mezzanine room at the Clock End at Highbury. Ken Friar suggested that Ray Kennedy would be a worthy beneficiary for the evening, a suggestion with which the organizing committee were delighted to comply.

Ted Drake, Jack Kelsey, virtually the entire Double side, Liam Brady and Pat Jennings were some of the former Arsenal players who agreed to attend, and the two hundred tickets for the 'Night of the Champions' were rapidly sold out. The evening of 2 November 1989 began with a champagne reception and then the highlights of the second half of that season's momentous Liverpool–Arsenal match were shown. When Alan Smith scored the first Arsenal goal, resounding cheers echoed throughout an otherwise deserted Highbury; in the last five minutes the lights were dimmed so that Michael Thomas's brilliant winner could be enjoyed to the full. Master of Ceremonies Bob Wilson then introduced Frank McLintock, who, after starting his speech stiffly and formally, rapidly launched into an impassioned battle cry which captivated everyone, especially the eleven middle-aged former gladiators. For a few brief moments, it was as if the clock had been turned back twenty years to the Highbury tunnel before a big game, with their captain urging them on to great deeds. The audience were spellbound, and McLintock's nostalgic recollections brought tears to a few eyes. The Arsenal manager, George Graham, received an award for snatching the title back for Highbury after an eighteen-year hiatus and echoed McLintock's words of praise in stressing Ray's crucial role in Arsenal's Double year. Tributes to Ray from Kenny Dalglish and Alan Hansen were shown on video, and Ray gave a spirited vote of thanks. Up until a few hours before the dinner it was not clear whether he would be well enough to attend. Fred Eyres, the former Manchester City goalkeeper and professional public speaker at football occasions, then gave a hilarious speech which put everyone in good spirits for the auction. Items on view included the shirt Michael Thomas had reputedly worn at Anfield, balls from championship games and a number of executive box seats, as well as several interesting pieces of memorabilia. The bidding was led by Roger Levitt, the now disgraced tycoon, who regarded it as a matter of honour to outbid everyone else for the crucial lots.

Ray's positive attitude to his illness made an impression on Richard Artus, who remembers the delighted look on the big man's face when he was introduced to a female guest who also had the disease. This gave Ray the golden opportunity to retract back into the world of Parkinson's and escape from the football world from which his illness had cruelly divorced him. Two hundred delighted Gunners' supporters spilled into the Islington evening, many of them holding mementoes from the auction or group photographs taken clustered round the League Championship trophy. The evening raised a substantial sum of money to help Ray to solve his immediate debts and prevent him from pressing forward with his depressing threat to sell his collection of championship medals.

At the end of his first week at the Middlesex Hospital, less than a year later, Ray told me:

> If I had my time over again and knew I had to pay the price of this illness for the thrill of playing for Arsenal and Liverpool, I'd do it. To play for one of them in a career is fantastic, but to be successful with both is more than anyone could dream of. In any case, I know I'll beat this illness eventually.

A few days after arriving home he told me on the phone:

> Apomorphine treatment has changed my life. At least I have days now when I feel normal. I look a lot better and at times it is difficult to tell I have Parkinson's. I am happier than I've been for several years and my family notice the enormous change.

Some weeks later, at the invitation of one of my patients, Kurt Lowy, an Arsenal supporter who had been instrumental in setting up JVC sponsorship for the club, I went to Highbury for the Arsenal–Liverpool game. After the match, I was able to talk to both Ken Friar and Peter Robinson about the possibility of Ray's long-awaited testimonial going ahead. Both were anxious to know how he was keeping and what the long-term outlook was. A week later it was finally agreed that Ray Kennedy's testimonial would take place at Highbury between an Arsenal Eleven and a Liverpool Eleven.

Thanks to the generosity of the Professional Footballers' Association, who again agreed to cover Ray's hospital bills, I was able to re-admit him for a period of assessment in February 1991. At Newcastle Station on the way down, his signature was so distorted and unrecognizable compared with that on his credit card that the booking office would not accept his ticket booking. During this distressing incident Ray had switched off and lost his ability to dispute the decision as he slumped helplessly, waiting for divine intervention. Fortunately this arrived in the form of a passer-by who chastised the bureaucratic official and vouched for Ray's identity. The greeting at the other end could not have been more different: a kindly Euston porter was there to help him off the train and into a taxi bound for the hospital.

During this second hospital admission Ray and I had long consultations, as he was hungry to learn everything he could about the illness and the initiatives being taken in the field of research. He ravenously read the handbooks for patients written by physicians and the idiosyncratic autobiographical accounts of patients. After I had told him about the Parkinson's Disease Society's Brain Bank at the Institute of Neurology, he was desperately keen to visit and see for himself the research that was being carried out. I had told him that many of the members of the Parkinson's Disease Society had agreed to bequeath their tissues to research and that more than two hundred brains were now stored in freezers, or in jars containing formalin, within the laboratory. A team of scientists were working there on certain aspects of basic research, dissecting the tissue and examining it with a whole range of new molecular biological probes. Ray did not seem at all put off by my descriptions of what he might see, so we set off together one day on the short journey across Bloomsbury to Wakefield Street where, on arrival, we were warmly greeted by Rita Nani, the administrative secretary. Ray was first shown a section of brain cut to expose the narrow strip of black tissue which is the seat of damage in Parkinson's disease. He was astonished to learn that this represented such a small portion of the total brain, making up no more than a few hundred thousand nerve cells out of a total figure of millions. He was then taught how to identify a Lewy body under the microscope. This is a small circular particle with a dense central core and an outer halo which resembles a bullseye and is found in many of the surviving pigmented nerve cells. Within a relatively short time, Ray became quite adept at recognizing these tiny structures. On seeing a cut section of brain he jokingly told me that it reminded him of the chicken pâté he had eaten the night before. On arriving in the freezer room, he asked whether the brains were sorted into vanilla, chocolate and strawberry. Despite these flippant quips, it was quite clear that he was fascinated with what was going on and impressed by the degree of commitment of the staff.

A few days later he was to return, this time at the request of the Parkinson's Disease Society and the *News of the World* newspaper, who were doing a promotional feature on Parkinson's disease around Gary Lineker. Lineker had donated a generous sum of money from a recent FIFA Fair Play Award to the Society as a token of respect for his grandfather, Harry, who had contracted the illness when Gary was fifteen. Lineker's grandfather had been probably the single most important figure in his first tentative steps towards a professional football career. He had stood out in all weathers to encourage his young grandson and had been there to promote him when the scouts came sniffing about. Gary now attributes many of his attitudes to football and his self-discipline on the pitch to his grandfather's influence. At the Brain Bank that day Ray met Gary Lineker and his wife, Michelle, and Elizabeth Ebbs, the first patient to receive apomorphine therapy in the United Kingdom. Representatives from the Parkinson's Disease Society were also in attendance. After the tour of the Brain Bank Gary Lineker told me:

> I miss my grandad very much and I'm sorry he can no longer see me play. He has a lot of bad days now, his vision is poor and he is often confused. It's nice to be in a position to help the Parkinson's Disease Society with donations and personal appearances even though the cure may come too late for my grandfather. It has moved me to see Ray with the illness too. He was a player I really admired for his attitude when I was starting out. Even though he laughs and jokes all the time, he told me that it is really a front and he is terrified of what is going to happen to him.

Ray was also able to talk with Elizabeth Ebbs and learn how apomorphine had helped her. Liz told Ray that she was now leading a near normal life four years after starting apomorphine, and was able to go on outings with her husband and children which had previously been impossible. She also told him that on some occasions she actually forgot that she had Parkinson's disease.

A month later Ray and I met again in the trophy room at Anfield, where I had been invited to give an after-dinner speech by the Liverpool Supporters' Club, who were holding a dinner in honour of Ray. On the top table that evening were Ronnie

Whelan, who was in his testimonial year and had replaced Ray in the Liverpool side in the early eighties, and Ray's old team-mates Tommy Smith, Ian Callaghan and Alan Kennedy. The whole of the boot room had also turned up to show their appreciation. The after-dinner speeches began with Tommy Smith relating the famous pre-match assassination of Manchester United by Shanks:

> They've got Alex Stepney in goal – couldn't catch a cold, full back Tony Dunn – couldn't catch a fish supper, Shay Brennan – someone told me he had a bad back. I'll tell you, he's got two bad backs and I've seen a juggernaut turn quicker than Bill Foulkes. Nobby Stiles, I've a gnome in my garden bigger. Now Paddy Crerand he's deceptive – he's slower than you think! Then there's their inside right – he's the worst player in the world.

At that point Reuben Bennett, Shanks's side-kick, had chipped in with 'You can say that again', following which Shanks started all over again to hoots of laughter from the players. Shanks concluded by saying, 'That leaves Best, Law and Charlton, only three men to beat'. Liverpool lost 4–0. Tommy then launched into a tirade of obscene and aggressive anecdotes, culminating in a frenzied diatribe against Emlyn Hughes.

Throughout the dinner, Ray oscillated between nervous restlessness and periods of immobility. At one point he told me that if he was asked to make a speech there and then he wouldn't be able to stand up, he was so stiff. I gave a short speech about my recollections of Ray as a player and light-heartedly discussing the theories put forward by Ray and his playing colleagues to explain the onset of his illness. I drew attention to the courage he was showing in facing up to the personal tragedy of Parkinson's disease. After the official entertainment, Ray also made a short speech thanking the Liverpool supporters and telling them that, although he still considered Arsenal to be the better club, he had little doubt that Liverpool were the better team and that his stay at Liverpool had been a much happier and more enjoyable one.

There was a small auction in which a Eurythmics Golden Disc, donated by the duo's road manager, was auctioned for £2,000 and a signed photograph of Ray went for £300. This was followed by an impromptu collection for Parkinson's disease, which raised £245, one unemployed docker putting in a £20 note. The next day I delivered this to the Society as it had been collected, in two pint glasses. When the formal proceedings had finished, people flocked round Ray, reminding him of the St Etienne game and the away goal in the Olympic Stadium in Munich. Many told him that they were praying for his recovery, others were shaking his hands and hugging him in what was an overwhelmingly moving show of warmth from a group of men who had been rolling around uncouthly in response to the most basic and obscene entertainment half an hour earlier. Ray became most excited, however, when he was introduced to a gentleman called Fred Roberts who also had Parkinson's disease and had been one of the first individuals to receive the experimental implantation of nerve cells from a human foetus. Ray's eyes lit up when he was told that the operation had helped, but was shocked when he felt the dent where the surgery had been carried out. He told me afterwards: 'I could never go through with that and be left with a hole in my head'. Fred Roberts later wrote to Ray from his Warrington home:

> ... Two years ago I underwent a foetal brain cell transplant at the Midland Centre for Neurosurgery in Smethwick. Twenty-five of these operations were performed during a twelve-month period and as far as I know, some patients showed some improvement. In my case there was an immediate benefit to speech and I was able to walk better. Choking was reduced and my shaking almost disappeared. I could reduce my pills by two-thirds, but after a few months my speech got worse again and so did my walking. The hospital have talked to me about the use of apomorphine, but they are not convinced that this is the best treatment. I am sure you would have realised by now, Ray, that a number of doctors are each studying different approaches to our problem. Depression, a feeling of hopelessness is with me constantly ... I find it almost impossible to explain to non-sufferers how Parkinson's affects me, the expression of being on or off, or freezing, can only be recognized by sufferers and doctors. ... I am not a religious person, but have found this prayer helpful –
> 'God grant me the serenity to accept the things I cannot change and the courage to change those I can and the wisdom

to know the difference'. Nice to meet you, Ray, you will beat
it one day,
   Regards,
     Fred
P.S. I am sorry to say I am a Manchester United supporter.

After the dinner at Anfield, Ray had returned to Southport to
'help wash dishes' in his friend Ian Kidd's restaurant, with his life
precariously balanced somewhere in the twilight zone between
order and disorder. That Saturday the Highbury Tannoy announced Ray's impending testimonial and a teenage fan sitting
next to me turned to his father and said, 'Who's Ray Kennedy?'

Ray arrived in London on the Monday before his testimonial
for press interviews and to start filming a video about his life.
Cara, Dale and Audrey Smith, his girlfriend, accompanied him.
On 25 April we all met for dinner at the Mayfair Hotel, chosen
because of its spacious and serene atmosphere. However, even
here, within minutes of sitting down, Ray's face went grim and
his right hand began to shake. His shoes were floating loose
under the table and his rigid, erect trunk was petrified. Apomorphine, as always, brought the body back to life, but the mind was
racing along so that he was unable to concentrate or express his
thoughts clearly. Unannounced, he left the dinner table and, ten
minutes later, I rescued him in the lavatory. His face was pale and
drenched with sweat, but he greeted me with: 'I'm all right,
doctor, I'm just over the moon and sick as a parrot'. During the
build-up to the testimonial, the press and media gave him
generous coverage. Saint and Greavsie mounted a special feature,
and his plight was highlighted on *News at Ten*.

Ray Kennedy's testimonial match took place on 27 April 1991
at Highbury. On the day of the game, two hours after waking,
he was crawling around the floor of his hotel room, convinced he
would never be able to crank himself up sufficiently to get to the
ground. He was starting to worry that no one would turn up,
although the promised presence of his old team-mates, Dalglish
and Souness, provided some reassurance.

Two months earlier, on 22 February, Kenny Dalglish had
shocked the Anfield faithful by announcing his resignation as
manager – a bombshell as unexpected as that dropped by
Shankly seventeen years earlier. Those close to Dalglish, however,

had noted an increasing secretiveness, unpredictability and reliance on magic rituals in the months prior to his departure. Communication, which had never been his strongest point in club matters, had virtually dried up altogether. There is little doubt that Dalglish's decision had come from a mind in turmoil and disarray. The pressure involved in keeping Liverpool at the top of the English game, and the moral courage needed to steer the devastated club forward after the grief of Hillsborough, had temporarily broken him. Ray's testimonial was to be Dalglish's first return to football of any sort. The new laird of Anfield, Graeme Souness, in eight short weeks had already begun to appreciate the enormous reconstruction exercise which would be necessary if Liverpool were to sustain their pre-eminence. He had inherited a side which had grown old together, and some of the great Anfield players were now getting stale or shell-shocked.

On arriving at Highbury for Ray's testimonial, Souness told me: 'Ray was not given the credit he deserved as a player, but he was never underestimated as a man by those who knew him'. A hardened Arsenal programme seller outside the ground who was interviewed by the *Ray of Hope* film crew, also sang his praises:

I feel sorry for Stanley Matthews. He knew nothing about football and they made him a knight. They used to say here that Storey was the hard man. Not so, it was Kennedy up the middle who took all the knocks. We couldn't believe it here when he was sold.

One of the fans outside the ground before the game told us: 'Everyone at school wanted to be Charlie George or Ray Kennedy. Those were the two different personalities, like John and Paul in the Beatles'.

By this time, Ray had finally managed to charge himself up and when he reached Highbury he was on an adrenaline high of the sort he must have experienced many times before big games. He was met by Ken Friar, who escorted him up to the board room, where the chairman and directors thanked him for his service to the club. Soon he was downstairs, rushing from room to room. 'I'm so high, doctor, I don't need any pills', he told me.

In the changing room before the match, Ray, Jimmy Case, Tommy Smith and Graeme Souness sat together chatting about the good old days. Soon they were all joking about the damage football had wreaked on their health. Case was deaf, Smith was crippled with arthritic knees and Kennedy couldn't speak because of Parkinson's disease. Graeme Souness, meanwhile, had only his thinning hair to worry about, blissfully unaware that within a year he would require major heart surgery. For professional football players, a suspended death occurs when they hang up their boots. Some are never rehabilitated.

On a glorious, sunny spring day, when no other First Division League football was on view, close on 20,000 fans waited expectantly to show their appreciation for a player who may have had bad patches and poor games, but who had never let either Arsenal or Liverpool down on the field of play, and had provided unforgettable moments of footballing skill which would be remembered by all those who regularly watched football from the terraces through the 1970s. To the youngsters, Ray Kennedy was just a name they had occasionally heard their fathers mention when harking back to the great days of Arsenal's Double or the vintage 1978 Liverpool team.

The two sides were made up mainly of first team players with a sprinkling of aspirant youths and one or two of Ray's old mates who were still in good enough shape not to make fools of themselves. Ian Rush was the major omission from the Liverpool side as a result of injury, and George Graham, although down as a substitute, decided it would be wiser not to participate. The full line-up was:

Arsenal XI	Jim Leighton, Michael Thomas, Nigel Winterburn, David Hillier, Andy Linighan, Tony Adams, David Rocastle, Paul Davis, Kevin Campbell, Perry Groves, Anders Limpar
Substitutes:	Pat Rice, George Armstrong, Jon Sammels
Liverpool XI	Bruce Grobbelaar, Steve Harkness, Steve Staunton, Steve Nicol, Jan Molby, Jimmy Case, Kenny Dalglish, Ray Houghton, Ronnie Rosenthal, Peter Beardsley, Graeme Souness
Substitutes:	Jimmy Carter, Mike Marsh, Glen Hysen, David Speedie, Jamie Redknapp, Ray Clemence.

Three o'clock arrived, with Cara and Dale Kennedy leading the sides onto the pitch, where they lined up on either side of the tunnel to await Ray's arrival. With Frank McLintock and George Graham there to give him moral support, he strode smartly, if a little disjointedly, between the corridor of players, waving and applauding to the appreciative crowd. For a brief moment he felt, for the first time in ten years, that adrenaline-induced invincibility and forgot about Parkinson's disease. To a respectful crowd ovation he then made his way back to the tunnel to take up his seat in the directors' box with his family. However, as he reached the crossroads under the stand where Don Howe and Frank McLintock had held their team talks in the Double year, he broke down sobbing. Ray told me afterwards:

> For so many people to turn up for me after twenty years was unbelievable. I felt excited and moved and upset all at the same time. It was great to see Graeme and Kenny playing together again, but I felt sad I couldn't be there with them on the pitch.

The game began with Souness baring his fangs as if to show Arsenal what was in store for them in the last few desperate weeks of the title race. He threw himself into the thick of things, laying on a number of balls for his old team-mates, Case and Dalglish, and played as if this were a decider for the championship. Murmurs of appreciation could be heard as he initiated a couple of neat one-twos with Dalglish, which made the Liverpool contingent in the crowd regret that their former and new managers were no longer available for first team selection. For one last time Dalglish had deprived Peter Beardsley of the number seven shirt. As early as the fifteenth minute 'The Supreme Being' was brought down in the area by Jim Leighton, and Molby opened the score for the Reds. However, within five minutes, the Gunners were level after a fine Kevin Campbell goal. The rest of the half continued with lively cut and thrust but there were no more goals. During the interval, Dalglish left hurriedly to catch a plane to Manchester and was replaced by David Speedie. Meanwhile, in the board room, Radford and Kennedy were gossiping about how their contemporaries had weathered the years. In the second half, with ten minutes to go, Speedie put Liverpool ahead and, right on the whistle, Beardsley made it 3–1 with Souness still on the pitch and fighting for every ball. It was clear that George Graham had made the right decision not to play. The final score was immaterial, but the crowd went home pleased that they had seen a serious game of football rather than a training session. The really serious encounter, between the two sides a few weeks later at Anfield, was to go to Arsenal, and was settled by a Paul Merson second half goal which effectively gave the Gunners the League Championship.

After the testimonial match, Paul Davis said: 'It was competitive all right. Graeme Souness badly wanted to win, you could tell by his tackling and the way he was shouting at his team-mates'. Souness confirmed this, justifying his attitude:

> The days of the non-competitive testimonial are over. People pay good money to see the game. Players receiving testimonials can no longer plead poverty. Playing with Kenny was easy and frustrating at the same time, but I was sorry George Graham didn't turn out. He's not that much older than me. I don't do many testimonials these days because every time I do someone wants to kick me.

As usual, Souness did not claim expenses in contrast to many of his colleagues. Football testimonials these days, especially those for the already wealthy, have a tendency to bear testimony to the unreliability of football players. Much is promised, nothing is arranged and, not infrequently, no one turns up. The public ever generous to those it has loved, usually proves more loyal than the beneficiary's fellow professionals. The testimonial for Ray was remarkable not just because he had not played for ten years, but for the impressive show of strength from his colleagues and former team-mates. Tommy Smith hitched a ride down with the Liverpool coach, and Ray Clemence rushed from a Tottenham youth game to be there to play in the second half. On Ray's day, the backbiting, bickering and mean-mindedness was put to one side and a ray of hope and compassion gleamed through.

In the players' lounge, Ray remained as high as a kite, talking freely to the press and all his old friends. After about an hour, however, while holding a huge imitation cheque with George Graham for the press to photograph, the spectre of James Parkinson returned and he tottered to a chair to sit down, drenched in perspiration and overcome with nervous exhaustion. The saviour, apomorphine, got him going sufficiently for him to leave the stadium hurriedly and return to the hotel.

The next day he could not remember going out onto the pitch at all, and was overcome by what the journalists had written about him in his testimonial programme. 'I never knew they thought so highly of me,' he said.

A few extracts from Ray Kennedy's testimonial programme are reproduced below:

Brian Glanville (*Sunday Times*)

Liverpool at their perceptive best realised what the rest of us had missed. Kennedy had all the attributes of a successful midfield man, save possibly speed. But what in the final analysis does speed matter, or rather, if a player is strong, technically adroit and his mind moves fast does it matter if he is not quick?

Harry Miller (*The Mail on Sunday*)

They come. They go. Those you remember, those you forget. Ray Kennedy and his contribution to Arsenal and Liverpool will be remembered for as long as football remains the people's game. He was not just a player of extraordinary ability, he was a genuinely nice guy. There was a warmth about Ray as a player ... long after he left Arsenal you could meet him in the corridors at Anfield, the car park at Tottenham or on the steps at Maine Road and he'd always greet you with a smile and the immediate question 'How's it going?' before you could ask about his own well-being.

Christopher Davies (*Daily Telegraph*)

It is probably true to say that the two biggest moves of Kennedy's career were from Arsenal to Liverpool and from striker to midfield. Rarely has such a seemingly improbable switch been made with such ease and success. Now the leading players in modern football have to be adaptable, but it is difficult to think of many who could make the type of change Kennedy did ... How England could have done with a player of his stature in the left midfield against the Republic of Ireland last month! ... The memories of Arsenal supporters today will be of Kennedy climbing over defences to head home. The Liverpool followers can remember sweet fifty yard passes with the left foot that aligned power with grace ... Ray made football look simple.

Brian Scovell (*Daily Mail*)

What I remember most about Ray Kennedy is what a nice guy he was when he was with Arsenal. Whatever the circumstances you could always talk to him and be courteously received. He always had a cheery greeting and a smile and often a joke. Typical Geordie we used to say of him. If he'd missed an open goal – and he missed his share – he was never afraid to talk us through it afterwards. He was thoroughly honest and almost self-deprecating.

Mark Lawrenson was among Ray's team-mates at Liverpool who contributed to the testimonial programme:

I first met Ray in 1971 when I was twelve. My parents took over a hotel in Blackpool but I continued my schooling in Preston, commuting by train. One Friday afternoon I just caught the train by the skin of my teeth for the journey home and one of the lads said Arsenal were in the rear carriage and I scuttled down to get autographs. They all signed including Ray who was playing cards with John Radford and a couple of the others. I went to see them play the next day at Blackpool. It wasn't a good game, but Arsenal went on to win the Double. Ray was the kind of player you could always rely on to support you when you were in trouble. I made my debut for Liverpool against Wolves in 1981 at left back. Ray was in front of me and it didn't take long to realise what a player he was. He was strong and powerful in the tackle and wholly committed, but what impressed me most was that he never gave the ball away ... the tragedy is you fall from superstar to obscurity very, very quickly. Many of those there today will not know who Ray Kennedy is.

A few days after the testimonial when I rang Ray, he said to me: 'If they think they've seen the last of me they're wrong. I'm going to visit every chairman in the First Division and ask them to give money for Parkinson's disease research'. Soon after, he began to attend charitable dinners as a special guest, and was the guest at Parkinson's Disease Society patient group meetings. The money raised at the testimonial would help Ray in his life among the chronically disabled, but the warm appreciation that he had received as one of England's finest post-war players had also replenished his determination to keep afloat. However, the next day nothing had basically changed and he was back staring at the empty walls.

At that time Ray was involved in a catalogue of perverse and painful relationships with women. Trevor told me that before the onset of Parkinson's disease Ray would never have let a woman get one over on him. Now the illness rendered him helpless and submissive for long stretches and his fear of isolation led to an unhealthy dependence. Cara and Dale, however, were always there to fortify and comfort him. Dale would sit on his feet to ease the cramp and Cara would attend to his mail and make phone calls. His mum continued to help with his washing and provide a sympathetic ear. Reconciliation with Jen seemed increasingly unlikely.

When I telephoned Ray I could usually work out what state he was in. When off he sounded low and disgruntled and would be full of complaints about his health. His stomach and chest would play up, his throat would be sore and he would feel generally off colour. In these phases he would agree with anything I suggested, especially if he was not particularly interested. Once he told me that he was preoccupied with a fear of being mugged and was terrified that he would be unable to defend himself.

During his second visit to London I had given him Dr Oliver Sacks's book, *Awakenings*, which vividly describes the dramatic and short-lived resurrection by L-dopa of a group of patients with Parkinson's syndrome who had been exiled to a long-stay institution in the United States. At the time of the First World War they had contracted sleepy sickness, or *encephalitis lethargica*, and had remained dormant, like spent volcanoes, for forty years. Sacks was able to give them L-dopa in the late 1960s and watch an astonishing transformation. Mobility and speech were regained, but many were suspended in a time warp with an incontinent nostalgia for their lives before the virus struck. After several weeks of treatment they also began to experience an increasingly brittle response to the drug, with alarming volleys of jerks, twitches, uncontrollable compulsions and tics and, even more distressingly, confusion, psychosis and mania. For most, their reincarnation lasted less than a year, when adverse reactions forced them to stop the medication and return to their motionless, apathetic vacuum. The L-dopa response of patients with this rare type of Parkinson's syndrome, in which nearly all the nerve cells in the black substance of the brain are dead, was to provide an ominous harbinger for what physicians were to encounter with L-dopa in a less drastic and more delayed way in Parkinson's disease. Ray went into Newcastle to see the film *Awakenings*, starring Robin Williams and Robert de Niro. Towards the end of the film his medication stopped working and he could hardly move. He was ashamed and frightened that people would think he was trying to be funny, or 'taking the mickey' as he trembled and shuffled out of the theatre. He also told me that he would be available to audition for *Awakenings 2*.

Two months after the testimonial Ray went on holiday with Audrey Smith to Cyprus. On his return, his relationship with Jenny improved a little and the two were talking again. Jenny told Cara, 'No one will love your Dad like I did'.

Profound swings in mood and mobility continued to occur from week to week. On good days he could manage an eighteen-hole round of golf or a game of tennis and, when striking the ball, he rarely froze. Between holes, however, he would sometimes stiffen, and throwing the ball accurately for a tennis service was difficult. He started to have dreams that he was not finished with football, and one night John Toshack had appeared before him and told him he'd make a good manager. On another occasion when I called, he was buoyant: 'My nerve cells are sprouting again, doctor. I'm getting two hours from each dose of Sinemet. If I eat nothing I get even longer, but fish and chips are a disaster'.

In July 1991 I visited Ray at his Tynemouth flat. Everything was spotlessly tidy. During the next few days I was able to experience at first-hand a little of what it is like to live with Parkinson's disease. In his best patches, I began to appreciate that driving force which had led to his successful career. At his worst – and best could transfer to worst within seconds – he was helpless and desperately insecure. After a game of ten-pin bowling at Whitley Bay he had to be lifted to his car by the bouncer, who thought that his left foot contortion was a twisted ankle. After a lunch we had together at his favourite Italian restaurant near St James's Park, and a dinner at the Gosforth Park Hotel, he was frozen to his seat.

Ray drove me to Keswick to see John Maley and his wife who were on holiday there in a rented apartment. On our arrival Ray was writhing and speaking so quickly it was difficult to keep up with him. After a cup of tea and scones, his face became drained of expression, his speech changed to a lugubrious drone and he flexed up. On seeing this, Mrs Maley commented, 'Eeh, Raymond, you're looking a lot better now'. This highlights a problem faced by all patients with Parkinson's disease. To relatives, carers and those closest to them, the wild, flinging, jerking movements and the pressure of thought induced by L-dopa therapy is less acceptable than the slowness and apathy of the disease itself. Relatives often beg for the dose to be reduced, a demand which is resisted strongly by the patient.

On the third day, I watched Ray crawling about the floor, his left leg twisted round in an agonizing cramp. An hour later he was racing around the house in a frenzy, as if he were trying to make up for lost time and squeezing as much life out of this period of release as possible, although much of this activity was aimless and disconnected. The illness appeared to be affecting his motivation and incentive (I remembered the headlines KENNEDY'S NOT TRYING at Swansea). He was having difficulty getting new plans off the ground and even more in seeing them through to completion. He seemed unable to make key decisions with respect to buying a new home and, though replete with sensible plans to raise funds for Parkinson's disease, he could not get things moving. Parkinson's disease was disorganizing his behaviour. The only thing that seemed to remain steady through ons and offs was his sense of humour.

I began to sense his alienation as we visited more and more of his regular haunts: his parents' home, Fenwick's for afternoon tea and the Metro Centre. His determination during his football days always to return home at the end of a season was a cry for help. His move south at seventeen had cut him off; later, as a star, he was put on a pedestal. Now he had a nervous disorder which was so protean that even people who had heard of Parkinson's disease could not comprehend it. Ray was going through the motions, but he and I knew that he did not really belong as a hero, a villain, or even a victim, of the North-East. Ray became more and more disconsolate as he drove me to Newcastle airport to catch my plane back to London. While we sat waiting for the plane, as usual, women were eyeing him up, but he did not notice: 'Look at all these people, not a care in the world. They don't know how lucky they are. I wonder how they'd cope with this illness. It is the hope of a cure which I know will come, doctor, which keeps me going'.

Throughout 1991 Ray's profile with the media remained high, culminating in the transmission of his life story, entitled *Ray of Hope*, on Channel 4 on Boxing Day. Many of the national newspapers gave it their Pick of the Day award. Transmitted to a football-crazy nation at peak viewing time, the programme served to introduce millions to the problems Parkinson's disease brings.

Ray continued to receive a motley selection of letters from fellow patients, well-wishers and cranks.

Dear Ray,
Please excuse the intrusion into your private life, but I was watching the television last night and was specially interested in the programme about you having Parkinson's disease, the reason being that my son-in-law was diagnosed as having the same illness two years ago. The only thing is he can't seem to accept it and doesn't talk about it outside the family. I wish he had seen the television last night, it would have given him so much heart but at the moment he is in Cyprus with the Red Arrows on their pre-season training as at the moment he is still able to work although he is medically downgraded in the RAF.

Ray – I was wondering if it was possible for you to drop him a line and tell him what is going on regards the injections you are taking. I would like you to mention to him what the specialist said about a possible cure within five to ten years. If I tell him I am sure he'll think I'm fobbing him off just to encourage him, but coming from you it will give him a lot of encouragement. He knows you suffer from the illness as we all spoke about it one night. He is a great football fan and loved playing the game but has had to give all that up. Like you he is in his thirties. I wish you well and dearly hope the cure comes for you, Kevin and all the other sufferers with Parkinson's. Good luck to you and God bless you and your family.

Dear Ray,
No doubt you are wondering why a nun is writing to you,

well I saw you on TV the time your testimonial match was played. You have Parkinson's disease like me but I have had it since 1979. When I saw you on TV I thought you looked so ill and I made up my mind to write to you. I believe you are on injections so may I ask what is in them? I am on Sinemet controlled release tablets and benzhexol. I shake a lot and am also at the freezing stage. This means that I get very stiff and can't move from one place, which I get in the morning and again in the afternoon. I am still able to fend for myself, wash and dress. I am a supporter of Arsenal and I am able to rejoice that we have won the League. My religion is a great support to me and now, I am not getting in my plug, but I pray a lot and I am enclosing a Medal of Our Lady. She is the mother of Jesus and like all mothers she is interested in all her children. I hope to hear from you and let me know how you are. I miss going out. When I see younger people much worse than me I thank God I am so well. With such an Irish name you and your family must surely come from the 'auld-sod'. I find it hard to write sometimes so please excuse this scribble. Up Arsenal everytime or do you still support Liverpool? I ask God to bless you and I pray for you and your family.

Ray was also contacted by physicians and healers. A retired Liverpool orthopaedic surgeon rang him and advised him to cut out all brown bread because it contained manganese which had been incriminated in Parkinson's disease. The surgeon later told me that he had recommended this to a man with Parkinson's disease at his church who had started the diet and subsequently improved. Manganese miners occasionally develop a syndrome resembling Parkinson's disease through inhaling the ore dust, but the brains of patients with Parkinson's disease do not contain excess manganese and, even in large quantities in the diet, manganese is harmless. I advised Ray against changing his diet. The desperate and understandable desire of patients to be released from an incurable disorder can render them vulnerable to unscrupulous quacks pedalling nostrums for pecuniary gain. One recent example of this was the arrival in the United Kingdom of an Israeli confidence trickster who claimed to represent a foundation which had been set up to find the cause for Parkinson's disease. After making contact with desperate patients through advertisements in the daily newspapers and backing his credentials by

quoting eminent doctors' names, he offered them a miraculous
natural cure of golden beans. These beans, just like ordinary
broad beans, did indeed contain L-dopa, but conferred no additional advantages. Many gullible and frightened Parkinsonians and
their relatives parted with considerable sums of money before
the con man fled to pastures new.

Throughout 1991 there were a number of distorted and
sensationalized reports in the national press of modest scientific
advances which were heralded by the daily press as being cures
or major advances. For example, an extract of gangliosides, a
fatty substance found in large quantities in cows' brains, was
reported on the television to be a cure for Parkinson's disease.
Ray listened to this alone at home and immediately jumped up
with joy and opened a bottle of champagne. He told me later
that he had felt like ringing me up immediately to break the
good news. I was left with the job of explaining to him that a
great deal more research would be needed before these claims
could be substantiated. When I had finished explaining the
scientists' findings, Ray dejectedly asked, 'So you mean if I was a
monkey, doctor, I'd be all right now?' He was equally excited
when he learnt that Jeremy Thorpe had entered the Midland
Centre for Neurosurgery for the experimental implant procedure,
although at no point did he express a desire to be referred there
himself. Thorpe's decision to go ahead with the operation received considerable publicity, but, after the operation, everything
went quiet and no progress reports were given.

After six to seven black weeks following a bout of 'flu, Ray
came back into hospital at the beginning of 1992. His off periods
were now much more malignant and difficult to escape from than
the year before and he had discontinued apomorphine injections.
Ray was becoming increasingly reluctant to use the apomorphine:
'I'm too vain, and it's making marks on my skin. Sometimes it
also shoots me up into the clouds and I can't think straight. In
any case I am feeling stronger now and don't seem to switch off
as much': From the outset he had been reluctant to inject into his
thighs and had restricted his sites of injection to the abdominal wall.

However, we were able to introduce him to a new method of
using apomorphine which he found more acceptable. Ray was
now taught how to inhale the drug through his nose.

At the time, a young Colombian doctor, William Fernandez,

was working with me and Ray used to joke to me that he wondered whether we were now giving him cocaine rather than apomorphine as he felt so good. It was also necessary for Ray to have a telescopic examination of his lower bowel. The physician allowed Ray to observe his large intestine during the examination: 'It was incredible, doctor, it looked like the Tyne Tunnel with a gigantic crane [the biopsy forceps]. There was a nurse standing by with giant gloves in a welder's suit and wellingtons. The tube was like a huge serpent. When the lights went out in the theatre I thought I might get a kiss on the back of my neck from the consultant.'

Philip Young, treasurer from the Parkinson's Disease Society, and David Collet, the chief fund-raiser, Ray and I visited the headquarters of the Football Association at 16, Lancaster Gate for a meeting with Mr Glenn Curtin, an FA executive. The place was flooded with journalists, as detailed proposals relating to the new Premier League were about to be announced. Ray got stuck in the entrance and had to be brought a chair, where he was passed by Sir Gordon McKeig and Bert Millichip, dignitaries from the Football League and Football Association, neither of whom acknowledged him. Ray used his new nasal inhaler to get him moving and we went upstairs to meet Mr Curtin. Ray had told me that the only other times he had been here were to attend disciplinary committees after his two uncharacteristic sendings-off at the end of his Liverpool career. The Football Association kindly agreed to give Ray all the support he wished for in launching his appeal to find a cure for Parkinson's disease, and agreed to donate money from the Charity Shield for Parkinson's disease. After the interview, however, Ray became nervous that he might be cut out of future negotiations and was not wholly reassured by me that, without him, nothing could be achieved.

A few weeks later Newcastle United, who were next to bottom in Division Two and in considerable financial difficulties, announced that Kevin Keegan had agreed to take over the manager's post from Ossie Ardiles. Ray, who had never been a great admirer of Kevin Keegan, was frustrated, but felt that his old team-mate had made a shrewd move: 'Keegan can't lose. The crowd will get behind him. If Newcastle stay up he'll be a Tyneside hero.' Ray told me that Kevin Keegan was not as virtuous as he appeared, and had always been very selfish: 'Kevin

knew I could see through him and that's why I think he kept
his distance from me at Liverpool.' At Liverpool, Keegan had
wanted to be involved in everything, taking the free kicks
from the half way line, taking the throw-ins and monopolizing
the play. His ambition knew no bounds and, Ray conceded
reluctantly, his attitude was faultless. He felt, however, that
Dalglish was a far better player. In training Ray found that if
he just stood still Kevin would be unable to go past him and
would be forced to pass, whereas Dalglish was deceptive and
could get round without parting with the ball. Keegan took
Terry McDermott away from his hamburger stall at Aintree
races to be his second in command and, after several threats
of resignation, squeezed money from the skinflint Newcastle
board. Batman and Robin managed to keep Newcastle up that
year, playing all the time to capacity crowds.

Ray had been lied to and manipulated so much during his
life in football that it was hard for him to now believe that
there were those who genuinely cared about him

> I know I've been wrong. I'm no saint, but if I was a com-
> plete waste of time people wouldn't bother with me, would
> they? You know what I believe? I am getting paid back for all
> my wrongdoings. When I was playing I always felt special
> and I had moments of contentment, but in the end I got
> greedy and overdid it. I got above my station and now I am
> getting punished.

Ray was unable to bring himself to visit St James's Park and
see his old team mates, nor indeed did he feel strong enough
to attend the Tynemouth branch of the Parkinson's Disease
Society meetings to which he had been invited on several occasions.

Ray was back down in London in April, and it was clear that his
illness was becoming increasingly difficult for him to cope with.
The really good periods of mobility were less frequent and many
of them were comprimised by intolerable fidgets of the neck,
arms and legs, and he was now quite helpless during off periods.
He would get trapped in the most embarrassing situations and,
on one occasion on visiting a dry cleaners close to the Middlesex
Hospital, he was unable to move and was rescued by Susan
Bishop, our nurse specialist. She was struck by his remarkable

calm during what must have been a most frightening, if all too frequent, episode. He told me that, when he was sitting in a car, the window would always steam up next to where he was sitting because his body gave off so much heat.

Despite missing the plane back from a holiday in Fuerteventura because of a muddle over the day of departure, Ray returned looking tanned and fit in time for the Parkinson's Disease Society Awareness Week. The library at the new Parkinson's Disease Society headquarters in Upper Woburn Square had been named after him, and a large photograph of him clutching the European Cup in Rome was hung on the wall. He had been asked to attend the official opening by the Princess of Wales, who was still bereaved after her father's death. Princess Diana looked strained and drawn, and at times during the guided tour, she was almost in tears. She asked Ray how his Parkinson's disease had begun and, when he began to explain to her that he was a footballer, she interjected, saying, 'Even I know that!' After listening politely to Ray's account of his illness, she then turned to Maureen, Ray's girlfriend, and asked where she came from. When she said, 'Newcastle', Princess Di replied, 'Where all the good people come from'. Afterwards, to the press, Ray said:

> I told the Princess I have to take pills every two hours and squirt a substance up my nose to control the disease. She was very sympathetic. She really is a fantastic woman and a true professional. It was brave of her to come so soon after her father's death. She kept smiling and kept all her sorrow to herself. I wanted to give her my sympathies over the death of her father but it was the wrong time. She is a very caring person, and her visit made me feel a lot better.

After I had explained to Ray about the designer drug MPTP, which had caused the Californian drug addicts to freeze, he began to ask me whether I felt it were possible that Ronnie Moran and Roy Evans might have put some toxin in his food before European games when he felt off colour. He was again threatening to sell his medals and told me that he was terrified of being alone. Without his kids, he said, he would probably have 'packed it all in by now'. On returning home after his holiday and a short stay in London, Ray learned that during his absence he had again been splashed all over the tabloids, this time to support the claim of the Professional Footballers Association for a bigger cut of the new Premier League's earnings. The *Daily Mirror*'s piece ran:

> England, Arsenal, Liverpool and Swansea Ray Kennedy's crippling agony has been eased by the PFA. The former golden boy, now wracked with Parkinson's disease, lost his wife, family, a £250,000 business and self-respect as people assumed his problems were due to drink or drugs. And it is only regular payments from the accident fund that have kept him smiling through the pain. PFA boss Gordon Taylor says: 'We have looked after many players such as Ray Kennedy . . . but for the PFA Kennedy would have been down and out. Even a £70,000 testimonial from 20,000 fans just managed to keep the bailiffs at bay which is where the PFA came in to help with his medical expenses'.

I had, in fact, never charged Ray during his numerous admissions to the hospital, but the cost of a private room and nursing fees were considerable, and Taylor and the PFA have continued to cover his expenses unreservedly. As a player Ray had shunned publicity, but within the space of two years he had become almost as well known to the public as in the heyday of his England career. He was now unquestionably the most famous patient with Parkinson's disease in the United Kingdom, in considerable demand at garden fêtes, and as a subject for articles in women's magazines. Sports writers were always asking him to give his verdict on crucial games involving Liverpool or Arsenal, and his career as a professional patient seemed to be taking off.

On 5 June 1992, an opportunity arose for Ray to fulfil one of his ambitions. Muhammad Ali and his entourage had eventually turned up in England to promote Hauser's biography on 'The Greatest'. Mary Baker, the welfare director of the Parkinson's Disease Society, had succeeded in the difficult task of arranging a meeting between Ray and Ali which would take place at Waterstone's bookshop in Leadenhall Market in central London.

On the morning of the planned meeting with Ali, I met Ray at the Parkinson's Disease Society headquarters. As always he was immaculately dressed. He told me that he had recently attended a reception in Newcastle in honour of Paul Gascoigne which had been filmed for television. Ray had been shocked by Gascoigne's clowning around and his lack of respect for the Mayor of Newcastle. Mary Baker, Ray and I set off by taxi into the City. The whole area around Waterstone's was blocked with traffic and the bookshop was swamped with eager fans all clutching their copy of Ali's biography. Ali sat serenely signing book after book surrounded by his aides, Thomas Hauser and Jeremy Robson, the publisher of the book in the United Kingdom. We were ushered downstairs to wait for Ali to complete the signing, and Ray became increasingly anxious at the thought of finally meeting his hero. He was constantly agonizing over what he could say and was fascinated to learn about Ali's Parkinson's syndrome. Members of the press and some of the Chrysalis film crew who had made *Ray of Hope* kept us company during the two-hour wait. Eventually Howard Bingham, Ali's loyal and long-standing guardian, came down the stairs and spoke to Ray: 'So you're the guy who is all nervous about meeting Muhammad? Don't worry he is just a normal guy'. Ray answered like a shot, 'No he's not, he's unique. There's no one like him.'

As the autograph hunters dwindled to a trickle, Robson's assistant came down to say that Ali would only meet Ray if the press and cameras left. The meeting was clearly a sensitive one for his public relations advisers. Ali himself frequently denies that he has a Parkinson's syndrome and the stigma of his illness and its potential repercussions for professional boxing were not something which his entourage wished to promote. During the wait I went up to get my own copy of Ali's biography signed. Ali, despite his impassive face, still had a twinkle in his eye.

Eventually Ali, surrounded by his followers, came down the narrow stairs to the basement of the bookshop and sat facing Ray, who immediately rose delightedly to shake Ali's hand warmly and repeatedly. Ray told Ali that he really was the greatest, most brilliant sportsman who had ever lived. To those of us who were used to seeing people react to Ray in a similar vein, it was a fascinating role reversal. I was keen to get a photograph for Ray, but Bingham told me to put my camera away. After a brief conversation, Ali bear-hugged Ray before autographing his book. It was all over in a few minutes and we were soon on our way, hotly pursued by journalists from the *Sunday Sun*, a local Newcastle newspaper. They had come down originally to report on the activities of Noel, the faith-healer who had treated Ray and was now carrying out a therapy session at a Regent's Park clinic. On the journey back to the Parkinson's Disease Society, Ray told me how saddened he was by Ali's appearance: 'I remember him when he was so quick-witted and lively that no one could defeat him. Today I didn't know what he'd do or say next. He seemed so slow and dim-witted, and his face was all bloated. I felt like crying.'

Just before the end of the meeting, Bingham had allowed me to take two shots of Ray with Ali. I later sent the negatives to Ray who took them into Newcastle to be enlarged. When they flopped out of the machine in the shop, people began crowding round in astonishment as they recognized Ali in the photographs. It had been clear to me, at the meeting, that Ali was now either unresponsive to medication or severely underdosed. His speech was virtually unintelligible, and all his movements were slow and diminished.

In the early summer of 1992, I decided to start Ray on a new medication called pergolide in the hope of being able to smooth out his motor swings and reduce his total daily dose of L-dopa. Pergolide is a drug quite closely related to ergot produced by a fungus that grows on rye husks. Ergot derivatives are responsible for St Anthony's Fire, and are used by doctors to assist the expulsion of the afterbirth and in the treatment of migraine. Pergolide is capable of artificially stimulating the dopamine receptors within the brain and imitating the effects of L-dopa. It is also quite closely related chemically to lysergic acid (LSD), the psychedelic spree drug of the sixties. Ray was able to build up the dose of pergolide and reduce his total dose of Sinemet with a gratifying reduction in the number of bad patches.

It was now almost two years since Ray had 'come out' fully, and, in tribute to his fortitude and resilience, in the autumn of 1992, at the Hyatt Carlton Hotel, he received the Evian Health Award which was presented to him by Tom Sackville, the Parliamentary Under-Secretary at the Department of Health. The other award in the sport and fitness section went to Imran Khan, the Pakistani cricketer, for his work in encouraging and promoting the need for immunization in inner city areas. The hotel in Portman Square brought back happy memories of former visits to the capital with Liverpool. Although Ray was able to cope with the luncheon, and switched on just in time to go up to receive his award, he was not strong enough to socialize. Straight after the dinner, he was whisked off by taxi to Heathrow airport to return to Newcastle.

Just before he left Ray told me that representatives from Christie's in Glasgow had visited his home to value his medals; they estimated them at £70,000–100,000. It was with relief some weeks later that I learnt that Ray had decided not to proceed with the sale. In the Christie's auction in which it had been proposed to sell Ray's collection, Bill Foulkes's European Cup winners' medal with Manchester United was sold for £30,000 to an Irish collector.

22 'They're doing a story on me, doctor'

The ghost sat down on the opposite side of the fireplace, as if he were quite used to it.
'You don't believe in me,' observed the Ghost.
'I don't' said Scrooge.
'What evidence would you have of my reality, beyond that of your senses?'
'Because,' said Scrooge, 'a little thing affects them. A slight disorder of the stomach makes them cheats. You may be an undigested bit of beef, a blot of mustard, a crumb of cheese, a fragment of an underdone potato. There's more of gravy than of grave about you, whatever you are!'

(C. DICKENS)

PERGOLIDE had virtually eradicated Ray's cramps and had enabled him to cut back considerably on his L-dopa tablets. The apomorphine sniffs continued to free him up in social situations, but were irritating his nose, and he was now using the inhaler infrequently. He was also turning in on himself more and more. His relationships with women were becoming increasingly convoluted and destructive. When I called, the answerphone always seemed to be on and, in August, I received several anguished calls from Maureen Wright.

Ray had become convinced that she was having affairs with four or five men at a time, they no longer went out, and a typical evening at home would consist of him grilling her, inquisitorially and relentlessly, about her movements during the day. A pattern emerged whereby he would leave her flat without warning in the evening and return later that night, convinced that in his absence another man had been there. He claimed to be able to smell aftershave; a towel was meaningfully left on the floor; the bed was warm. He was unshakeable in his belief that his fears were justified. Ray also told me that, for the first time in his life, he was beginning to experience difficulties with his sexual potency and was firmly of the conviction that Maureen was putting something in his drinks to damp down his ardour: 'It sounds far-fetched I know, doctor. I wish you were here, I could show you all the clues'. Ray asked the porter where Maureen worked to keep an eye open for any men friends who might come to see her. The accusations rained down.

One night Maureen watched a television programme on schizo-phrenia, and took down a self-help telephone number, in the hope that Ray would ring up. In fact, she had accidentally transposed two of the digits so that when he rang the number a man answered. This set Ray off on an elaborate exercise of detection in which, over several days, he played with different permutations of the phone number until he came up with a code which linked him to one of Maureen's alleged lovers. Ray was increasingly frightened and dismayed about his difficulty in having a trusting relationship with a woman; a terror of ending up as a 'lonely cripple staring at the walls of an institution' lay at the root of these tensions.

An appointment was fixed up for Maureen and him to go to Relate, but their relationship deteriorated so drastically in the interim that Ray did not turn up. As his liaison with Maureen disintegrated Ray renewed his stormy relationship with Audrey Smith. He told me: 'Maureen's too clever, she can tie knots round me with words'. Maureen also booked an appointment for him to see a clairvoyant, making the appointment under another name so that he would not be recognized. Ray was convinced that this was a set-up and that Maureen had told the woman all about him. The clairvoyant told him that the book that he was involved in writing would be a bestseller, if he expressed his emotions more, that he had done a lot of travelling in his life and that he was having a close relationship with someone who loved him, but whom he could not trust.

On 23 August I met Ray at Anfield for the Arsenal game. He looked exhausted and told me, 'I'm going nuts, doctor'. Trevor, who was also there, expressed concern about his elder brother's behaviour. However, during his stay at Anfield, Ray was able to relax briefly and renew acquaintances with former friends; Graeme Souness took care of him personally.

In issue 15 of the Liverpool fanzine, *Through the Wind and Rain*, the following letter appeared:

The day we played Arsenal I stood waiting for my mate on
Anfield Road. He was late, so I stood there watching for all
the familiar faces. All of a sudden I noticed coming past me a
very familiar face indeed – The Great Ray Kennedy. A truly
great player, a wonderful person whose battle against PD puts
the rest of us moaning bastards to shame. Shame and embarrassment was exactly what I felt as dozens of 'Liverpool fans'
walked past and around Ray, totally oblivious of who he is.

If you've got his video (and if not why the hell not?) you'll
know that one of the main symptoms of the disease is the
way Ray gets flustered around groups of people. As he
walked up Anny Road he looked nervously around him. He
needn't have worried, none of the ignorant gits knew who he
was. I went over to him and found myself saying 'All right
Ray, how are you?'.

He looked straight at me, no different from the great Ray of
the 70s; he looked bronzed fit as a fiddle. He shook my hand
firmly and said 'I'm okay, thank you, son, okay thanks'. When
I let go my hand was covered in sweat and he took out a
tissue to mop his brow. He went through the Shankly Gates,
pushing through all the ignorant people. I hope the club treats
him with the respect he deserves; more than some fans who
have forgotten there was a team here before Barnes and Co.

On his return home his paranoia and jealousy became fixed on
Audrey. Dr Jackson, his new general practitioner, recommended
that he see a psychiatrist, inquiring whether he would prefer to
see a male or female doctor. Ray opted for a woman and was
accompanied to the first consultation by Audrey. Ray had previously told me that at one time he had been deadly serious about
proposing marriage to Audrey despite the turbulence of their
relationship. He had become convinced that she cared for him
after an episode in York when she had stayed uncomplaining by
his side for four hours while he was cramped up. They had
bought a small flat together in Gosforth and an apartment in
Hull, both of which had been put up for sale. While Ray was
seeing the elderly lady psychiatrist, Audrey was telling the nurse
outside that Ray had begged her to go back to him and, despite
her better judgement, she had agreed. The consultation was a
disaster. Ray felt that the psychiatrist was demeaning and authori-
tarian, that she refused to listen to his story and continually

interrupted him. She concluded that he was paranoid and had not come to terms with his Parkinson's disease. She also told him that he was incapable of ever having a deep relationship with a woman, and that she found it difficult to understand how a man in his physical state was able to attract so much female-company! Ray told me afterwards: 'There's nothing wrong with me, doctor. It's just that I've got involved with two women who are not good for me. When I'm not with them I'm all right'. The trouble was that Ray could not bear not to be with Audrey as he sat helpless and alone in his flat.

I arranged for Ray to be admitted urgently to the Middlesex Hospital. Delusional jealousy and paranoia are well-recognized, if uncommon, responses to long-term dopamine replacement therapy. On his arrival at the hospital, Ray was able to speak sensibly and dispassionately about his recent behaviour. However, he appeared more preoccupied, prickly and distant than usual, and the jokes were fewer. The main purpose of his admission had been to separate him from the seeds of his delusion. For the first day or two he made desperate efforts to get hold of a Newcastle-upon-Tyne telephone directory so that he could continue his disordered investigation into Audrey's possible men friends. When I asked him why he was wasting his time doing this, he replied that for him it was like doing a jigsaw, he loved to put all the pieces into place and solve the mystery.

Within a few days, however, he was back to his old self, and his recovery was accelerated by visits from Frank McLintock, members of the Parkinson's Disease Society and Malcolm and Terry, his old North London friends. One night he went out with friends and returned to the ward the worse for wear in the early hours of the morning. He greeted me the following day with a smile and a joke: 'I've found the cure for Parkinson's disease, doctor. It's called the Capricorn Club in Goodge Street'. He was able to talk about his plans to raise money for the Parkinson's Disease Society, and his hopes of buying a small bungalow in the North-East. He remained only partially persuaded by my explanations that his paranoia had got out of hand as a result of his medication, his illness and his depression. I attempted to reduce his medication as much as I could, but this was possible only to a limited degree because of the return of intolerable slowness and abdominal cramp.

Shortly before his discharge he told me that he planned a holiday in the sun, which I encouraged him to take alone. A few days later I learned that he had disappeared without informing his parents of his whereabouts. On his return he was dejected and dispirited. His parents' misgivings, that he had gone on holiday with Audrey, had been confirmed, and the trip had proved a disaster: his jealousy had magnified and he had been informed, not for the first time, that Audrey was pregnant. During his off periods he felt increasingly vulnerable and dominated. Ray, in turn, contributed to Audrey's own insecurity and jealousy.

Ray got back home just in time for the christening of Janet's baby son, Leon. The day was a happy diversion for Ray, who was able to have a partial reconciliation with Michael, although he told me afterwards that his younger brother hadn't asked once about his illness. He also jokingly said: 'It's the first time all the Kennedys have been together and not had a fight'.

Although Ray knew in his heart that Audrey and he were bad for each other, he was unable to leave her alone. Love oscillated with hate as they each strove to dominate and control the other, hell-bent on self-destruction. Audrey's desperation and anger with Ray's continuous accusations led to physical retaliation, despite her diminutive size. Ray began to suspect that Audrey was setting him up for a sensational story in the Sunday papers. Ray had begged his recently acquired home help not to come any more, because he became increasingly suspicious about her, and a proposed interview with a film maker was cancelled at the last minute because 'the fella's story didn't add up'.

Despite the unsatisfactory first consultation with the psychiatrist, I encouraged him to go again. Fortunately, the second consultation went somewhat better, although Ray was keen to spend time talking to the younger nurse who he felt understood him better than the doctor. He again complained to me that the psychiatrist kept putting words into his mouth and that she was only interested in starting him on drugs. A third and final consultation did more harm than good. The doctor kept Ray waiting some time, whereupon he became more and more anxious. He got the impression that she resented his character and that she was more concerned about the potential costs of his treatment than getting to the root of his problem. He again sensed that she wanted to enforce a relationship in which she exerted control over him, and that he should take a submissive, deferential role. The consultation terminated with Ray telling the psychiatrist that she did not understand him and that she was trying to put words into his mouth. He left feeling insecure and distressed, and vowing never to see her again. He told me desperately, 'Every year it's getting harder and harder to cope with this illness, doctor'.

After another torrid night of warfare with Audrey, Ray determined to sever the Gordian knot and the following day attended a meeting of young patients with Parkinson's disease at Whitley Bay. One of them was receiving apomorphine and told Ray that he had demanded it from his specialist after watching *Ray of Hope* on television on Boxing Day. The drug had changed his life. Ray complained to me that every time he tried to talk to one of the patients a carer would butt in, answering for the patient: 'It's the carers that need treatment, doctor, not the patients. I don't think anyone who has not got this illness can even start to understand what it's like'. Even the noise of the carers' voices became too much for Ray and, as had happened so frequently over the past two years, he was obliged to excuse himself and sit quietly to compose himself.

In another desperate attempt to escape from his increasingly humiliating relationship, he visited a gym owned by a lady he had known for ten years. One of her friends who had recently been divorced invited Ray round for the evening and no sooner had he arrived than things started to go desperately wrong:

> She seemed to be doing everything to annoy me deliberately. One of her children put loud music on, and she started to discuss her rare blood group and whether or not I should stick with Audrey if the baby was mine. I couldn't take it any longer and left, but on the way home I felt dizzy and dazed, and felt certain she'd put something in my food, and had to call my mum to tell her I was feeling bad.

Ray's relationship with Jenny had improved considerably during all this. Jen had told him that she was pregnant, that she was hoping to sell her house and live with the father of her expected child, with whom she had been having a relationship for some time. Ray had never met him, but had heard that he was a 'nice, quiet fellow'. Ray was able to discuss these developments rationally and without malice or jealousy. He also talked glowingly about his new nephew, Leon, whom he enjoyed visiting and whom he felt would be good for his mum and dad in keeping them young. The volcano had gone to sleep, his thoughts were no longer irrational, impassioned, irregular and fearful. Once I'd steered him off the subject of women, he was back to the same old Ray, positive, quick-witted and brimming with hope.

Transient paranoia, rapidly dismissed and carrying no lasting conviction, is an almost universal human experience. All of us have experienced the feeling on entering a crowded room when all eyes seem to be directed towards us, or the suspicion that, when a group of acquaintances suddenly stop talking, that they must have been conspiring in some way. The more sensitive, inward-looking of a lay audience listening to a lecturer in psychology talking about personality types may conclude that they share the hysterical, obsessive, paranoid or schizoid traits of the individuals under discussion, whereas the thicker-skinned extrovert may see these characteristics in their friends or even in the lecturer. Beliefs that others experience similar feelings to ours, and the assumption that external events are directed towards us in some meaningful way, inspire an environmental sensitivity which has probably been helpful in human survival. The famous may suffer justifiable paranoia and, undoubtedly, there are some individuals whose acute perceptiveness enables them to pick up nuances and signals which are denied to the rest of us in everyday social contact. There is no absolute way of distinguishing a normal belief from a paranoid delusion and only when the fear becomes persistent and fixed, and influences the behaviour and actions of the individual can it be considered in any way morbid. Paranoia has jokingly been referred to as 'total awareness' and this blur between perceptive sensitivity and morbidity is reflected in the amusing anecdote: 'I may be paranoid, doctor, but that still doesn't stop people following me!'.

What is reality, what delusion? This question with its implied paradox is never more pertinent than when applied to morbid jealousy. Intense feelings of possession directed towards a loved sexual partner are commonplace and rooted in proprietorial, competitive and controlling urges. However, when behaviour

becomes abnormal as a result of distressing irrational thoughts
and disordered preoccupations centred on the partner's infidelity,
then illness is present. Intercurrent physical illness or an assault
on a patient's self-esteem, such as a broken marriage or delayed
promotion, may trigger a paranoid delusion. Isolation, prison, a
trip to a strange land, partial deafness, alcohol or cocaine abuse
are other precipitants. In truth, however, these are really no more
than the sparks which ignite a keg of gunpowder. Paranoid
reactions tend to occur particularly in sensitive, emotionally
labile, vulnerable individuals who lack self-confidence. These
people are often slightly rigid, stubborn and proud, as well as
being self-centred, aggressive and touchy. Ray's personality fits
the stereotype closely. The train of events often develops from
feelings of shame. In Ray's case, possible fears about his failing
potency and, perhaps, concern about his inability to sustain a
lasting female relationship may be relevant. In some individuals,
envy may also be a factor as may a lust to exert extreme control
over a loved one. 'A real or imagined discovery – the jealous
flash – sets in motion the delusion.'

People started to look at Ray and whisper and, although he
was used to this as a famous figure, he was now convinced that
they were being rude and disrespectful. When he rang his
solicitor in London, the secretary asked whether it was Ray
Kennedy on the phone and, when he replied in the affirmative,
she responded, 'I thought so, I can tell by the awful accent'. Little
things like this became of more significance because Ray's mood
and morale had deteriorated so much.

Jealousy includes a peculiar, but passionate desire for the
absolute truth. Proust described this desire in *À la Recherche du
Temps Perdu* in the character of his hero, Swann:

> 'All manner of actions from which he would have recoiled in
> shame such as spying, putting adroitly provocative questions
> to casual witnesses, and listening at doors seemed to him now
> to be precisely on a level with the methods of scientific
> investigation with a genuine intellectual value and legitimately
> employable in the search for truth'.

A patient of Pierre Janet, the French medical psychologist,
whom he nicknamed 'The Gunman' because of his powerful build
and his part-time employment in strong-arm jobs, presented for

medical help because he could not get a job. Janet was immediately impressed by the hostility of the man's body language and his threatening appearance. After a course of successful therapy, the Gunman was able to describe in a four-page letter how he had lived his life:

> No one in whom I could confide, no one that I might call a true friend. The things I loved most, and those that I loved, were taken away. There was not one thing that I could really call my own. Defence after defence I threw up to ward off more hurt, retreating, ever retreating into my shell. Until finally I became a snarling animal at bay. The few people I did know slowly left me, people shunned me on the street. I became suspicious of everyone. I looked for trouble to present itself almost everywhere and looking for it I found plenty. I tried to smash my way through life's barriers, crushing those that opposed me, fighting, snarling, to retain my place in the world. In doing so I created a world of hate, which finally overpowered me.

Pierre Janet, analysing this case, commented that he had often heard the term paranoid personality used as a descriptive term for this disturbance, however, he was concerned that this implied a pathological or diseased brain as the underlying cause. He accepted that some of these cases are determined by organic disease, but considered that the majority of paranoid attitudes cannot be regarded as clearly abnormal:

> Many paranoid individuals see the world as we do, without hallucination, even if they describe it differently. Their capacity for continuous thinking is if anything above average and their capacity for logical thought although unusually tortuous is not necessarily abnormal.

The jealous person is always checking and re-checking, seeking those crucial tell-tale signs of betrayal, cross-questioning incessantly which sometimes culminates in the desperate use of force to cajole a confession.

Fear of loneliness and rejection stalked Ray in his cramped apartment. When I asked Ray if he minded if Audrey had other men he replied, 'No, doctor, but I want to get to the truth'. The so-called rivals remained vague, shadowy figures, contrasting sharply with the detailed descriptions of the lovers' treacherous behaviour. Ray remained persuaded through the autumn that he was being set up, and laid traps in his house to deflect silent intruders.

Trevor changed his locks twice, as Ray was adamant there was a conspiracy against him and felt unsafe even in his own house. Ray was now convinced that people were out to get him, and could see omens in every little incident. Trevor was taken out with him in his car to try to vindicate his story, but nothing happened. As they returned home, Ray commented to his brother, 'It's a quiet night tonight'. However, as soon as Ray got home, he rang Trevor to say that someone had set him up at the local McDonalds. Trevor rang me on several occasions to express his concern about his brother's behaviour. I asked him to persuade Ray to come for treatment and that he was not well. Trevor said to me, 'All I want, doctor, is for you to get my brother back for me.' Ray's distrust even spread to his own family, and he was constantly smelling strange vapours which he interpreted as poisons in the environment.

People are a bit like crystals, they have fault lines. If intolerable pressure is exerted, those lines influence how each of us breaks. Parkinson's disease brings with it a pervasive maladjustment, feelings of hopelessness, worry, tension, hypochondriasis and irritability. For years the world had been subtly altered for Ray. Everything was uncanny, portentous and peculiar. He had felt uncomfortable, perplexed and at the same time excited, but did not know why; now these indefinite premonitions had become clearer, the vague menace of life had been transformed into a more definite threat and his suspiciousness had become a conviction. Events that, for so long, had confused him now fitted into place. He felt trapped and yet at the same time protected within a black labyrinth deep below the world outside. When he looked up occasionally, a field stretched out towards a green felt horizon.

The Newcastle vendetta continued. Mechanics were commanded to strip his car down; everyone was now under suspicion, and Ray clamoured for a safe house. I had many worrying phone conversations with him, including one conducted on a deserted

Whitley Bay beach with Ray walking seawards to find fresh air.
Ray asked me what would happen if his pills stopped working
and the gases closed in again. Thirty minutes later, he was back
home dismantling the plugs in his room in a desperate attempt to
locate the fumes.

In January 1993, he finally agreed to come back to hospital.
Veronica accompanied him to Newcastle Station and got him on
the train. Just as she was leaving, relieved that at last help was at
hand, Ray reappeared flushed and wild-eyed, telling her he
couldn't go because the gases were all around. An air ticket was
hurriedly fixed, and finally, albeit with considerable difficulty,
Ray was on his way to the Middlesex Hospital.

When he arrived late in the evening, he recognized me, but
there was no customary joke or warm greeting. He told me his
twisted right arm was being controlled by outside forces, the
fumes were everywhere and his tormentors were in the building.
He wanted to leave immediately and switched on the oxygen
mask to try to protect himself. His Parkinson's disease was now
incorporated into his delusions. After much persuasion, he reluctantly agreed to stay the night.

The following day, again with considerable difficulty, I was
able to get him to discontinue pergolide, which I felt had
unmasked the psychosis, and to accept a small dose of sulpiride,
which would help to block the overstimulated dopamine
receptors.

Improvement in his mental state was slow; the poisons and
toxins kept closing in and even on cold nights Ray slept with his
window wide open. In those early weeks, virtually everyone on
Campbell Thompson ward, including me, was involved in the
conspiracy. Encouraging patches of lucidity, however, began to
appear with flashes of his sense of humour. Before setting off to
see a dentist, he told us: 'Tell the dentist I'll be bringing my own
gas with me!'

Frank McLintock was a daily visitor, but Ray did not want to
see anyone else. He complained of a muzzy head and sedation,
and developed a prodigious appetite, which was nurtured by
Victor the porter and the nurses who supplemented the hospital
menu. Veronica Kennedy also sent a small hamper.

As he improved, Audrey made weekly visits; she was now
definitely pregnant. Ray was excited about becoming a father

again, and also talked a lot about Leon, Janet's son. Gradually, his confidence increased and he started to leave the hospital for Sunday walks and to fetch his dry cleaning. The number of visitors increased: first Veronica and Trevor, then Cara and Dale. Jimmy Case, just transferred from Halifax to Wrexham, popped in, and there were visitors from Highbury and the Parkinson's Disease Society. There were also several new female friends and admirers from his past.

As the pergolide washed out of his brain and the hallucinations and ideas of reference receded, he began to realize how ill he had been. Depression set in with fears that he might become that ill again. Nevertheless he was back in the real world and able to state that Parkinson's disease was easy to cope with compared with what he had just come through. On sharing his terrifying experience with another patient on the ward, he was astonished to be told: 'Oh, don't worry, Ray, every time I open my wardrobe I see a lion's face'.

By March Ray was well enough to go home. All traces of paranoia had gone, and I joked with him that once the jigsaw he had been toiling with for three weeks was finished he could leave the ward. He was looking forward to his mother's chips, and was determined to find a home and resume his fund-raising for the Parkinson's Disease Society. As he left his last words to me were: 'Thanks for all you've done, doctor. You've done a good job!'

23 Chimera

I am going to make me a big sharp axe
Shining steel tempered in the fire
I'll chop you down like an old dead tree
Dirty old town, dirty old town.

(EWAN MACCOLL)

KENNEDY to Keegan, on to Case, headed back to Kennedy, a little one-two with Case and out wide to Heighway. Number five, Kennedy, receives the ball out on the left, brings it down with his chest, holds it momentarily, then lifts a looping cross into McDermott's path. McDermott deceives to go right, then swivels round, hits a flat ball twenty yards up to Dalglish; Dalglish flicks on to Johnson who skews it back to Kennedy. Kennedy, on the edge of the box, hardly lifts back his standing peg, but the ball dips viciously into the top right-hand corner. Kennedy, again attacking the defence, wins a corner, taken by Dalglish. Kennedy hangs back waiting for pickings on the edge of the box. A high hanging ball is chipped on by Souness and knocked back across to Kennedy, who rifles a piercing drive. With Liverpool in possession again down the right, the ball swirls across to the left to Alan Kennedy, who crosses long to Johnson's head. The ball flies across the face of the goal. Kennedy, broad-shouldered, with great economy of movement, drifts past one player, then swings a dangerous ball out towards Case. Just as the game is dying, Case hits a screamer from forty yards. The Kop is singing now: 'Champions, champions, champions'. Reds weave patterns on the park; Kennedy is all angles and oblique balls, a prowler in the shadows of the box.

Solid as a rock, Kennedy's head swivels as the cross comes over and the ball explodes up, out and between despairing hands. Kennedy is bullocking forward, bulldozing on like a Chieftain tank, moving wide; Radford draws off, Graham waits lean and hungry and George hovers like a cat waiting to pounce. The ball bobs around and drops to Armstrong, who loops a seemingly impossible cross back for Kennedy to knock forward for a Radford strike into the yawning goal. Twenty minutes gone and Rice is driving a long ball forward onto Kennedy's head and the ball is in the net again. The exultant North Bank tumbles forward.

A McDermott cross falls to Kennedy who forces his way between two men, rounds the goalkeeper and drives in low. A little jump and a clap. A master of the loose ball in the box, with a sixth sense even in the mud, Kennedy ebbs and flows languidly on the left, provider and opportunist.

Scores of games with intangible permanence on anonymous grounds under inclement skies, with Kennedy dictating from the fringes, scheming trajectories and killing chips: I hear these mesmeric radio waves and picture disjointed fragments of play in Brownian motion in my sleep. Movement is the mirror of the soul, but the soul turned into a ghost on 5 December 1981.

Kennedy had a dream too. He was running normally through the park, kicking a ball to Dale. The toffee on his boots had melted and he no longer bobbed and weaved like a drunken marionette to the tune of capsules. His right arm had lost its ungiving angular stiffness and had ceased to palpitate. His jaw no longer sagged in disbelief, and saliva no longer hung from the corners of his mouth. The doctor said he could go back to work. One last time he rose from the tunnel, dribbled and juggled, checked and volleyed past the disappointed moaning bastards and out into clear water. The ghost was chasing shadows again in the fading light.

Postscript

Ray was bound over to keep the peace after an almighty skirmish with Audrey. However, the two of them were to share great happiness with the birth of their daughter Alannah. Despite his differences with Audrey, Ray was drawn to the baby and spent long hours at Audrey's home, happy in the baby's company. The birth also brought Audrey and Ray closer together again.

With the proceeds from the Arsenal testimonial Ray was able to buy a bungalow in New Hartley, no more than a stone's throw from the park where, a quarter of a century earlier, he had been scrutinized by the League scouts. This new home allowed Ray to visit Audrey, and when things got too stressful for both of them he could retreat to the security of his own place. Their relationship began to blossom and Ray told me:

> 'I'm still considering asking Audrey to marry me. Audrey and I have known each other for five years now and the baby's come along and we want to get things sorted out.'

Audrey was also more enthusiastic about their relationship, although she admits:

> 'Ray and I have had some upsets and we have problems other couples don't because we've got Parkinson's.'

As the summer wore on Ray steadily began to pick himself up after the traumas of the previous winter, although again there were days when he was so tired and lethargic that he couldn't get going until midday. Cara and Dale were regular visitors to the bungalow and were there to help him settle in and sort things out. The squirmy, twitchy fidgets which had been building up inexorably before his last hospital admission were now greatly reduced, and eating was again a pleasure rather than a disjointed ordeal.

In one of our frequent telephone conversations, which now often drifted to football matters and particularly the decline of

Liverpool Football Club, Ray reminded me of his own personal conflict:

> 'I never believed I was good enough to be a top footballer. I felt with me in the side it was like ten teas and one coffee. I was twenty-seven and playing for England before I started to have any belief in myself.'

He also told me how he could recognize people with Parkinson's disease in the street and felt the urge to go over to them and say 'Have you got Parkinson's? Well so have I. It's horrible, isn't it?' His self-pity, however, never lasted more than a few seconds, and he would then change tack and tell me how lucky he had been to pack so many happy memories into such a short time.

In early September the hardback edition of *Ray of Hope* was launched. Ray, with moral support from Audrey and baby Alannah, embarked on a hectic ten-day schedule of book signing and interviews. At a literary lunch in Birmingham Ray made his maiden public speech as a Parkinsonian. As he nervously rose the microphone collapsed, but David Frost and other literary guests leapt to Ray's aid and held the microphone in front of Ray. Ray's nerves melted as he sensed that the audience were sympathetic, and his confidence rose so much that he was able to discard the short written speech I had prepared for him and express his true feelings to rapturous applause. At the end of the dinner Frost gave him a signed copy of his own book, in which he had written, 'You are an inspiration to us all.' Later that year David Frost was to select *Ray of Hope* as one of his two book choices for 1993.

Ray's medals, caps and shirts, which had been lodged in Christie's safe earlier in the year, were auctioned in Glasgow in sixty lots on 21 October 1993. The Arsenal Double medals went to a private collector for £17,000 and Gordon Taylor of the Professional Footballers Association bought Ray's three European Cup Winner's medals for £31,080, the £16,000 paid for the 1977 Rome final against Borussia Münchengladbach beating the previous British record for a football medal. With fourteen lots unsold, Ray's unique collection raised £88,000. Gordon Taylor told the press afterwards:

> 'What Ray won may never be repeated. We wanted such

quality memorabilia to stay in football and at the same time to help one of our members.'

The Professional Footballers Association is proposing to exhibit Ray's medals at a new football museum in Manchester, and Ray was so delighted that a significant part of his collection had remained in good hands that he immediately resolved to let Gordon Taylor take care of the four unsold medals as well. Ray had reluctantly sold his medals to provide financial security for himself and his children.

A second occasion to talk about Parkinson's disease occurred just before Christmas 1993 with an invitation to talk to a group of Merseyside general practitioners in the new Bob Paisley suite in the Centenary stand at Anfield. It was anticipated that Ray would speak for no more than a few minutes and then the video of his life would be shown. Ray eloquently expressed to the audience of doctors what it was like to have Parkinson's disease and, guided by his old mentor Bob Paisley, whose picture hung on the wall behind Ray as he spoke, the video became irrelevant, such was the power of Ray's thirty-minute soliloquy.

'I don't want you to feel sorry for me and I don't want to be seen as Mr Parkinson, but I hope what I have said to you tonight will help you understand more.'

Appendix 1

England Under-23s

DATE	OPPONENTS	SCORE	APS.	GLS.
1972				
Jan	WALES	2-0	1	—
1973				
Jan	HOLLAND	3-1	1	—
March	CZECHOSLOVAKIA	1-0	Sub	—
May	DENMARK	1-1	1	—
	HOLLAND	0-1	Sub	—
Oct	POLAND	0-0	1	—
			4(2)	—

England Career

DATE	OPPONENTS	SCORE	APS.	GLS.
1976				
March	WALES	2-1	1	1
May	WALES	1-0	1	—
	N. IRELAND	4-0	1	—
	SCOTLAND	2-1	1	—
1977				
March	LUXEMBOURG	5-0	1	1
May	WALES	0-1	1	—
June	SCOTLAND	1-2	1	—
	BRAZIL	0-0	Sub	—
	ARGENTINA	1-1	Sub	—
Sept	SWITZERLAND	0-0	1	—
Oct	LUXEMBOURG	2-0	1	1
1979				
Oct	BULGARIA	2-0	1	—
1980				
March	SPAIN	2-0	1	—
May	ARGENTINA	3-1	1	—
	WALES	1-4	1	—
June	BELGIUM	1-1	Sub	—
	ITALY	0-1	1	—
			14(3)	3

Appendix 3

Club Roll of Honour
Figures in brackets indicate substitute appearances

CLUB	SEASON	LEAGUE		FA CUP		LEAGUE CUP		EUROPE	
		APS	GLS	APS	GLS	APS	GLS	APS	GLS
ARSENAL	1969–70	2(2)	1	—	—	—	—	(2)	1
	1970–1	41	19	9	2	5	2	8	3
	1971–2	37	12	6(2)	1	4	2	6	4
	1972–3	34(1)	9	1	—	1	—	—	—
	1973–4	42	12	3	1	1	—	—	—
LIVERPOOL	1974–5	23(3)	5	—	—	4	3	4	2
	1975–6	29	6	2	—	1	—	10	4
	1976–7	41	7	8	1	2	—	9	1
	1977–8	41	4	1	—	9	1	9	2
	1978–9	42	10	7	1	1	—	2	—
	1979–80	40	9	8	—	6	—	1	—
	1980–1	41	8	2	1	9	2	9	2
	1981–2	15(3)	2	—	—	3	—	4	1
SWANSEA	1981–2	18	2	—	—	—	—	—	—
	1982–3	21	—	—	—	2	—	3	—
	1983–4	3	—	—	—	—	—	2	—
HARTLEPOOL	1983–4	18(5)	3	—	—	—	—	—	—
		502	109	49	7	48	10	69	20

Appendix 4

Honours

European Cup winners' medal: 1977, 1978, 1981
UEFA Cup winners' medal: 1970, 1976
European Super Cup winners' medal: 1977
League Super Cup runners-up medal: 1978
League Championship medal: 1971, 1976, 1977, 1979, 1980
FA Cup winners' medal: 1971
FA Cup runners-up medal: 1972, 1977
League Cup winner' medal: 1981
League Cup runners-up medal: 1978

Appendix 5

When Did Ray Kennedy's Parkinson's Disease Begin?

A. J. Lees

Department of Neurology, The Middlesex Hospital, Mortimer Street, London, U.K.

Summary: Ray Kennedy's Parkinson's disease probably began during his distinguished career as a professional soccer player at least 10 years before the first unequivocal physical signs and 14 years before the diagnosis was finally made, when he was 35 years old. Early prodromal symptoms included intermittent subtle disturbances of movement and posture affecting the right arm and leg, mild facial immobility, episodes of profound malaise and lack of energy, inner feelings of tremulousness, excessive unprovoked bouts of perspiration, and accompanying feelings of heat. Abnormalities of movement in the right arm can be seen in video footage of soccer games up to 8 years before his disability came to medical attention. Many of his premorbid personality traits are characteristic of those believed to be associated with the subsequent development of the malady. At least in some patients with Parkinson's disease, the search for instigating aetiological factors should focus 10–20 years before the cardinal signs can be recognized with certainty. **Key Words**: Premorbid personality – Early diagnosis.

The onset of Parkinson's disease is so gradual that many patients, even with hindsight, may be uncertain as to when their symptoms began although they can usually indicate when they first became aware of their presence. This difficulty may be shared by close friends and relatives who also fail to notice slow, subtle changes in body language and physiognomy. Paradoxically, those who see the

A videotape segment accompanies this article.
Address correspondence and reprint requests to Dr A. J. Lees at The Middlesex Hospital, Mortimer Street, London, W1N 8AA.

patients infrequently may be immediately struck by an altered facial expression, quality of voice or posture, and diminished physical alacrity. The disorder is not infrequently picked up at routine medical check-ups or following elective surgery. In many patients, there is an element of denial or neglect of symptoms at the time of presentation. The earliest symptoms are vague and are not unreasonably misconstrued as evidence of strain, overwork, or mild melancholia. The patient, puzzled and frustrated by inexplicable malaise and torpor then may become genuinely depressed. The diagnosis, therefore, usually remains unsuspected until a resting tremor of the fingers or, less commonly, the foot appears.

The diagnostic triad of a coarse resting tremor, rigidity, and bradykinesia does not show itself until 70% of the ventrolateral groups of pars compacta nigral neurones have been destroyed. The presence of Lewy bodies in the surviving nerve cells is also central to contemporary clinicopathological concepts of Parkinson's disease. The frequency of Lewy bodies in the substantia nigra of individuals dying without recorded signs of Parkinson's disease in life rises steadily from 2% of the population in the 6th decade to 10% in the 9th decade (1,2). These incidental Lewy body brains have significantly more nerve cell loss in the ventrolateral nigral tier than do age-matched control brains without Lewy bodies (3,4). The prevalence of Parkinson's disease rises from a very low level in middle age in 2% of the whole population living into tneir 9th decade (5). The 3-decade difference in the 2% prevalence figures for incidental Lewy body cases and Parkinson's disease could indicate that neuronal nigral loss in Parkinson's disease begins decades before cardinal signs appear. Furthermore, the marked degree of nigral cell loss already present in patients dying with mild Parkinson's disease of short duration suggests that there must be a period of time during which compensation is more or less effective.

If the duration of this 'presymptomatic phase' of Parkinson's disease could be ascertained with accuracy, it would help narrow the search for aetiological factors to a specific time period. More accurate means of early detection of Parkinson's disease will also become vital if a neuroprotective agent for nigral neurons becomes available. In the absence of biological markers for Parkinson's disease, increased sophistication in the recognition of early psychomotor disturbances may be needed.

Association soccer players are acutely aware of the mechanical capabilities and limitations of the human frame and must be extremely fit if they are to compete at the highest level. During their playing careers, they are continually under the eye of a fickle public, demanding coaches, and managers, and subject to the unquenchable thirst of the media. Ray Kennedy's meticulous recollections, analysis of extensive video footage of his playing career, and corroborative statements from his family and numerous professional colleagues provide further support for the view that in some patients at least, subtle aberrations of psychomotor behaviour may be present for many years before the diagnosis of Parkinson's disease can be established with conviction.

RAY KENNEDY THE SOCCER PLAYER

Ray Kennedy, a miner's son from Seaton Delaval, Northumberland, had a distinguished career as a professional soccer player. At the age of 18, he played a pivotal role as a lethal striker in the 1970/1971 Arsenal League and Cup double winning team and, over the next four seasons, had a regular place in the side during which he gained England Under-23 honours and notched 53 goals. He was a bulldog of a player, strong and powerful, adept at shielding the ball, and able to ride tackles, but with a deft touch and a cultured left foot. In the summer of 1974, he was signed by Bill Shankly for Liverpool for a fee of £180,000. During the next 7 years of virtually uninterrupted triumphs, he made 381 appearances for Liverpool and scored 72 goals. At Liverpool, he won three European Cup Winner medals, four League Championship medals, one League Cup, and one UEFA Cup Winner's medal, and gained 17 full England International caps. This was all the more remarkable because on his arrival at Anfield, he looked awkward, slow, and jaded and had briefly drifted into the reserves. The Liverpool manager, Bob Paisley, however, was able to remodel him into a determined, powerful left-sided midfield player who read games instinctively and had a swift, decisive distribution of the ball.

In 1982, he joined Swansea then in the First Division, for £20,000 less than his purchase price from Liverpool and played for a further season and a half. He then had a brief spell in the lower divisions with Hartlepool Rovers before taking a player-coach post in Cyprus and finishing his direct contact with soccer as a youth coach at Sunderland in 1985.

RAY KENNEDY'S PARKINSON'S DISEASE

Premorbid Personality Traits

By nature, Ray Kennedy is dynamic, determined, modest, organized, and somewhat over-controlled. Although highly disciplined on the field of play, he has a short fuse off it and has always been prone to episodic uncontrolled bouts of aggression. He attributes much of his success in soccer to a deep-seated fear of failure, and from his early twenties, he has experienced mild claustrophobia. Although of solitary, somewhat suspicious disposition he has an engaging wit and canny sense of self-preservation. He is a habitual nonsmoker.

Prodromal Signs (1970–1982)

At Arsenal when receiving training instructions, Kennedy was frequently accused of looking vacant and, to his coach, he appeared unresponsive and inattentive. Kennedy recalls vividly one hot day during a training match an inability to do up his shirt buttons with the fingers of his right hand because of what appeared to him to be an inexplicable loss of finger dexterity. After match practice, Kennedy would be so lacking in strength and energy that he would go to bed and sometimes sleep for several hours in the afternoon.

On moving to Liverpool in 1975, he noticed that his right hip was involuntarily pushing forwards when he walked, causing him to move in a different way from usual and feel occasionally slightly off balance. At this time, his right foot sometimes scuffed on the floor and his right arm and leg felt tired and tense. After a year or two, this seemed to pass, but even when back to full fitness on the pitch he felt exceptionally weary after training and it became a standing joke at home that he was always too tired to go anywhere or do anything, always wanting to sit down for a few minutes to have a rest.

> At Liverpool I could never understand why I was the odd man out, particularly after a match. Players react in different ways after a game, but looking round I realized that nobody had my after match routine. Usually the adrenaline is still pumping and most of the lads would be talking about what happened on the pitch, grabbing a coke or chicken leg. They were always doing something – all except me. I used to slump hunched in my seat too tired to talk or move.

He and some of his fellow players remember his considerable uncoordination and asynchrony in carrying out star jumps in training where the right arm had to be raised and the left leg kicked out simultaneously, alternating rapidly with the left arm and right leg. Examination of video material showed that after the Football Association Cup final against Manchester United in 1977 his right arm was flexed and he moved it extremely slowly.

In the 1978 video of the Aston Villa against Liverpool match, Kennedy comes out on the pitch last, leaden stiff, awkward, and slightly stooped. In the May 1980 match against Arsenal, his face looks frozen and dazed after he has scored a goal and in the Bristol City match in the same season his right arm at times did not swing fluently.

> I tried to kid myself I was more tired because I had worked harder than the others during a match, yet I knew it was not the case. The odd thing was I could always perform for the full ninety minutes and was rarely the one to be substituted.

In the last 18 months of his time at Liverpool, he describes feeling that his body was beginning to rebel against the rigour and intensity of team training, increasing feelings of anxiety and depression, and mounting feelings of tiredness.

Unequivocal Onset of the Disease to Diagnosis (1982–1986)

In 1982, lying on a sunbed, he began to notice that it was extremely difficult for him to get his right arm comfortable and he became aware of some brief, intermittent twitches of the right index finger that disappeared immediately on changing the posture of his hand. On one or two occasions after this, he again noticed tremulous movements of his fingers. At the age of 31, he inexplicably began to become more wooden and lacklustre in his performance with increasing slowness. His speed of thought and ability to read games deteriorated alarmingly, culminating in him being accused of not trying by Toshack, the Swansea manager. In training, he began to get hot, dry, choking sensations in his throat and noticed that his right arm felt tense and would adopt a curious flexed posture. Extended highlights of the Swansea matches between FC Braga and Paris Saint-Germain at the beginning of the 1982 season show him 'carrying his right arm', which appears flexed at the elbow, tense and stiff. His kinetic melody also seems to be disturbed giving him a mechanical stiff appearance. I have shown these video films to a group of medical students aware of the physical signs of Parkinson's disease but unaware of Ray Kennedy's illness, and a number of them were able to pick him out from the other players as having some disturbance of movement. It became increasingly difficult for him to keep fit and to stretch wide for balls on his right hand side. In a match against Southampton in 1982/83, he was taken off before half-time because he appeared so slow and he was stripped of the captaincy of the Swansea team. The physiotherapist at Swansea noted that his right thigh muscles were continuously stiff and in spasm and he missed a number of matches as a result of what was put down to a hamstring injury. He was unable to put his right foot on the ground properly on starting to move, but noticed that if he ran for 5 min this disability would slowly wear off. During this period of his career, he became increasingly morose, irascible, and miserable and made only 21 League appearances during the 1982–83 season. He was transferred to Hartlepool Rovers in 1983 and immediately had an injury to the right Achilles tendon. Despite the relatively low standard of play, he found he was unable to keep up and was getting slower and slower, describing himself as a carthorse. In 1984, when much slimmer and fitter, coaching a team in Larnaca, Cyprus, the tremor reemerged and this time affected the whole of his right hand.

He also noticed that his speech would become extremely slurred after even small quantities of alcohol. During training, he was experiencing increasing chest discomfort, muscular aches down the right side, and a choking sensation. In the summer of 1984, he took up coaching boys in holiday camps throughout England and would have to drive long distances. During these journeys, he noticed that he had a tendency to veer involuntarily towards the middle of the road and also that when swimming he would tend to diverge to the right. His right arm often felt tense and uncomfortable when driving and he would keep shifting the position of the right elbow as it rested on the window sill. People had begun to comment that he looked unwell and he found it extremely difficult to dexterously cross his legs when sitting down. He was noted to be slumped in a chair like an old man when sitting in a hotel lounge and he appeared to have great difficulty in coordinating hand movements. During coaching, he appeared reluctant to kick the ball, especially with his right foot and he seemed extremely slowed down when running. By 1984, he was aware of writing difficulties:

All my life I prided myself on being a neat writer so whenever anyone asked me for an autograph it was with pride. I signed with my own distinctive signature, but at the summer camp I found it increasingly difficult even to write my name. It got to a stage when I knew people were laughing at me as their children showed the pathetic scribble supposed to be my name. In the end I was forced to take pictures to my room and sign them in my own time because of the embarrassment.

In 1985, when playing soccer with a local team in the North East, it was noticed that his speech was slurred, that he was short on stamina, and struggled to get moving. He was able to run reasonably well, but had great difficulty in fastening his boot laces and seemed to be always putting his right hand towards his mouth. Because he was landlord of a public house, these problems were put down to excess alcohol, stress, and difficulty coming to terms with giving up soccer. By 1986, he was unable to rub shampoo into his hair with his right hand and had great difficulty shaving. His handwriting had become almost illegible and he was complaining of shaking of the right hand. He was referred to hospital by his general practitioner whose notes record tenseness, tremulousness, and chest discomfort extending back 4 years. Examination by a consultant cardiologist notes that he had a frightened appearance, was perspiring profusely, and had uncoordinated movements. He was finally referred for a neurological opinion in 1986 when the diagnosis of Parkinson's disease was made as soon as he walked into the room. He remembers not being able to turn the pages of a newspaper in the waiting room and having great difficulty in finding a comfortable position in which to sit. Examination revealed facial hypomimia, lid retraction, slowness of initiation of finger movements on the right with cogwheel rigidity, and loss of arm swing.

Current Medical Condition (1986–1991)

Neurological examinations carried out in 1986 recorded an intermittent resting tremor of the right hand, increasing rigidity in the right arm and leg, mild slurring of speech, a stooped posture and facial immobility. There was no evidence of cognitive impairment, cerebellar or autonomic dysfunction, and the plantar reflexes were both down-going. A CT brain scan was normal and there were no abnormalities of copper metabolism.

Levodopa therapy was started with striking improvement in

his disabilities, but over the next 2 years his levodopa requirements increased rapidly, so that by 1988 he was receiving 600
mg of levodopa, bromocriptine in a dose of 5 mg twice a day
and selegiline (Deprenyl) 5 mg bid. By 1990 he was experiencing
an increasing fragility of motor response to an increasingly
complicated regimen of medication. He was now taking Sinemet
(25/100 mg) 12 to 14 tablets/day ad lib, bromocriptine 10 mg/
day and selegiline 5 mg bid. A 200 mg dose of Sinemet took 30
to 45 min to work and lasted about 2 h. Unpredictable off
periods were increasingly frequent lasting from 30 min to 4 h,
during which he would have almost complete blocking of gait,
and an inability to take more than a few shuffling steps. During
off periods his speech was slurred, he became indecisive and was
covered in profuse perspiration. His face was masked and his
hand movements were slow and laborious. A resting tremor was
occasionally present, but painful off period dystonia of the left
foot was more frequent, particularly in the early morning. During
periods of mobility, there was mild chorea of the head, trunk and
limbs with racing of thoughts and mild unsteadiness. At these
times, he was fully functionally independent and able to play
golf, tennis and tenpin bowling.

In 1990 he was started on apomorphine injections with marked
benefit. A single subcutaneous injection of 5 mg apomorphine
'switches him on' within 7 min and lasts for 1 h. He uses between
1 and 6 injections a day to liberate him from refractory off
periods. He is also now taking Sinemet 50/200 mg every 2 hours
throughout the waking day at fixed intervals and a restricted
protein diet.

DISCUSSION

Inward-looking, over-controlled, tense, perfectionistic individuals
who make a religion of success and have a tendency to decompen-
sate with panic attacks or depression seem at particular risk of
acquiring Parkinson's disease (6). A study of monozygotic twins
discordant for Parkinson's disease revealed that the affected sibling
was more self-controlled from the 1st decade of life onwards, and
for 10 years before the onset of motor disabilities was more
anxious, less confident, less dominant, and less lighthearted. The
affected twin was also significantly more likely to have been a

nonsmoker of tobacco (7). The association between Parkinson's disease and habitual nonsmoking has been confirmed in a large number of other case-controlled epidemiological studies. It seems more likely that this is an epiphenomenon rather than due to neuroprotective effects of tobacco. It is possible that premorbid neurobehavioural traits of Parkinsonians may lead to smoking aversion in adolescence. Eatough and colleagues have looked retrospectively at the personalities of patients developing Parkinson's disease before the age of 40 who had been recently diagnosed and found that compared with age-matched controls and with a control group of patients with rheumatoid disease, the Parkinsonians were premorbidly significantly more cautious, conventional, unassuming and rigid in thought, and had had more major adverse life events in early childhood (8). Neuropsychological abnormalities have been demonstrated in the earliest stages of Parkinson's disease and include a poverty and slowness of ideation and a disfluency in switching from one cognitive set to another (9). Similar mild, relatively nonspecific deficits have also recently been found in a group of heroin addicts exposed to the neurotoxic designer drug MPTP and who had only the mildest signs of Parkinson's disease (10). Ray Kennedy's personality fits closely this pattern of behaviour and, in hindsight, his unexpected and alarming loss of soccer playing vision when at Swansea may well have been due to early bradyphrenia.

Patients with Parkinson's disease have difficulty in initiating spontaneous facial gestures leading to considerable problems with nonverbal communication and the misconception that they are cold, distant, and unfeeling. Early photographs and video clips confirm that Ray Kennedy had a slightly deadpan, anxious look and this together with a lack of cadence in his speech might indicate psychomotor retardation. In a group of patients with depression scored on rating scales for Parkinson's disease, facial hypomimia, monotonous speech, and reduced arm swing were much more commonly found than in age-matched controls (11). Dorros (12) in his autobiography states that he believes Parkinson's disease may affect behaviour and emotions for many years before it becomes clinically apparent. In his late childhood, his parents complained that he always looked sad or angry in family photographs and when he was teaching students at least 10 years before the onset of his illness, one pupil asked him to smile more because he looked continuously grim. At a routine health check-up some years before the onset of Parkinson's disease, it was specifically commented that he had a phlegmatic appearance. Considerable evidence now indicates that depressive illness may precede the motor signs of Parkinson's disease by many years in up to 20% of patients (13). Dorros also complained of pain in one shoulder for 2 years before the diagnosis was made in his mid-30s and experienced 'typists' cramp', a rounding of his shoulders, and restless, irritable, impatient behaviour.

Fatigue is a physiological occurrence and complaints of chronic tiredness are amongst the commonest of nonspecific symptoms. However, not uncommonly, it may be a presenting symptom of Parkinson's disease with physical exhaustion leading to reduced spontaneous movement, complaints of temporary weakness and impaired precision, and apathy or mental fatigue causing diminished capacity for mental effort, lack of initiative, and poor concentration.

Although Ray Kennedy throughout his career had to work hard on his fitness and weight, his physical stamina during matches was never in question. Despite this, for at least 10 years before Parkinson's disease was confirmed, fatigue marred his everyday life. Dramatic physical deterioration may follow severe physical effort in Parkinson's disease and the patient then has to take time out to recover and presumably replenish dopamine reserves. A disinclination to continue motor tasks or put an adequate amount of effort into a particular movement is also characteristic. Kennedy, after training, would go straight to bed and sleep and 3–4 years before the disease appeared was unable to train properly because of instant feelings of exhaustion. Some of his complaints bear striking resemblance to the chronic fatigue syndrome (14), which is a protean syndrome with many causes, but underlying depressive symptomatology is often found. Kennedy's contrasting gritty performance during League matches might represent a form of kinesia paradoxica. Compensatory reserves within the nigrostriatal system are considerable, but severe emotional stress, physical exhaustion, and even peripheral trauma may trigger decompensation. I have encountered two or three patients whose Parkinson's syndrome emerged during times of stress and then temporarily submerged sufficiently completely for me to retract the diagnosis, only to reaffirm it 1 or 2 years later. A syndrome of 'fixed fright' superficially resembling the physical signs of early Parkinson's disease has been reported occasionally in severe shellshock (15). It is also of interest that transient Parkinsonism has been reported in association with heavy alcohol ingestion (16). Ray Kennedy observed that even small amounts of alcohol had a profound effect on his ability to move and speak. Some of his inexplicable drenching sweats may be explained on the basis of panic attacks. However, on occasions even the slightest mental or physical exertion would elicit sweating in the absence of any associated tension or panic. This was sometimes accompanied by burning hot feelings in rooms where everyone else felt cold.

Gowers (17) noted 'increased perspiration which may be general and profuse on the least exertion of mind and body' and described a Parkinsonian patient who could not even dictate a letter without first taking her coat off so intense was the perspiration. Ivan Vaughan, in his autobiography, also alludes to excessive physical fatigue with perspiration occurring some months before the onset of finger tremor (18). Vaughan had also noticed that his trouser belt had tended to shift spontaneously to the left so the buckle was constantly off centre, for 2 years before other signs appeared and had noted that on days when he was tired he was aware of difficulties with sequential movements, which he had to carry out by breaking them into their individual bits (18).

For 13 years before the diagnosis was made, Ray Kennedy had intermittent subtle, but definite, disturbances of movement and posture down the right side of his body. These included impaired finger dexterity, mild uncoordination of the right leg, difficulty in switching rapidly from some sequential movements to others and abnormal posturing of the right hand and leg. Four years before the diagnosis was made, he complained of tightness and aching and stiffness in the right leg and began to experience a number of musculo-skeletal injuries. He was also aware of motor unease, tension, and restlessness down the right side. Charcot (19) described these early symptoms of Parkinson's disease as follows:

They complain of a nearly permanent sensation of traction and tension in most of the muscles. There is also a feeling of utter prostration and fatigue, in short an indefinable uneasiness which shows itself in a perpetual desire for a change in posture.

Although many soccer players reach a watershed in their professional careers at ~ age 30, Ray Kennedy's decline from the top level was precipitous and unpredicted by his fellow players. In patients exposed to the designer toxin MPTP with only very mild Parkinson's syndrome, muscular stiffness, slowing down, aching of muscles, easy fatigue, and balance and coordination problems were the earliest complaints (20). Tremor can be intermittent and transitory in the early stages of Parkinson's disease as in Kennedy's case. Gowers (17) describes a patient who noted a transient tremor following the sounding of a fire bell. Each time the bell went off for the next 2 years he experienced tremor, but at no other time until his Parkinson's disease established itself. Video footage of Ray Kennedy's playing career confirms that his Parkinson's disease indisputably began in 1982, 4 years before the diagnosis was made, illustrating the immense difficulty in making an early diagnosis.

His astute observations during his playing career also lend strong circumstantial support to the notion that there may be a long (relatively asymptomatic) phase of the illness. About one in five patients give tantalising accounts of isolated focal episodes of slowness under stress, habitual postural abnormalities, uncoordination, drooling of saliva at night, muscular tension, internal feelings of tremulousness under stress, or a tendency to veer to one side when walking or swimming for many years before Parkinson's disease is diagnosed. Recently, in a family with four affected siblings with L-dopa-responsive Parkinson's syndrome studied with fluorodopa positron emission tomography (PET) scans, a fit, 35-year-old sibling was found whose fluorodopa uptake was so reduced that one would predict Parkinson's disease. On examining this man, he gave an unsolicited account of recurrent internal feelings of tremulousness under stress, chronic fatigue, and aches and pains in one arm. He had a positive glabellar tap sign with increased blink reflex excitability on neurophysiological examination and mild slowness of finger movements on the right suggesting that he was in the earliest phase of Parkinson's syndrome.

Although many of the prodromal symptoms described by Ray Kennedy are ubiquitous and non-specific especially in the middle-aged and elderly, in a young man of his level of fitness they assume greater significance. Parkinson's disease remains a clinical diagnosis, but greater sophistication and analysis of the range of normal movement and posture may improve early detection or at least pinpoint groups of individuals at particular risk of developing the disease. If an effective neuroprotective agent become available in the near future, it will become necessary to find clinical parameters to screen for the earliest phase of Parkinson's disease.

Acknowledgement: I am grateful to Ray Kennedy for his courage and frankness in describing his symptoms and for permission to plough through his scrap books and memorabilia. I am also grateful to Phil Boersma, John Burgum, Jimmy Case, Ray Clemence, Mike Croagan, Dr W. B. Davis, Frank McLintock, Lawrie McMenemy, Bertie Mee, Sammy Nelson, John Radford, Peter Robinson, Richard Shepherd, Tommy Smith, Colin Todd, John Toshack, and Ray's mother for providing invaluable information. I am also grateful to Jimmy Case and BBC Sport for providing video clips of Ray Kennedy's soccer playing performances.

LEGEND TO VIDEOTAPE

Video caption shows Kennedy's body movements (he wears no. 5 shirt in all games) during his Liverpool and England playing days when no detectable movement disorder is apparent. In comparison, however, in the 1981 season his right arm has adopted a flexed posture and does not swing fluently, and his movements are more mechanical.

REFERENCES

1. Gibb WRG, Lees AJ. The relevance of the Lewy body to the pathogenesis of Parkinson's disease. *J Neurol Neurosurg Psychiatry* 1988; 51:745–752.
2. Gibb WRG. The epidemiology of Lewy bodies. In: Fahn S, Marsden CD, Calne DB, Goldstein M, eds. *Recent developments in Parkinson's disease, vol.2.* New Jersey: Macmillan, 1987:1–13.
3. Forno LS. Concentric hyalin intraneuronal inclusions of Lewy type in the brains of elderly persons — 50 incidental cases, relationship to Parkinsonism. *J Am Geriatr Soc* 1969; 17:557–575.
4. Fearnley JM, Lees AJ. Ageing is not involved in the pathophysiology of Parkinson's disease. *Brain* (in press).
5. Mutch WJ, Dingwell-Fordyce I, Downie AW, Paterson JG, Roy SK. Parkinson's disease in a Scottish city. *Brit Med J* 1986; 292:534–536.
6. Todes CJ, Lees AJ. The pre-morbid personality of patients with Parkinson's disease. *J Neurol Neurosurg Psychiatry* 1985; 48:97–100
7. Ward CD, Duvoisin RC, Ince SE, Nutt JD, Eldridge R, Calne DB. Parkinson's disease in 65 pairs of twins and in a set of quadruplets. *Neurology* 1983; 33:815–824.
8. Eatough VM, Kempster PA, Stern GM, Lees AJ. Premorbid personality and idiopathic P.D. *Adv Neurol* 1990; 53:335–337.
9. Lees AJ. The behavioural neurology of Parkinson's disease. In: Stern GM, ed. *Parkinson's disease.* Baltimore: Chapman and Hall, 1990:389–413.
10. Stern Y, Tetrud JW, Martin WRW, Kutner SJ, Langston JW. Cognitive change following MPTP exposure. *Neurology* 1990; 40:261–264.
11. Rogers D, Lees AJ, Smith E, Trimble MMR, Stern GM. Bradyphrenia in Parkinson's disease and psychomotor retardation in depressive illness. An experimental study. *Brain* 1987; 110:761–776.
12. Dorros S. *Parkinson's: A patient's view.* Washington DC: Seven Locks Press, 1989.
13. Santamaria J, Tolosa ES, Valles A, Bayes A, Blesa R, Masono J. Mental depression in untreated Parkinson's disease of recent onset. *Adv Neurol* 1986; 45:443–446.
14. Wessely S, Thomas PK. The chronic fatigue syndrome — myalgic encephalomyelitis or

postural fatigue. In: Kennard C, ed. *Recent advances in clinical neurology, vol.6*, Edinburgh: Churchill Livingstone, 1990:85–131.

15. Grinker RR, Spiegel JP. War neuroses in N. Africa: the Tunisian campaign Jan–May 1943. Prepared and distributed for the Air-Surgeon Army Air Forces by the Josiah Macy Jr. Foundation, 1943, pp. 14–17, 40–44.

16. Carlen PL, Lee MA, Jacob M, Livshits O. Parkinsonism provoked by alcohol. *Ann Neurol* 1981; 9:84–86.

17. Gowers WR. In: *A manual of the nervous system, vol.2*, 2nd ed. Connecticut: Hafner Dorien, 638–653.

18. Vaughan I. *Ivan – Living with Parkinson's disease*. London: MacMillan, 1986.

19. Charcot JM. In: *On diseases of the nervous system, vol.1*. London: New Sydenham Society, 1877:134–156.

20. Langston JW. MPTP-induced Parkinsonism: how good a model is it? In: Fahn S, Marsden CD, Jenner P, Teychenne P, eds. *Recent developments in Parkinson's disease*. New York: Raven Press, 1986:119–126.

Index

Discover more about our forthcoming books through Penguin's FREE newspaper...

Penguin
Quarterly

It's packed with:

- exciting features

- author interviews

- previews & reviews

- books from your favourite films & TV series

- exclusive competitions & much, much more...

READ MORE IN PENGUIN

In every corner of the world, on every subject under the sun, Penguin represents quality and variety – the very best in publishing today.

For complete information about books available from Penguin – including Puffins, Penguin Classics and Arkana – and how to order them, write to us at the appropriate address below. Please note that for copyright reasons the selection of books varies from country to country.

In the United Kingdom: Please write to *Dept. JC, Penguin Books Ltd, FREEPOST, West Drayton, Middlesex UB7 OBR*

If you have any difficulty in obtaining a title, please send your order with the correct money, plus ten per cent for postage and packaging, to *PO Box No. 11, West Drayton, Middlesex UB7 OBR*

In the United States: Please write to *Penguin USA Inc., 375 Hudson Street, New York, NY 10014*

In Canada: Please write to *Penguin Books Canada Ltd, 10 Alcorn Avenue, Suite 300, Toronto, Ontario M4V 3B2*

In Australia: Please write to *Penguin Books Australia Ltd, 487 Maroondah Highway, Ringwood, Victoria 3134*

In New Zealand: Please write to *Penguin Books (NZ) Ltd,182–190 Wairau Road, Private Bag, Takapuna, Auckland 9*

In India: Please write to *Penguin Books India Pvt Ltd, 706 Eros Apartments, 56 Nehru Place, New Delhi 110 019*

In the Netherlands: Please write to *Penguin Books Netherlands B.V., Keizersgracht 231 NL–1016 DV Amsterdam*

In Germany: Please write to *Penguin Books Deutschland GmbH, Friedrichstrasse 10–12, W–6000 Frankfurt/Main 1*

In Spain: Please write to *Penguin Books S. A., C. San Bernardo 117–6⁰ E–28015 Madrid*

In Italy: Please write to *Penguin Italia s.r.l., Via Felice Casati 20, I–20124 Milano*

In France: Please write to *Penguin France S. A., 17 rue Lejeune, F–31000 Toulouse*

In Japan: Please write to *Penguin Books Japan, Ishikiribashi Building, 2–5–4, Suido, Bunkyo-ku, Tokyo 112*

In Greece: Please write to *Penguin Hellas Ltd, Dimocritou 3, GR–106 71 Athens*

In South Africa: Please write to *Longman Penguin Southern Africa (Pty) Ltd, Private Bag X08, Bertsham 2013*

READ MORE IN PENGUIN

BIOGRAPHY AND AUTOBIOGRAPHY

Freedom from Fear   Aung San Suu Kyi

This collection of writings gives a voice to Aung San Suu Kyi, human rights activist and leader of Burma's National League for Democracy, who was detained in 1989 by SLORC, the ruling military junta, and today remains under house arrest. In 1991 her courage and ideals were internationally recognized when she was awarded the Nobel Peace Prize.

Friends in High Places   Jeremy Paxman

'The Establishment is alive and well ... in pursuit of this elusive, seminal circle of souls around which British institutions revolve, Jeremy Paxman ... has written a thoughtful examination, both poignant and amusing' – Jessica Catto in the *Independent*

Last of the Hot Metal Men   Derek Jameson

Following on from his hugely successful *Touched by Angels*, Derek Jameson presents the second volume of his astonishing memoirs. Here is the inside story of the ten years when he was editor of three national newspapers, ended up unemployed and then bounced back as a media megastar. 'The great personality of today' – David Frost

When Shrimps Learn to Whistle   Denis Healey

The Time of My Life was widely acclaimed as a masterpiece. Taking up the most powerful political themes that emerge from it Denis Healey now gives us this stimulating companion volume. 'Forty-three years of ruminations ... by the greatest foreign secretary we never had' – Ben Pimlott in the *New Statesman & Society*

Stone Alone   Bill Wyman with Ray Coleman

Ruthless, cynical, electrifying and exuberant – the Stones played a revolutionary soundtrack for the sixties. Offstage, bass guitarist Bill Wyman has always been 'the silent Stone'. But here he reveals the intimate and gripping story of the 'bad boys' of British rock and the era they helped to shape.

READ MORE IN PENGUIN

A CHOICE OF FICTION AND NON-FICTION

Travels in Nepal   Charlie Pye-Smith

'It is refreshing to find a travel writer bothered to grapple with facts instead of simply gossiping about the view from the train window ... This gives his account – which in itself is an attractive description of a beautiful, mountainous nation – a tough and interesting backbone' – *Independent*

Greenmantle   John Buchan

Richard Hannay undertakes a perilous mission to pursue the elusive 'Greenmantle'. His success or failure could change the outcome of the First World War.

Lucky Jim   Kingsley Amis

'A classic comic novel, a seminal campus novel, and a novel which seized and expressed the mood of those who came of age in the 1950s. But there is more to it than that ... Its university setting functions primarily as the epitome of a stuffy, provincial bourgeois world into which the hero is promoted by education, and against whose values and codes he rebels, at first inwardly and at last outwardly' – David Lodge

A Gentleman of Leisure   P. G. Wodehouse

Redolent with the sights, sounds and smells of rural English life, *A Gentleman of Leisure* also contains all the wit and vivacity we have come to expect from the inimitable Wodehouse.

Shots from the Hip   Charles Shaar Murray

His classic encapsulation of the moment when rock stars turned junkies as the sixties died; his dissection of rock 'n' roll violence as citizens assaulted the Sex Pistols; superstar encounters from the decline of Paul McCartney to Mick Jagger's request that the author should leave – Charles Shaar Murray's *Shots from the Hip* is also rock history in the making.

READ MORE IN PENGUIN

A CHOICE OF FICTION AND NON-FICTION

City on the Rocks Kevin Rafferty

'Rafferty has filled a glaring gap on the Asian bookshelf, offering the only comprehensive picture of Hong Kong right up to the impact of the Tiananmen Square massacre' – *Business Week*. 'A story of astonishing achievement, but its purpose is warning rather than celebration' – *Sunday Times*

The Anglo-Saxons James Campbell (ed.)

'For anyone who wishes to understand the broad sweep of English history, Anglo-Saxon society is an important and fascinating subject. And Campbell's is an important and fascinating book. It is also a finely produced and, at times, a very beautiful book' – *London Review of Books*

Arabian Sands Wilfred Thesiger

'Following worthily in the tradition of Burton, Doughty, Lawrence, Philby and Thomas, it is, very likely, the book about Arabia to end all books about Arabia' – Lord Kinross in the *Daily Telegraph*

Ah, Sweet Mystery of Life Roald Dahl

In this compelling collection of tales Roald Dahl's urbane and sophisticated wit is directed at the unfathomable mysteries and eccentricities of rural life.

Ways of Seeing John Berger

Seeing comes before words. The child looks before it can speak. Yet there is another sense in which seeing comes before words ... These seven provocative essays – some written, some visual – offer a key to exploring the multiplicity of ways of seeing.

READ MORE IN PENGUIN

A CHOICE OF NON-FICTION

The Time of My Life Denis Healey

'Denis Healey's memoirs have been rightly hailed for their intelligence, wit and charm ... *The Time of My Life* should be read, certainly for pleasure, but also for profit ... he bestrides the post-war world, a Colossus of a kind' – *Independent*. 'No finer autobiography has been written by a British politician this century' – *Economist*

Chasing the Monsoon Alexander Frater

'Frater's unclouded sight unfurls the magic behind the mystery tour beautifully ... his spirited, eccentric, vastly diverting book will endure the ceaseless patter of travel books on India' – *Daily Mail*. 'This is travel writing at its best. Funny, informed, coherent and deeply sympathetic towards its subject' – *Independent on Sunday*

Isabelle Annette Kobak

'A European turned Arab, a Christian turned Muslim, a woman dressed as a man; a libertine who stilled profound mystical cravings by drink, hashish and innumerable Arab lovers ... All the intricate threads of her rebellious life are to be found in Annette Kobak's scrupulously researched book' – Lesley Blanch in the *Daily Telegraph*

Flying Dinosaurs Michael Johnson

Hundreds of millions of years ago, when dinosaurs walked the earth, we know that there also existed great prehistoric beasts call pterosaurs that could fly or glide. Now you can make these extraordinary creatures fly again. *Flying Dinosaurs* contain almost everything you need to construct eight colourful and thrillingly lifelike flying model pterosaurs – from the pterodactylus to the dimorphodon.

The Italians Luigi Barzini

'Brilliant ... whether he is talking about the family or the Mafia, about success or the significance of gesticulation, Dr Barzini is always illuminating and amusing' – *The Times*. 'He hits his nails on the head with bitter-sweet vitality ... Dr Barzini marshals and orders his facts and personalities with the skill of an historian as well as a journalist' – *Observer*

READ MORE IN PENGUIN

A CHOICE OF NON-FICTION

Riding the Iron Rooster Paul Theroux

Travels in old and new China with the author of *The Great Railway Bazaar*. 'Mr Theroux cannot write badly ... he is endlessly curious about places and people ... and in the course of a year there was almost no train in the whole vast Chinese rail network in which he did not travel' – Ludovic Kennedy

Ninety-two Days Evelyn Waugh

In this fascinating chronicle of a South American journey, Waugh describes the isolated cattle country of Guiana, sparsely populated by an odd collection of visionaries, rogues and ranchers, and records the nightmarish experiences travelling on foot, by horse and by boat through the jungle in Brazil.

The Life of Graham Greene Norman Sherry
Volume One 1904–1939

'Probably the best biography ever of a living author' – Philip French in the *Listener*. Graham Greene has always maintained a discreet distance from his reading public. This volume reconstructs his first thirty-five years to create one of the most revealing literary biographies of the decade.

The Day Gone By Richard Adams

In this enchanting memoir the bestselling author of *Watership Down* tells his life story from his idyllic 1920s childhood spent in Newbury, Berkshire, through public school, Oxford and service in World War Two to his return home and his courtship of the girl he was to marry.

A Turn in the South V. S. Naipaul

'A supremely interesting, even poetic glimpse of a part of America foreigners either neglect or patronize' – *Guardian*. 'An extraordinary panorama' – *Daily Telegraph*. 'A fine book by a fine man, and one to be read with great enjoyment: a book of style, sagacity and wit' – *Sunday Times*

READ MORE IN PENGUIN

A CHOICE OF NON-FICTION

Ginsberg: A Biography Barry Miles

The definitive life of one of this century's most colourful poets. 'A life so dramatic, so dangerous, so committed to hard-volume truth, that his survival is a miracle, his kindness, wisdom and modesty a blessing' – *The Times*. 'Read it to the end' – Michael Horovitz

Coleridge: Early Visions Richard Holmes

'Dazzling … Holmes has not merely reinterpreted Coleridge; he has re-created him, and his biography has the aura of fiction, the shimmer of an authentic portrait … a biography like few I have ever read' –*Guardian*. 'Coleridge lives, and talks and loves … in these pages as never before' – *Independent*

The Speeches of Winston Churchill David Cannadine (ed.)

The most eloquent statesman of his time, Winston Churchill used language as his most powerful weapon. These orations, spanning fifty years, show him gradually honing his rhetoric until, with spectacular effect, 'he mobilized the English language, and sent it into battle'.

Higher than Hope Fatima Meer

A dramatic, personal and intimate biography drawing on letters and reminiscences from Nelson Mandela himself and his close family, *Higher Than Hope* is an important tribute to one of the greatest living figures of our time. It is also a perceptive commentary on the situation in South Africa. No one concerned with politics or humanity can afford to miss it.

Among the Russians Colin Thubron

'The Thubron approach to travelling has an integrity that belongs to another age. And this author's way with words gives his books a value far transcending their topical interest; it is safe to predict that they will be read a century hence' – Dervla Murphy in the *Irish Times*

READ MORE IN PENGUIN

A CHOICE OF BESTSELLERS

The Darling Buds of May H. E. Bates

Here come the Larkins, in the first of their hilarious rural adventures, crashing their way through the English countryside in the wake of Pop, the quick-eyed, golden-hearted junk-dealer, and Ma, with a mouthful of crisps and a laugh like a jelly.

Down with Superwoman Shirley Conran

This cheerful, friendly reference book is filled with sensible and practical advice. Shirley Conran tells you everything you need to know about all aspects of running a home using minimum effort and achieving the best results. Completely updated and expanded from her internationally bestselling *Superwoman*, it is now twice the size of the original.

Eva Fraser's Face and Body Programme Eva Fraser

Following the huge success of her facial workout, Eva Fraser now brings you her complete health and beauty programme, which reverses the signs of ageing – naturally. In her new book she shares with us her daily fitness programme as well as her philosophy for youthfulness of mind and body.

Better Than Life Grant Naylor

The sequel to the internationally bestselling *Red Dwarf* finds Lister, Rimmer, Cat and Kryten trapped in the ultimate computer game: Better than Life. BTL transports you directly to a perfect world of your imagination, a world where you can enjoy fabulous wealth and unmitigated success. It's the ideal game with only one drawback – it's so good, it will kill you . . .

Keith Richards: The Biography Victor Bockris

'The year's best book about rock music . . . The Rolling Stone was a dream topic, being both the rocker who took drugs until his teeth needed replacing, and the faintly aristocratic type who could still talk about it in complete sentences. Bockris sat back and let the story tell itself' – Giles Smith in the *Independent*, Books of the Year

READ MORE IN PENGUIN

A CHOICE OF BESTSELLERS

Brightness Falls Jay McInerney

'The story of a disintegrating marriage set in New York in the frenzied few months leading up to the Wall Street crash of 1987. It is his biggest, most ambitious novel yet – a sort of *Bonfire of the Vanities* with the added advantage of believable, likeable characters' – Lynn Barber in the *Independent on Sunday*

Chicago Loop Paul Theroux

'Like *Doctor Slaughter*, this novel watches a character blunder to disaster through emotionless, anonymous sex . . . [a] fast-paced horror-excursion into what Theroux once called "subterranean gothic"' – *Sunday Times*

The Russian Girl Kingsley Amis

'Dazzling skill with dialogue and . . . no less dazzling ability to conjure up minor characters – policemen, academics, businessmen, Russian émigrés – who, for all their hilarious oddity, somehow remain believable' – *Evening Standard*

Dunster John Mortimer

'Masterly . . . Part thriller, part observer of current mores, realistic yet full of ambiguities, Dunster raises every kind of question, moral and psychological, while spinning along at a cracking pace' – *Financial Times*

Rum Punch Elmore Leonard

For bail bondsman Max Cherry, control is slipping away fast. His ex just moved in with some Cuban artist, the mob is into his business, and he's broken the golden rule: never fall in love with a client . . . 'A brilliant and subversive book' – A. Alvarez in the *Sunday Telegraph*